THE
340B PROGRAM HANDBOOK

Integrating 340B into the Health-System Pharmacy Supply Chain

ANDREW L. WILSON, PharmD, FASHP

Vice President, 340B Solutions
McKesson U.S. Pharmaceutical
Richmond, Virginia

Any correspondence regarding this publication should be sent to the publisher, American Society of Health-System Pharmacists, 4500 East West Highway, Suite 900, Bethesda, MD 20814, attention: Special Publishing.

The information presented herein reflects the opinions of the contributors and advisors. It should not be interpreted as an official policy of ASHP or as an endorsement of any product.

Because of ongoing research and improvements in technology, the information and its applications contained in this text are constantly evolving and are subject to the professional judgment and interpretation of the practitioner due to the uniqueness of a clinical situation. The editors and ASHP have made reasonable efforts to ensure the accuracy and appropriateness of the information presented in this document. However, any user of this information is advised that the editors and ASHP are not responsible for the continued currency of the information, for any errors or omissions, and/or for any consequences arising from the use of the information in the document in any and all practice settings. Any reader of this document is cautioned that ASHP makes no representation, guarantee, or warranty, express or implied, as to the accuracy and appropriateness of the information contained in this document and specifically disclaims any liability to any party for the accuracy and/or completeness of the material or for any damages arising out of the use or non-use of any of the information contained in this document.

Acquisitions Editor: Daniel Cobaugh

Editorial Project Manager, Special Publishing: Ruth Bloom

Production Manager: Johnna Hershey

Cover & Page Design: David Wade

Library of Congress Cataloging-in-Publication Data
Names: Wilson, Andrew L., editor. | American Society of Health-System
  Pharmacists, issuing body.
Title: The 340B program handbook : integrating 340B into the health-system
  pharmacy supply chain / [edited by] Andrew L. Wilson.
Description: Bethesda, MD : American Society of Health-System Pharmacists,
  [2018] | Includes bibliographical references and index.
Identifiers: LCCN 2018003699 | ISBN 9781585285983 (pbk.)
Subjects: | MESH: Pharmaceutical Services--economics | Government Programs |
Economics, Pharmaceutical | Health Plan Implementation | United States
Classification: LCC RS100 | NLM QV 736 AA1 | DDC 362.17/82--dc23 LC record available at https://lccn.
  loc.gov/2018003699

Printed in Canada.

ISBN: 978-1-58528-598-3

10 9 8 7 6 5 4 3 2 1

Dedication

The 340B Handbook

is dedicated

to my wife Janet

for her support through this and the many professional projects in our life together.

Table of Contents

Table of Contents

Preface

The 340B program remains among the most significant supply chain savings opportunities for eligible nonprofit hospitals and government grantee clinics. Nearly 45% of U.S. hospitals participate in the 340B program ranging from small rural hospitals to the largest academic medical centers (AMCs) and integrated delivery networks (IDNs).[1,2] The regulatory boundaries and operational requirements present a significant challenge to achieve results and mitigate risk. An active 340B program engages a broad spectrum of institutional resources in pharmacy, finance, compliance, and information technology, among others. The goal of community benefit for the care for the uninsured, underinsured, and low-income patients can be well-served through 340B program participation results.

Key elements of the 340B program are not fully outlined in law and regulation. Due to constraints on government oversight authority, formal regulatory guidance exists in only a few areas of the program. 340B program oversight by the Health Resources and Services Administration (HRSA) Office of Pharmacy Affairs (OPA) is supported through guidance documents, frequently asked questions (FAQs) posted on HRSA and Apexus web sites, a call center, and structured training programs through Apexus, the 340B Prime Vendor.

OPA fosters a view of compliance through on-site and desk audits with the primary result of program alignment across covered entities on key policy issues and compliance activities. The primary consequences of audit findings result in posting of violations on the HRSA web site and repayment of unearned 340B discount to manufacturers.[3] OPA, Apexus, 340B Health, and numerous established and independent consultants provide support to 340B program participants, primarily by offering compliance-focused and policy-based solutions.

Pharmacy leaders in 340B hospitals experience a strong tension between meeting detailed and complex 340B compliance requirements as well as supporting technical supply chain efficiency and effectiveness goals, including drug shortages and achieving health-system financial objectives. Drug shortages, formulary changes, supply chain efficiency, and other operating concerns are amplified and complicated by 340B. In addition to health-system operations challenges, the complexities of pharmacy regulation, including state board and Drug Enforcement Administration (DEA) requirements and the requirements of the Drug Supply Chain Security Act (DSCSA), must also be considered.

The *340B Program Handbook* is designed as a practical guide for pharmacy leaders, hospital administrators, business managers, and pharmacy supply chain professionals implementing, maintaining, or overseeing a high-performing 340B program. *The 340B Handbook* content focuses on financial, business, and supply chain performance constraints and opportunities in the face of unique 340B options and compliance constraints.

The *Handbook* is designed to offer well-organized, practical information that considers and integrates 340B into the current care delivery model, information systems, and the increasingly complex healthcare supply chain beyond 340B. In seeking 340B advice, hospitals generally engage "340B experts" and receive guidance that honors 340B program requirements. In contrast, the *Handbook* assembles a group of professionals who work with 340B every day to provide a framework for building and managing an effective contemporary supply chain that integrates 340B program requirements.

ASHP members in pharmacy leadership positions (vice presidents, directors of pharmacy, assistant directors of pharmacy), pharmacy business managers, supply chain leaders, and health-

Preface

system compliance officers outside pharmacy should find the *Handbook* to be a practical guide to implementing 340B and as a support in managing leadership conversations regarding 340B program expectations.

Andrew L. Wilson, PharmD, FASHP

REFERENCES

1. Medicare Payment Advisory Commission: Overview of the 340B Drug Program, May 2015. http://www.medpac. gov/docs/default-source/reports/may-2015-report-to-the-congress-overview-of-the-340b-drug-pricing-program. pdf?sfvrsn=0. Accessed November 1, 2017.

2. Health Policy Brief: The 340B Drug Discount Program, *Health Affairs*, September 14, 2017. DOI: 10.1377/ hpb20171409.000175 http://www.healthaffairs.org/do/10.1377/hpb20171409.000175/full/. Accessed November 1, 2017.

3. Health Resources and Services Administration Office of Pharmacy Affairs: Program Integrity. https://www.hrsa.gov/ opa/program-integrity/index.html. Accessed November 1, 2017.

Contributors

CONTRIBUTING EDITOR

Andrew L. Wilson, PharmD, FASHP

Vice President, 340B Solutions
McKesson U.S. Pharmaceutical
Richmond, Virginia

CONTRIBUTORS

Krist Azizian, PharmD

Chief Pharmacy Officer
USC Norris Cancer Hospital,
  Keck Hospital of USC
University of Southern California
Los Angeles, California

William Black, MBA, PharmD, MS, BCPS

Pharmacy Operations Manager
University of Utah
Salt Lake City, Utah

Kavish Choudhary, PharmD, MS

Senior Director
Inpatient and Infusion Pharmacy Services
University of Utah Health
Salt Lake City, Utah

Charles Cooper, MBA, RPh

340B Program Director
Fairview Pharmacy Services
Minneapolis, Minnesota

Heather Easterling, MBA, PharmD

Director, Pharmacy Services
Medical University of South Carolina
Charleston, South Carolina

Marcus Farbstein, MBA, RPh

Director, Public Policy & Government Markets
Medivation
613 Langston Lane
Falls Church, Virginia

John P. Gray, PharmD, MS, BCPS

Medication Safety Officer
Keck Medical Center of USC
University of Southern California
Los Angeles, California

Christopher Hatwig, MS, RPh, FASHP

President
Apexus
Irving, Texas

Douglas J. Hosie, MBA, RPh

System Director of Pharmacy
Rochester Regional Health
Rochester, New York

Julie Houston, CPhT

Senior Director, Retail 340B Solutions
McKesson U.S. Pharmaceutical
Boise, Idaho

Kim Le, PharmD*

Director
Health System Value and Outcomes
Tesaro, Inc.
Los Angeles, California

Lauren Meekins, PharmD, MS, BCPS

Clinical Manager
UNC Shared Services Center Pharmacy
University of North Carolina at Chapel Hill
Raleigh, North Carolina

*At the time that Chapter 12 was written, Dr. Le was Director of Pharmacy and Investigational Drug Services at USC Norris Cancer Hospital.

Contributors

Gregg Niemiec, BS, RPh

Managing Consultant, 340B Solutions
McKesson U.S. Pharmaceutical
San Antonio, Texas

Shuchi Parikh, JD

Associate
Powers, Pyles, Sutter & Verville
Washington, DC

Fern Paul-Aviles, PharmD, MS, BCPS

*Director, 340B and Regulatory Program
    Compliance*
Carolinas Healthcare System
Charlotte, North Carolina

Katheryne Richardson, PharmD

Vice President
Apexus
Virginia Beach, Virginia

Lisa N. Schatz, PharmD, BCPS

Managing Consultant, 340B Solutions
McKesson U.S. Pharmaceutical
Wilmington, North Carolina

Kevin A. Scheckelhoff, MBA, RPh

Assistant Vice President, 340B Solutions
McKesson U.S. Pharmaceutical
Richmond, Virginia

Christopher S. Shain, PharmD, BCPS

Assistant Vice President, 340B Solutions
McKesson U.S. Pharmaceutical
Fenton, Missouri

Steven Sundberg, PharmD

Director of Pharmacy
Advocate Healthcare Pharmacy Central
    Supply Center
Algonquin, Illinois

William von Oehsen, JD

Principal
Powers, Pyles, Sutter & Verville
Washington, DC

Madeline Carpinelli Wallack, PhD, MS

Principal
RxX Consultants
Minneapolis, Minnesota

Barbara Straub Williams, JD

Principal
Powers, Pyles, Sutter & Verville
Washington, DC

Acknowledgments

I would like to acknowledge the support of my McKesson colleagues—those who contributed to this volume and those who support the supply cad service chain for the many hospitals and clinics that engage in the 340B program.

I would also like to acknowledge the insight and continued focus of the Apexus leadership team and 340B University colleagues in building and communicating with the community of 340B program stakeholders. Thanks to the current and past leadership of the HRSA Office of Pharmacy Affairs; 340B Health along with friends, colleagues, customers, and clients in covered entities; group purchasing operations; manufacturers; 340B administrators; and consultants.

Andrew L. Wilson
April 2018

CHAPTER 1

Introduction to the 340B Program: Current Perspectives

Andrew L. Wilson, PharmD, FASHP

The 340B program has been a part of the hospital pharmaceutical supply chain for more than 25 years. From a modest start, through steady program growth, the 340B program's impact has multiplied abundantly for participating covered entities. Growth of the 340B program in the hospital marketplace has been underpinned by the addition of new hospitals, the extension of hospital care delivery into ambulatory care areas covered by 340B, and innovative program development led by participants.

GROWTH OF THE 340B PROGRAM

As program participants explored practice boundaries and used technology to support effective management of patient data, dispensing, purchases, and inventory for the 340B program, the Health Resources and Service Administration (HRSA) Office of Pharmacy Affairs has proffered guidance. Their guidance has included technical details, tracking, and audit requirements with an eye to keeping the 340B program on course. The participant-driven nature of 340B program development, along with the diversity, breadth, and scope of the 340B program participants, has led to a complex "organic" set of guidance materials rather than a structured, well-designed whole. As a result, 340B hospitals now contend with a complex set of rules and guidance in implementing and managing the 340B program. The flexible nature of guidance, as opposed to clear, straightforward rules and regulations, has fostered an extensive education and support industry through programs, meetings, and on-line resources. Moreover, other support has come from software providers, consultants, and an array of program tools.

However, it is only in the past 5 years that circumstances have aligned to create today's impactful 340B program. The scope of 340B financial impact; greater HRSA oversight through audits; and the active interest of Congress, manufacturer stakeholders, and others in the healthcare community have created a high level of focus on covered entities' 340B program performance.

Current public dialogue regarding the 340B program revolves around the program's size and growth based on participant count, purchase amount, and total drug discount earned, along with the collateral interest in hospital use of savings and program entry requirements. The public dialogue from manufacturers and others has shifted to program intent, the use of 340B savings, and compliance with 340B rules and guidance as well as a focus on fostering transparency from participants—both covered entities and manufacturers.

A common criticism regarding the 340B program is that hospitals are "gaming the program" in ways that are not congruent with the original intent of the 1992 legislation. Absent a disagreement regarding Congress's explicit wishes, the combination of modest detail in the original law with the sweeping changes in healthcare makes the current 340B program more pervasive and impactful than even the most enlightened drafter could have predicted.

With nearly half of nonprofit hospitals participating and 45% of all hospital drug purchases in 2016 coming under the program's auspices,[1-3] the 340B program has certainly grown beyond its initial concept and possibly beyond the wildest dreams of its authors and proponents from a quarter century ago. Depending on the viewer's perspective, the program has either outgrown its original intent[4] or has outperformed its earliest vision to become a key element of a hospital's ability to provide community benefit[5]—or both.

Regardless of this difference in perspective, policymakers and participants have come to take the 340B program seriously. The HRSA Office of Pharmacy Affairs and its surrogate, the 340B Prime Vendor program, have devoted substantive thought and resources to building the framework of the current 340B program within the boundaries and powers specified in the statute. Covered entities are well-advised to consult the tools, programs, and information provided on the Internet.[6,7] However, the original 1992 statute's lack of enabling language has limited the development of definitive rules for many aspects of the 340B program. This gap leads to a challenge for participants and critics in outlining program requirements and objectives in a definitive form. Practically speaking, there is flexibility in application of the most basic elements of the program, defining eligible patients, and covered outpatient drugs. HRSA plans to fill the 340B community's needs for direction through audit standards and active communication on compliance topics and best practices through the Prime Vendor. Readers of this *Handbook* are deeply engaged in 340B and probably believe the program contains some measure of uncertainty, even with HRSA's guidance. However, they are probably focused on meeting 340B program requirements for securing discounted medications to treat their eligible patients while seeking a conservative approach and best practices.

THE HEALTHCARE MARKET ENVIRONMENT

The healthcare marketplace, public health needs, and the resources to support and deliver pharmaceutical care in 2018 differ dramatically from 1992. The 340B tools available to participants have kept pace, particularly with increasingly sophisticated "split billing" virtual inventory and contract pharmacy management software. Nevertheless, the 340B program is a creature of the pharmaceutical care marketplace—a rapidly changing part of the U.S. healthcare system and an area that has transformed materially in 25 years.

Consolidation, acquisition, and diversification have defined the recent healthcare market. Insurers, pharmacy benefit managers (PBMs), retail pharmacies, distributors, and manufacturers have merged. Hospitals have also consolidated through mergers and acquisitions, developed into groups, and acquired related healthcare services and technology—becoming *integrated delivery networks* (IDNs). As the focus of care moved the ambulatory setting, hospitals have transitioned to providing these services through movement of inpatient services, growth and the purchase of physician practices, building of diagnostic and other services, and development of the associated competencies. As a program designed to support ambulatory care, this shift alone provides a key engine for 340B program growth.

A host of expensive, targeted biologics, specialty drugs, and biosimilars now treat diseases in a complex market where drug costs and prices are multiples higher than in years past. These expensive agents are where health plans, PBMs, manufacturers, and others seek to manage costs to deliver effective care and value. In this market, substantive price increases with rebates through the Medicaid Drug Rebate Program (MDRP) and PBMs have driven greater discounts and financial advantage. The *gross-to-net bubble* that supports MDRP and PBM discounts[8] also delivers a similarly scaled financial result to 340B hospitals. In addition to the actual prices and discounts supported under 340B, contract pharmacy relationships between covered entities and retail pharmacies arguably convert some or all of the funds that would pass through rebates to others in the pharmacy supply and provider chain for captured prescriptions. Although not necessarily driving the changes in the pharmaceutical marketplace, the 340B program's financial results are clearly driven by them, particularly since 2012.[8]

The *value of therapy* is broadly defined as clinical success at a competitive cost. In the case of pharmaceuticals, the 340B program materially alters drug cost for program participants, changing the results of this equation. Although critics of the program, and even the federal government,[9] point to apparently irrational "higher cost" choices made by 340B facilities, a more focused understanding would demonstrate that the choices are made in an economically sensible way.

The lack of a published 340B price makes the economic basis of a 340B hospital's choices opaque to all but the covered entity. Although the covered entity can "do the math" for their formulary choice or business plan, it is uncommon to test the result against alternative non-340B economics. The 340B hospital has no incentive to do so, nor any real opportunity to provide these services at a group purchasing organization (GPO) price under 340B program rules. It is reasonable to consider the choice to open an infusion center or specialty pharmacy and to develop or purchase a clinic practice as materially supported by 340B financial considerations; however, 340B versus non-340B economic comparisons are generally external, post hoc, and based on broad estimates of 340B discounts.

At its core, the 340B program might be best described as a government-supported GPO—a statutory version of a hospital GPO—a membership organization with access to a catalog of discounted prices. However, consider it: (1) a government GPO with a statutory price formula driving deep discounts, (2) a pricing formula that limits price increases to the Consumer Price Index for Urban Consumers (CPI-U), (3) a payer mix threshold for group membership (disproportionate share hospitals [DSH] patient percentage), and (4) detailed, complex rules of participation that include granular management of purchases and inventory as well as a requirement that discounted drugs only be dispensed in treatment of specifically qualified patients. The latter two items are key elements of 340B program guardrails and a limiter on 340B program growth based solely on 340B financial leverage.

CURRENT SCALE AND SCOPE OF THE 340B PROGRAM

The current scale and scope of 340B program rules and guidance are the result of a responsive regulator seeking to provide clarity and uniformity over a period of large-scale change for healthcare. Beyond the covered entities' positive financial results and the support of care for the uninsured and underinsured, the results generated by 340B participation require adherence to the complex, nuanced, and often challenging set of rules and guidance. The initial legislation creating the 340B program did not foresee the numerous changes and trends in the healthcare marketplace, particularly for hospitals that now constitute the majority of drug purchases under the program. The transition to ambulatory care, the consolidation of care into the hospital marketplace, and transformation of hospital-based care to 340B-eligible ambulatory sites was never a goal, nor a certainty.

A matrix of published guidance, frequently asked questions (FAQs), and educational programs provides the framework for managing a 340B-compliant supply chain, while HRSA audits interpret the scope and nature of compliance. To an extent, the 340B program functions under the consent of the governed as guidance documents are subject to interpretation, generally function under a broad consensus, and may be missed, misinterpreted, and implemented in a variety of ways. HRSA and Apexus exercise influence through education, communications, and most formally in audits. Active enforcement actions are rare because covered entities and manufacturers seek to follow HRSA's guidance and interpretations. In the base case, covered entities seek to understand the rules and to implement them effectively.

The existence of a cadre of 340B managers and the recent development of a full credentialing program for an Advanced 340B Operations Certificate[10] speaks to the commitment of covered entities and their employees, as does the existence of counterparts in the offices of participating manufacturers and distributors. The industry of third-party administrators, consultants, services, blogs, software, tools, and shared listserv opinions adds clarity to applying the rules, while adding an element of confusion or inadvertent misdirection in some instances. Over time, the flow of advice and consensus leads to an active 340B community seeking the latest and most current audit results and call center interpretations.

340B is often viewed independently as a component or subset of all hospitals in a limited context. Considering the depth and pervasiveness of 340B requirements and the number of participating hospitals, this is no longer the best and most appropriate view. Although 340B is considered a growing and influential subset of the health-system pharmacy operations universe, the structure, accountability, and supply chain mastery required to fully manage and capture 340B discounts bring an unprecedented element of business discipline to health-system pharmacy not present in their non-340B peer organizations. Revenue cycle performance, detailed posting of charges associated with the actual national drug codes (NDCs) purchased and the framework for electronic medical record (EMR) software, electronic data interchange (EDI), and other connections to the supply chain bring a higher level of discipline to inventory management. Health-system pharmacists are rightly focused on a broad variety of operations, clinical, safety, regulatory and other professional rules, regulations, and guidance. 340B health-system pharmacies support a level of attention to business affairs that rivals their focus on patient care, controlled substances, sterile products, and state pharmacy regulations.

WHERE DOES 340B GO FROM HERE?

How did we get here from a modest niche program enacted as section 340B of the Veterans Healthcare Act of 1992? Although the 340B program has arguably grown well beyond its original vision, the changes that brought us here have as much, or even more, to do with the larger changes in healthcare and their impact on participants than the 340B program itself.

The visibility of the 340B program and its growth over time have provided a context of consensus for changes to the 340B program that may add to its health and longevity. These include the potential for greater transparency in the scope of savings benefit, support for transparency, and covered entity reporting requirements, perhaps including a standardized methodology for calculating savings and requirements for how savings are used. Humility is advisable in forecasting the future of 340B at a time when healthcare appears poised to continue transformation and change. The 340B program is unique and perhaps not completely understood, but it has become an integral element of healthcare delivery in the United States.

REFERENCES

1.   Medicare Payment Advisory Commission, Report to Congress: An Overview of the 340B Program. http://www.medpac.gov/docs/default-source/reports/may-2015-report-to-the-congress-overview-of-the-340b-drug-pricing-program.pdf?sfvrsn=0. Accessed November 3, 2017.

2.   Fein A. Drug Channels, EXCLUSIVE: The 340B Program Hits $16.2 Billion in 2016; Now 5% of U.S. Drug Market. http://www.drugchannels.net/2017/05/exclusive-340b-program-hits-162-billion.html. Posted May 18, 2017; accessed November 5, 2017.

3.   Berkeley Research Group. Measuring the Relative Size of the 340B Program: 2012–2017 http://340breform.org/wp-content/uploads/2017/02/July-2017-BRG-White-Paper_Percent-of-Sales.pdf. July 2017; accessed November 3, 2017.

4.   Conti RM, Bach PR. Cost consequences of the 340B drug discount program. JAMA. 2013; 309(19): 1995–1996.

5.   Waxman H. We Must Protect Vital '340B' Drug Discounts for Safety Net Hospitals. https://www.huff-ingtonpost.com/rep-henry-waxman/we-must-protect-vital-340_b_6201768.html. Accessed November 5, 2017.

6.   Health Resources and Service Administration Office of Pharmacy Affairs. The 340B Drug Pricing Program https://www.hrsa.gov/opa. Accessed November 5, 2017.

7.   Apexus 340B Prime Vendor Program. https://www.340bpvp.com/controller.html. Accessed November 5, 2017.

8.   Fein A. Drug Channels: New Data Show the Gross-to-Net Rebate Bubble Growing Even Bigger http://www.drugchannels.net/2017/06/new-data-show-gross-to-net-rebate.html. Posted June 14, 2017; accessed November 5, 2017.

9.   Payment for Drugs under the Hospital Outpatient Prospective Payment System, OEI-03-09-00420. https://oig.hhs.gov/oei/reports/oei-03-09-00420.pdf. Issued October 22, 2010; accessed November 5, 2017.

10. Apexus Advanced 340B Operations Certificate Program. https://www.apexus.com/apexus-advanced-340b-certificate-program/. Accessed November 5, 2017.

CHAPTER 2

A Historical Perspective on the 340B Program's Purpose

William von Oehsen, JD

The 340B drug discount program recently celebrated its 25th anniversary. Until the last 5 or 6 years, the rationale for establishing the 340B program has never been challenged. To the contrary, stakeholders and policymakers have embraced the program's purpose and sought ways to expand its reach. Like an adolescent faced with competing pressures and demands, the 340B program is going through an identity crisis. The pharmaceutical industry asserts that the program is being used more widely than Congress intended. Some within the government contend that the program should be used to reduce Medicaid and Medicare drug spending. Safety net providers, on the other hand, cite the program's legislative history in support of their view that 340B savings are intended to pay for the uncompensated care they deliver to vulnerable patients. This chapter undertakes a historical assessment of the 340B program's role and purpose from the perspective of key stakeholders.

COVERED ENTITIES: THE 340B PROGRAM SUPPORTS UNCOMPENSATED CARE FOR VULNERABLE PATIENT POPULATIONS

From the standpoint of safety net hospitals, community health centers, and other providers participating in the 340B program, Congress established the program based on a simple concept. Namely, because manufacturers derive significant revenue from selling their drugs within the U.S. healthcare market, they should do their part to support the U.S. healthcare providers and programs that deliver essential services to indigent and other vulnerable patients who cannot afford to pay for such services. 340B program participants, referred to in the law as "covered entities," are highly dependent on Medicaid, Medicare, federal grants, state and local subsidies, and other tax-supported funding sources. By providing discounts on their drugs, manufacturers alleviate some of the burden on taxpayers of paying for vital covered entity services that would otherwise be uncompensated. Covered entities take care of some of the most challenging patient populations—ranging from the poor who face a host of socioeconomic barriers to care, to those who struggle with complex and expensive illnesses such as hemophilia and HIV, to those who need special services to access and receive appropriate care. By enacting the 340B program, Congress understood that covered entities are on the frontline of caring for these vulnerable populations and are in the best position to use 340B program savings to invest directly in the services that patients need most. This understanding is reflected in the program's legislative history, which explains that the purpose of the program is to enable covered entities to stretch scarce resources so they can reach more eligible patients and provide more comprehensive services.[1]

KEY POINT

Covered entities take care of some of the most challenging patient populations—ranging from the poor who face a host of socioeconomic barriers to care, to those who struggle with complex and expensive illnesses.

Therefore, it is not surprising that prior to the current debate over the 340B program's purpose, numerous healthcare initiatives spearheaded by the Administration, Congress, and the private sector have resulted in 340B program growth. Some of the more important initiatives are described below.

- **HRSA grant condition requiring 340B participation**—In 2000, the Health Resources and Services Administration (HRSA) published a rule requiring HRSA grantees and sub-grantees to either join the 340B program or provide good cause for nonparticipation. Grantees that choose not to participate in the 340B program must demonstrate the appropriateness of their drug purchasing practices.[2] Virtually all grantees and sub-grantees eligible to participate in 340B have enrolled in the program as a result of this grant condition.

- **Dispensing 340B drugs through contract pharmacies**—HRSA issued guidelines in 1996 permitting covered entities to dispense their 340B drugs through contracted pharmacies, but limited such arrangements to no more than one per covered entity site.[3] In 2010, HRSA issued guidelines that significantly expanded the contract pharmacy program by eliminating the one-to-one limitation and replacing it with what is commonly called the "one-to-many" rule, under which covered entities can enter into as many contract pharmacy arrangements as they desire.[4] Contract pharmacies allow covered entities to fill more of their patients' prescriptions with 340B drugs.

- **Alternative methods demonstration projects**—In 2001, HRSA launched a program that allowed covered entities to experiment with different contracting models on a demonstration basis.[5] Prior to publication of the 2010 contract pharmacy guidelines, alternative methods demonstration projects (AMDPs) were the only vehicle for one-to-many pharmacy arrangements. AMDPs were also used to allow two or more covered entities, serving a common patient population, to form a network that could enroll in the program in its own name and not have to keep separate inventories for the respective patients of network members.[6]

- **HRSA promotion of 340B to states**—HRSA previously provided funding to the National Conference of State Legislatures (NCSL) to promote 340B state initiatives and to monitor state legislation that affected the 340B program. Although HRSA no longer provides these grants, NCSL continues to host a web site that tracks 340B legislation at the state level.[7]

- **Heinz Foundation promotion of 340B partnerships**—The Heinz Foundation has assisted governors in determining whether and to what extent their states might achieve savings through the 340B programs. For example, the Heinz Foundation prepared a 2005 report for the state of Rhode Island estimating that it could save up to $18.8 million over a five-year period by expanding its use of the 340B program to inmates, the elderly, and others.[8]

- **Expanded hospital eligibility under the Affordable Care Act (ACA)**—Under the original 340B legislation, only one category of hospitals qualifies as 340B covered entities, namely, public or nonprofit acute care hospitals with a disproportionate share hospital percentage above 11.75%.[9] The ACA added four new categories of covered entities: free-standing cancer hospitals, critical access hospitals, sole community hospitals, and rural referral centers.[10] The ACA also formally recognized children's hospitals as covered entities under the 340B program.[11]

It is not surprising that initiatives like the ones above, combined with the relentless market pressure on covered entities to reduce costs, resulted in significant growth of the 340B program.

MANUFACTURERS: PROGRAM WAS INTENDED TO HELP UNINSURED

Expansion of the program, especially under the ACA, appears to have been the trigger that propelled the drug industry to mount a public relations and legislative campaign criticizing 340B program growth and advocating for reform.[12] PhRMA, which represents brand name drug-makers, and BIO, which represents biotechnology companies, began to reach out to other organizations for support in trying to reform the 340B program. In February 2013, these efforts culminated in publication of a white paper criticizing the program.[13] The white paper took aim at the growth of the 340B program and especially the use of 340B drugs to treat insured patients. One day later, the *New York Times* published an article describing the growing rift between the 340B provider community and drug manufacturers.[14] The organizations that sponsored the white paper, along with others, unveiled a new industry coalition called the Alliance for Integrity and Reform of 340B (AIR 340B). AIR 340B hired a public relations firm to publicize alleged abuses within the 340B program and to advance 340B reform measures. AIR 340B's web site (www.340Breform.org) prominently features the white paper and various studies questioning the commitment of covered entities, primarily 340B hospitals, to indigent care.

This is not the first time that the pharmaceutical industry has tried to reform the 340B program. In the mid-1990s, the industry asked Congress to amend the 340B program in ways that, if enacted, would have either destroyed the program or reduced its scope to the point of making it irrelevant. The first reform effort was focused on making participation in the program completely voluntary for manufacturers by eliminating the penalty for nonparticipation, namely, exclusion of a manufacturer's drugs from coverage under Medicaid and Medicare Part B.[15] The second effort would have required covered entities to bill all patients at actual acquisition cost for their 340B drugs.[16] An exodus from the program would likely have occurred for manufacturers under the first proposal and for covered entities under the second.

What is new about AIR 340B's recent reform efforts is its position that the program has a narrower purpose than helping to shoulder the burden of covered entities' uncompensated care. According to AIR 340B's web site, the purpose of the program is to make drugs more affordable to uninsured patients.[17] AIR 340B has, therefore, been vocal in its complaints about use of the 340B program for insured patients. When covered entities fill prescriptions with 340B drugs for insured patients—through either in-house or contract pharmacies—they can capture more revenue because the difference between a drug's acquisition cost and the reimbursement received for the drug is greater when a 340B drug is used. AIR 340B views this practice as "profiteering" and even describes it as fraudulent, especially when covered entities purposefully target insured patients for expanding their 340B pharmacy programs.[18] HRSA, on the other hand, has explicitly recognized the right of covered entities to "work within the reimbursement policies of the public and private health insurance plans they work with" to exercise "billing flexibility" and generate the "income that 340B was enacted to create."[19]

STATES: 340B SAVES MEDICAID DOLLARS

More recent disagreement over the intent of the 340B program has also clouded its already complicated relationship with the Medicaid drug rebate program. In creating the 340B program, Congress recognized that, when a 340B hospital or clinic dispenses or administers a covered outpatient drug to a Medicaid patient, the manufacturer is at risk of giving two discounts on the same drug: (1) an up-front 340B discount to the covered entity at the time of purchase and (2) a post-purchase rebate to the Medicaid program after Medicaid pays the covered entity for the drug and submits a rebate request to the manufacturer for that drug. Congress included provisions in both the 340B and Medicaid drug rebate statutes to protect manufacturers from this duplicate discount problem.[20] Congress had to expand that protection when it chose to extend the Medicaid rebate program to drugs covered and reimbursed by Medicaid managed care organizations.[21] But starting with California in 2009, states began eyeing the 340B program as a way to save money, not just to protect manufacturers from duplicate discounts.

Facing the largest year-end shortfall ever recorded, in 2009 the California legislature mandated, as part of an emergency budget-balancing bill, that covered entities carve in 340B drugs for California Medicaid (Medi-Cal) beneficiaries and pass their 340B discounts on to the state by billing such drugs at no more than actual acquisition cost (AAC) plus a dispensing fee.[22] The AIDS Healthcare Foundation challenged the law in court, arguing that the mandatory carve-in and AAC billing requirement for 340B drugs violated Medicaid procedural standards and the equal protection clauses of both the U.S. and California constitutions. Although the district court issued a permanent injunction to prevent implementation of the law, the Ninth Circuit ultimately decided in favor of Medi-Cal and vacated the permanent injunction.[23] In 2012, Illinois followed the California model by enacting an even more expansive 340B mandatory carve-in and AAC billing law.[24] As in California, Illinois adopted the changes as a cost-saving measure to address a budget shortfall in the state's Medicaid program.[25]

HRSA first established the requirement that 340B drugs be billed at AAC shortly after passage of the 340B law. The duplicate discount provisions in the 340B and Medicaid statutes directed the Secretary of the Department of Health and Human Services (HHS) to develop a mechanism that would ensure manufacturers do not give 340B discounts and Medicaid rebates on the same drug.[26] Within just a few months of the 340B law's enactment, HRSA, on behalf of HHS, responded to this directive by developing a two-part mechanism to avoid duplicate discounts.[27] First, each covered entity passes its 340B discount through to the state by billing the state Medicaid agency for each 340B drug dispensed or administered to a Medicaid patient at a price that does not exceed the drug's AAC plus a dispensing fee that the state has established.[28] Second, the state Medicaid agency excludes from its manufacturer rebate requests any Medicaid claim involving payment of a 340B drug. HRSA's mechanism was effective in protecting manufacturers from duplicate discounts and compensating states for the loss of their rebates. However, because the 340B ceiling price is less than what a state would have paid even if it had received its Medicaid rebate, the AAC billing rule actually created a windfall for states.[29] HRSA withdrew its AAC billing policy in March 2000, but states probably noticed that their drug budgets shrank when 340B drugs are paid at AAC.[30]

KEY POINT

In the program's legislative history, the program's purpose "is to enable covered entities to stretch scarce federal resources as far as possible, reaching more eligible patients and providing more comprehensive services."

There is no evidence in the legislative history of the 340B program that Congress established the program to save money for the Medicaid program. As noted in the program's legislative history, the program's purpose "is to enable covered entities to stretch scarce federal resources as far as possible, reaching more eligible patients and providing more comprehensive services."[31] The legislative history also makes clear that Medicaid relief from the high cost of drugs was the intent of the Omnibus Budget Reconciliation Act of 1990 (OBRA 90), which established the Medicaid drug rebate program, not the bills passed by Congress to establish the 340B program and a sister drug discount program for the Department of Veterans Affairs.

> [i]t is evident that OBRA 90 has achieved its objective of generating savings for the Medicaid program. However, other entities—notably the Department of Veterans Affairs, federally funded clinics, and public hospitals, have continued to experience substantial increases in their outpatient drug costs. The Committee is persuaded that, without intervention, the DVA and federally-funded clinics may continue to experience substantial drug price increases as manufacturers try to limit their rebates to Medicaid. In the view of the Committee, the federal government simply cannot continue to allow the DVA, federally-funded clinics, and their patients to remain unprotected against manufacturer price increases.[32]

The above language makes clear that Congress' purpose in enacting the 340B statute was to benefit covered entities, not state Medicaid programs. Accordingly, Congress did not intend for states to receive a windfall by paying 340B drugs at AAC.

Notwithstanding this legislative history, CMS established a federal AAC reimbursement requirement for all covered outpatient drugs, including those purchased through the 340B program, when it published its covered outpatient drug rule on February 1, 2016.[33] States have apparently interpreted CMS's AAC payment rule as a signal that, despite the legislative record to the contrary, they are entitled to the windfall representing the difference between a drug's 340B price and the post-rebate net price that Medicaid would otherwise have paid. For example, even though CMS only applied the 340B AAC billing rule to retail drugs reimbursed on a fee-for-service basis, several states apply the rule more broadly. HRSA's 340B technical assistance contractor Apexus recently reported that 21% of states require AAC billing of both fee-for-service and managed care claims.[34] California and Iowa have extended the rule to non-retail drugs, often referred to as physician-administered drugs.[35]

OIG, MEDPAC, AND CMS: 340B CAN REDUCE MEDICARE PART B COSTS

Since the beginning of the 340B program, Medicare has reimbursed 340B providers no differently than non-340B providers. Although Congress and CMS have instituted significant changes to Medicare drug reimbursement methodologies over the years, neither has taken any action that resulted in covered entities being paid at lower rates.

In 2008, CMS specifically considered and rejected the suggestion that the Medicare Part B program pay lower rates to 340B hospitals for physician-administered drugs. CMS requested information on the impact of 340B discounts on outpatient prospective payment rates for separately-paid drugs and asked whether Medicare should adjust payment to 340B hospitals in light of their lower drug costs.[36] In comments submitted to a CMS advisory panel called the CMS Ambulatory Payment Classification Panel (APC Panel), representatives of the drug industry, hospital pharmacists, cancer centers, physician groups, and other stakeholders were united in their view that 340B hospitals should receive the same level of reimbursement as non-340B hospitals because that is how Congress designed the 340B program.[37] The APC Panel noted in its February 2009 report to CMS that "[m]ost commenters felt that 340B hospitals should receive the same payment for drugs and biologicals as non-340B hospitals, because the intent of the program is to enable 340B hospitals to use the money they save on drug costs to pay for other services for the uninsured."[38] The APC Panel recommended that CMS "pay 340B hospitals in the same manner as it pays non-340B hospitals."[39] When CMS published its 2010 outpatient rates in November 2009, it accepted the APC Panel's recommendation, noting that commenters "were generally opposed to differential payment for hospitals based on their 340B participation status."[40]

The HHS Office of Inspector General (OIG), like CMS, also considered and rejected the idea of cutting Medicare Part B reimbursement to 340B hospitals for separately payable drugs. In October

2010, the OIG issued a report to CMS analyzing whether Medicare should pay the same rates to 340B and non-340B hospitals even though 340B hospitals pay less for drugs.[41] The OIG concluded that Medicare payments exceeding acquisition costs for 340B hospitals "was an expected result given the purpose of the 340B Program."[42] In reaching that conclusion, the OIG confirmed that the purpose of the program is for hospitals to use their 340B savings—the difference between reimbursement rates and lower acquisition costs—to help serve their low-income patients. The OIG noted that 340B hospitals receive reimbursement rates that are higher than their acquisition costs "based on the fact that the populations served by these entities are disproportionately low-income, uninsured, and underinsured."[43]

PRACTICE POINT

> With the changing political climate in Washington, DC, however, past assumptions about the relationship between the 340B and Medicare programs are being re-examined.

With the changing political climate in Washington DC, however, past assumptions about the relationship between the 340B and Medicare programs are being re-examined. Five years after issuing its report on Medicare reimbursement of 340B drugs, the OIG revisited its analysis because "some policymakers have questioned whether a portion of the savings mandated through the 340B Program should be passed on to Medicare and its beneficiaries."[44] The OIG ignored its prior analysis and identified three alternative payment methodologies that would redistribute 340B program savings to Medicare Part B. Separately-payable Part B drugs are currently reimbursed at 106% of average sales price (ASP).[45] The OIG recommended that Part B reimbursement for 340B drugs be reduced to 100% of ASP under the first methodology, ASP minus 14.4% under the second, and at the 340B ceiling price plus 6% of ASP under the third.[46] Building on the OIG's study, the Medicare Payment Advisory Committee (MedPAC) formally recommended to Congress that it reduce Part B reimbursement to 340B hospitals by 10% of ASP.[47] MedPAC is an independent agency established by Congress to advise it on issues affecting the Medicare program.

CMS has taken the latest step toward cutting Part B reimbursement for 340B drugs, and this time the proposed payment cut could actually be adopted. On July 13, 2017, CMS issued a proposed rule that would cut Medicare reimbursement for separately-payable Part B drugs to ASP minus 22.5%.[48] The rule would also require hospitals to identify non-340B Part B claims using a modifier.[49] Failure to include the modifier might result in a non-340B claim being paid at ASP minus 22.5% since CMS would presume such drugs were purchased through the 340B program.[50] If CMS finalizes its proposed rule, it would do so based on a new perspective that 340B program savings can be shared with the Medicare program and that covered entities and their patients are no longer the exclusive beneficiaries of the program.

340B IDENTITY CRISIS

After 20 years of apparent consensus around the purpose of the 340B program, a battle has emerged over competing versions of that purpose. The debate over the program's purpose is moving in two entirely different directions. According to manufacturers, the program's purpose is narrower than that supported by covered entities. They assert that the sole purpose of the program is to make drugs more affordable for uninsured patients. A growing number of Medicaid and Medicare policymakers, on the other hand, believe the program's purpose is broader than the traditional covered entity view. They believe the program is available to help reduce costs for the Medicaid and Medicare programs. In short, the 340B program is going through a major identity crisis.

KEY POINT

Over the past 25 years, the covered entity community has become increasingly dependent on the 340B program as a financing mechanism to support care delivery and community benefit.

Ironically, if the drug industry is successful in limiting program use to uninsured or under-insured individuals, it would be at the expense of the Medicaid and Medicare programs. States like California and Illinois would see Medicaid reimbursement to 340B hospitals climb because Medicaid-covered drugs would no longer be 340B eligible. And aspirations by OIG, MedPAC, and CMS to save Medicare Part B dollars would go unfulfilled. Similarly, if the Medicaid and Medicare programs are successful in using 340B discounts to save program dollars, drug industry efforts to limit 340B utilization to uninsured and underinsured patients could not be achieved without driving up Medicaid and Medicare costs. Meanwhile, the covered entity community has become increasingly dependent on the 340B program as a financing mechanism. Many covered entities claim that, if the program were scaled back or if they were required to pass their 340B discounts to payers like Medicaid and Medicare, they would be forced to cut services, or worse, close their doors.

In light of these competing and conflicting interests, it is tempting to conclude that Congress got it right in drafting the 340B legislation the way it is and that the 340B program should be left untouched. There appears to be consensus among stakeholders that the 340B program could benefit from greater transparency and that covered entities should make available to the public how they use their 340B savings.[51] Perhaps covered entities should be allowed to take this step on a voluntary basis before Congress opens up the program for reform.

SUMMARY

This chapter undertakes a historical assessment of the 340B program's role and purpose from the perspective of key stakeholders. Until recently, the rationale for establishing the 340B program has never been challenged. After 20 years of apparent consensus around the purpose of the 340B program, a battle has emerged over competing versions of that purpose. The debate over the 340B program's purpose is moving in two entirely different directions.

Stakeholders and policymakers embraced the program's purpose and sought ways to expand its reach prior to the current debate. Over the 25-year history of the 340B program, the Administration, Congress, and the private sector have spearheaded a number of healthcare initiatives that resulted in 340B program growth, especially under the ACA. Recent program growth appears to have been the trigger that propelled the drug industry to mount an effort criticizing 340B program growth and advocating for reform.

REFERENCES

1.   HR Report No. 102-384 (II) at 12 (1992) (accompanying H.R. 2890, Purpose and Summary, Background and Need for the Legislation: Current Law).

2.   *See* Final Notice Regarding HRSA Grant Requirement—Participation in the 340B Drug Pricing Program, 65 Fed. Reg. 6,383 (February 9, 2000).

3.   *See* Notice Regarding Section 602 of the Veterans Health Care Act of 1992; Contract Pharmacy Services, 61 Fed. Reg. 43,549, 43,551, 43,555 (August 23, 1996).

4.   *See* Notice Regarding 340B Drug Pricing Program—Contract Pharmacy Services, 75 Fed. Reg. 10,272, 10,275 (March 5, 2010).

5.   *See* Press Release, HHS, New HHS Initiative Will Expand Access to Prescription Drugs for Safety Net Patients (June 18, 2001).

6.   *See* HRSA, 340B Drug Pricing Program & Pharmacy Affairs, Alternative Methods Demonstration Project Summaries, http://www.hrsa.gov/opa/implementation/alternativemethods/amdprojects.html (last visited November 18, 2016) for a list of approved AMDPs. The AMDP program has been discontinued by HRSA.

7.   *See* NCSL, States and the 340B Drug Pricing Program, http://www.ncsl.org/research/health/340b-drug-pricing-program-and-states.aspx (Accessed October 10, 2017).

8.   *See* Federal Drug Discount and Compliance Monitor, vol. 2, no. 4, Heinz Foundation Calls For Increased State Use of 340B (April 2005).

9.   42 U.S.C. § 256b(a)(4)(L).

10. *Id.* at § 256b(a)(4)(M)-(O).

11. *Id.* at § 256b(a)(4)(M). Congress intended to add children's hospitals to the program under the Deficit Reduction Act of 2005 (DRA), but HRSA delayed implementing this directive due to legal complications surrounding how the relevant DRA provision was drafted. Under the DRA, they were added indirectly to the 340B program by including them in the manufacturer pharmaceutical pricing agreements, but they were not included in section 340B directly. *See* DRA, Pub. L. No. 109-171, § 6004, 120 Stat. 61.

12. "Drug Discount Policy for Hospitals, Clinics Under Scrutiny," Kaiser Health News (June 23, 2014), *available at* http://khn.org/news/drug-discount-policy-340b/ (Accessed October 10, 2017).

13. PhRMA, et al, *The 340B Drug Discount Program: A Review and Analysis of the 340B Program* (Winter 2013), http://www.bio.org/sites/default/files/340B%20White%20Paper%20FINAL.pdf. Accessed October 10, 2017.

14. Andrew Pollack, *Dispute Develops over Discount Drug Program*, N.Y. Times, February 12, 2013. http://www.nytimes.com/2013/02/13/business/dispute-develops-over-340b-discount-drug-program.html. Accessed October 10, 2017.

15. Balanced Budget Act of 1995, H.R. 2491, 104th Congress (1995) (as reported by H. Comm. on the Budget, Oct. 17, 1995). The penalty for non-participation in the 340B program was later inserted in the proposed legislation, which was ultimately vetoed by President Bill Clinton on December 6, 1995.

16. Welfare and Medicaid Reform Act of 1996, H.R. 3734, 104th Congress (1996) (as reported by H. Comm. on the Budget, June 27, 1996).

17. *See* AIR 340B web site (2017), *available at* http://340breform.org/about-the-340b-program/ (Accessed October 10, 2017).

18. *See, e.g.,* Bill Sarraille, *OPA's Challenges in Implementing Health Care Reform Considerations from Manufacturers' Perspective* at the 15th Annual 340B Coalition Conference (July 12, 2011).

19. HRSA, Hemophilia Treatment Center Manual for Participating in the Drug Pricing Program Established by Section 340B of the Public Health Service Act, II.K, (July 2005), *at* https://docs.340bpvp.com/.../resourcecenter/htc_policy_manual_340b_template.docx. Accessed October 10, 2017.

20. 42 U.S.C. § 256b(a)(5)(A) and § 1927(a)(5).

21. 42 U.S.C. § 1927(j)(1).

22. Cal. Welf. & Inst. Code § 14105.46 (2009).

23. *AIDS Healthcare Foundation v. Douglas*, --- Fed. Appx. ----, 2016 WK 6599919 (9th Cir. November 8, 2016).

24. 305 Ill. Comp. Stat. § 5-5.12(l) (2012).

25. *See* "Governor Quinn Signs Law to Save Medicaid," Illinois Government News Network (June 2012), *available at* http://www3.illinois.gov/PressReleases/ShowPressRelease.cfm?SubjectID=2&RecNum=10307 (Accessed October 10, 2017).

26. 42 U.S.C. § 256b(a)(5)(A) and § 1927(a)(5).

27. In an effort to implement parallel provisions in the 340B and Medicaid drug rebate programs, HHS articulated this mechanism in both HRSA guidelines and in a Medicaid drug rebate release addressed to state Medicaid directors. *See* Medicaid Drug Rebate Program Release No. 33, at 4-7 (November 1993); Notice Regarding Duplicate Discounts, 58 Fed. Reg. at 27,293 (adopted as proposed at 58 Fed. Reg. 34,058).

28. Medicaid Drug Rebate Program Release No. 33, at 6 (November 1993); Notice Regarding Duplicate Discounts, 58 Fed. Reg. at 27,293 (adopted as proposed at 58 Fed. Reg. 34,058); and Notice Regarding section 340B Drug Pricing Program – Program Guidance Clarification, 65 Fed. Reg. 13,983, 13,984 (March 15, 2000).

29. The 340B ceiling price for a given drug is its average manufacturer price (AMP) minus its drug-specific unit rebate amount (URA). Manufacturers are free to give sub-ceiling discounts on their 340B drugs and often do through the 340B prime vendor program. Medicaid reimbursement is typically higher than 340B AAC, even taking into account the rebates states collect. A study by the Congressional Budget Office (CBO) in 2005 confirmed that 340B pricing is lower than the net final price to Medicaid. CBO, "Prices for Brand-Name Drugs Under Selected Federal Program," p.11 (June 2005). According to the report, the average 340B price is 51% of average wholesale price, whereas the net final price to Medicaid is 64% of average wholesale price. *Id*. at 11-12.

30. 65 Fed. Reg. 13,983, 13,984 (March 15, 2000).

31. H.R. No. 102-384(II)(1992) at 12 (accompanying H.R. 2890, Purpose and Summary, Background and Need for the Legislation: Current Law).

32. H.R. No. 102-384(II)(1992) (accompanying H.R. 2890, Purpose and Summary, Background and Need for the Legislation: Current Law).

33. 81 Fed. Reg. 5,170 (February 1, 2016).

34. Katheryne Richardson, Presentation at 340B Coalition Summer Conference (July 10, 2017).

35. *See* Informational Bulletin 16-9, Louisiana Department of Health and Hospitals (April 19, 2016), *available at* http://new.dhh.louisiana.gov/assets/docs/BayouHealth/Informational_Bulletins/2016/IB16-9.pdf (Accessed October 10, 2017); Informational Letter No. 1638-MC, Iowa Department of Human Services (March 21, 2016), *available at* https://dhs.iowa.gov/sites/default/files/1638-MC_Update-340B_DrugPricing%20Program.pdf (Accessed October 10, 2017).

36. Final Rule, Medicare Program: Changes to the Hospital Outpatient Prospective Payment System and CY 2009 Payment Rates, 73 Fed. Reg. 68,502, 68,655 (November 18, 2008).

37. *See* "Drugs, Biologicals, and Pharmacy Overhead: Testimony Before the Advisory Panel on Ambulatory Payment Classification (APC) Groups Meeting" [PowerPoint Slides], The Pharmacy Stakeholder Group (Aug. 5-7, 2009); Stuart Gordon and William von Oehsen, "Interplay Between 340B Pricing and HOPPS Drug Reimbursement: SNHPA Testimony Before the Advisory Panel on Ambulatory Payment Classification (APC) Groups Meeting" [PowerPoint Slides], Safety Net Hospitals for Pharmaceutical Access (February 18-20, 2009).

38. CMS Advisory Panel on Ambulatory Payment Classification Groups, APC Panel Meeting Report, February 18-19, 2009, https://www.cms.gov/Regulations-and-Guidance/Guidance/FACA/APC-Panel-Archives-Items/CMS1237161.html (hereinafter "APC Panel Meeting Report"). Accessed October 10, 2017.

39. APC Panel Meeting Report, p. 29.

40. 74 Fed. Reg. 60,316, 60,501 (November 20, 2009).

41. Memorandum Report to Donald M. Berwick, Administrator, CMS from Stuart Wright, Deputy Inspector General for Evaluations and Inspections, HHS OIG (Oct. 22, 2010), *available at* https://oig.hhs.gov/oei/reports/oei-03-09-00420.pdf (Accessed October 10, 2017).

42. *Id.*

43. *Id.*

44. OIG, Part B Payments for 340B-Purchased Drugs, OEI-12-14-00030 Executive Summary (November 2015).

45. 77 Fed. Reg. 68,210, 68,216 (November 15, 2012).

46. OIG, Part B Payments for 340B-Purchased Drugs, OEI-12-14-00030, p. 11 (November 2015).

47. MedPAC, Report to Congress: Medicare Payment Policy (March 2016).

48. Medicare Program: Hospital Outpatient Prospective Payment and Ambulatory Surgical Center Payment Systems and Quality Reporting Programs, 82 Fed. Reg. 33,558, 33,633-34 (July 20, 2017).

49. *Id.*

50. *Id.*

51. *See* "Hospital Group Seeks to Beef Up Case for 340B Drug Discount," CQ Roll Call (March 25, 2016), *available at* http://www.commonwealthfund.org/publications/newsletters/washington-health-poli-cy-in-review/2016/mar/march-28-2016/hospital-group-seeks-to-beef-up-case-to-340b-drug-discount (Accessed October 10, 2017). In addition, AIR 340B's web site (www.340Breform.org) states that Alliance Members believe "[a] 340B program should directly support access to prescription drugs for uninsured, indigent patients," and "[r]eform, transparency, accountability and oversight are needed to ensure that the program meets this public health objective."

CHAPTER 3

340B Program Requirements and Compliance Issues

William von Oehsen, JD,
Barbara Straub Williams, JD, and
Shuchi Parikh, JD

This chapter summarizes the requirements and compliance issues applicable to providers and manufacturers that choose to participate in the 340B program. It also examines the enforcement authority of the federal agency charged with administering the program, the Health Resources and Services Administration (HRSA), which is located within the Department of Health and Human Services (HHS). Most of the 340B program's requirements are set forth in the 340B statute. As of April 2018, HRSA has issued only one regulation governing the 340B program; that regulation has still not been implemented.[1] All other instructions from HRSA are issued as guidance. Both providers and manufacturers struggle with discerning their 340B compliance responsibilities because, in the absence of implementing regulations, the program's only legally binding requirements are those found in the 340B statute. In most cases, it is drafted in broad terms. HRSA guidance deserves deference by program participants, but some policies may be unenforceable if they stray too far from the plain meaning of the law. For this reason, 340B providers and manufacturers would be well-advised to seek legal counsel to clarify their 340B rights and responsibilities.

KEY POINT

HRSA has issued only one regulation governing the 340B program, and that regulation has yet to be implemented. 340B rules are typically articulated as guidance and may be subject to change as HRSA considers new information and audit results.

PROGRAM ELIGIBILITY

Only certain healthcare providers are eligible to become "covered entities" under the 340B statute.[2] The original legislation allowed public or nonprofit acute care hospitals with a disproportionate share hospital (DSH) percentage above 11.75%, certain grantees, and federally qualified health center (FQHC) look-alikes to enroll in the 340B program.[3] The Affordable Care Act (ACA)[4] made five additional hospital categories eligible for the 340B program: children's hospitals,[5] cancer hospitals, sole community hospitals (SCHs), rural referral centers (RRCs), and critical access hospitals (CAHs).[6] Each of these categories of covered entities must meet additional criteria to participate in the 340B program (discussed below). A qualifying grantee may also be an outpatient department of a qualifying hospital. In these circumstances, the entity may register as a grantee or qualify under the hospital's registration. HRSA encourages grantees with more than one qualifying grant to register under each grant in case the grantee loses one of the grants.

Hospital Eligibility

Both the eligibility criteria and compliance requirements applicable to the six categories of 340B hospitals vary by category. If a hospital qualifies under more than one category, it may participate under any one of the categories under which it qualifies, but must comply with the requirements relevant to the category it selects.

DSH Adjustment Percentage

Each hospital category, with the exception of CAHs, must meet a DSH adjustment threshold to participate in the 340B program.[7] Acute care hospitals, children's hospitals, and cancer hospitals must have DSH adjustment percentage that exceeds 11.75%, based on the hospital's most recently filed Medicare cost report.[8] Hospitals designated as SCHs or RRCs must have a DSH adjustment percentage of at least 8%.[9] A hospital must contact HRSA if its DSH adjustment percentage falls below the requisite level based on its filed Medicare cost report and must stop purchasing 340B drugs immediately.

Hospitals can only become prospectively eligible for the 340B program. According to one of the three court cases addressing the 340B program, covered entities cannot become retroactively eligible for participation in 340B based on an amended Medicare cost report with a qualifying DSH percentage.[10]

Organizational Status

Each category of eligible hospital must meet the "government function" requirement, which mandates that a hospital be the following:

- Owned or operated by a unit of state or local government (a state, county, or city).
- A public or private nonprofit corporation that has been formally granted governmental powers by a unit of state or local government.
- A private nonprofit hospital with a contract with a state or local government to provide healthcare services to low income individuals who are not entitled to benefits under Medicare or Medicaid.[11]

For-profit hospitals and hospitals that are not legally or contractually obligated to care for low-income patients are, therefore, not eligible to participate in the program.

KEY POINT

HRSA relies on a 340B hospital's Medicare cost report to determine whether a hospital and its child sites are eligible to participate in the 340B program. Pharmacists should confer with the hospital's Medicare cost report personnel to avoid violations of 340B eligibility requirements.

Defining the Scope of an Eligible DSH Hospital

Although the 340B statute is relatively clear in identifying the kinds of hospitals eligible to participate in the program, it is less specific about the scope of a qualifying hospital. HRSA has relied in large part on a 340B hospital's Medicare cost report for distinguishing between hospital facilities that are eligible and ineligible.

The Medicare Cost Report Test. HRSA policy states that outpatient facilities that are an "integral component" of a hospital are eligible to participate in the 340B program.[12] HRSA refers to these clinics as "child" sites.[13] Through informal guidance, HRSA has stated that hospitals must register all off-site outpatient clinics that use 340B.[14] HRSA defines an *off-site clinic* as one that is outside the four walls of the hospital or uses a different street address. Clinics that share the same street address as the hospital but have a different suite address are considered within the four walls.[15] If an off-site facility houses multiple clinics, each of the clinics must be registered in the HRSA database.[16] When a hospital submits a child site registration request, HRSA reviews the hospital's Medicare cost report worksheets A and C and confirms that the costs and charges for the clinic appear in a reimbursable outpatient or ancillary line to determine whether a facility is an integral component of the hospital. HRSA reviews electronic data from the Centers for Medicare & Medicaid Services (CMS) to verify the cost report information, but asks the covered entity to submit documentation if the CMS data do not match the covered entity's registration request.

New Off-Site Hospital Clinics. Section 603 of the Bipartisan Budget Act of 2015 (BBA 2015) specifies that, unless a hospital off-campus provider-based outpatient department was billing under the hospital outpatient prospective payment system (OPPS) prior to BBA 2015's date of enactment (November 2, 2015), it will not be paid under OPPS and instead will be paid "under the applicable payment system" beginning January 1, 2017.[17] Exceptions to this provision are off-campus emergency department services,[18] departments that are on-campus of a "remote location" of the provider (i.e., another facility that provides inpatient services and is not co-located with another hospital or on another hospital's campus),[19] rural health clinics (RHCs), and certain FQHCs and FQHC look-a-likes.[20]

CMS published final rules to implement Section 603 on November 14, 2016.[21] Because clinics subject to Section 603 are not reimbursed under the same Medicare payment system as other hospital outpatient clinics, some stakeholders questioned whether these clinics would be eligible for the 340B program. However, both the statutory language of Section 603 and CMS's statements in the preamble to its final rule indicate that Section 603 clinics are considered part of the hospital.[22] As part of a 340B eligible hospital, these clinics should be eligible for 340B.

GPO Prohibition

DSH hospitals, children's hospitals, and cancer hospitals are subject to a 340B eligibility criterion that states that they may not purchase covered outpatient drugs through a group purchasing organization (GPO) or similar arrangement.[23] This requirement is commonly referred to as the *GPO prohibition*. A hospital that violates the GPO prohibition will become ineligible for participation in the 340B program. Hospitals are required to cease purchasing covered outpatient drugs through a GPO on the effective date of their registration in the 340B program. Importantly, the GPO prohibition does not apply to SCHs, RRCs, or CAHs. The GPO prohibition only applies to *covered outpatient drugs*, which means that GPOs can still be used to purchase inpatient drugs as well as any outpatient drug that falls outside the definition of a covered outpatient drug. Covered entities must adhere to the GPO prohibition even if a manufacturer does not make 340B pricing available.[24]

KEY POINT

Although the penalty for violation of the prohibition on diversion or duplicate discounts is generally only repayment of the 340B discount, HRSA takes the position that a hospital that violates the GPO prohibition is ineligible for participation in the 340B program during the period of the violation. Hospitals may not purchase covered outpatient drugs through a GPO beginning on the effective date of their registration in the 340B program unless they comply with the criteria summarized below.

One exception to the GPO prohibition is that hospitals may purchase drugs through the GPO operated by HRSA's prime vendor, Apexus. In addition, hospital departments may use a GPO for covered outpatient drugs if those facilities meet the following criteria:

- They are located at a different physical address than the parent.
- They are not registered on the HRSA 340B database as participating in the 340B program.
- They purchase drugs through a separate pharmacy wholesaler account than the 340B participating parent.
- The hospital maintains records demonstrating that any covered outpatient drugs purchased through the GPO at these sites are not utilized or otherwise transferred to the parent hospital or any outpatient facilities registered on the HRSA 340B database.[25]

Further details about HRSA's application of the GPO prohibition can be found in a 340B program release dated February 7, 2013.[26] Prior HRSA guidance on the prohibition was narrow, infrequent, and—in some cases—inconsistent.

Eligibility for Grantees and FQHC Look-Alikes

The following grantees and clinics are eligible for the 340B program:

- FQHCs and look-alikes
- Ryan White HIV/AIDS program grantees
- AIDS drug assistance programs
- Hemophilia treatment centers
- Native Hawaiian health centers
- Black lung clinics
- Title X family planning clinics
- Sexually transmitted disease clinics
- Tuberculosis clinics[27]

Grantees must register every service location that purchases or uses 340B drugs.[28] These locations must be authorized within the scope of the grant upon which the covered entity's 340B status is based.[29]

Eligibility Requirements Applicable to All Covered Entities

Although, as described above, hospitals and grantees have to meet different requirements to qualify for 340B participation, there are two eligibility-related requirements— ensuring annual recertification and maintaining auditable records—that apply to all covered entities.

Annual Recertification

The ACA added a provision requiring covered entities to ensure at least annually that their information on the HRSA database is accurate.[30] To implement this provision, HRSA established an annual recertification process. HRSA announces a period each year, generally about 3–4 weeks in length, during which covered entities must recertify or they will be terminated from the 340B program. The period generally differs for hospitals and grantees. The covered entity's designated Authorizing Official must attest to several statements, including (1) the covered entity meets all eligibility requirements, (2) its information on the HRSA database is accurate, and (3) it will disclose to HRSA if it discovers a breach of 340B eligibility or compliance requirements.[31]

Auditable Records

All covered entities must maintain auditable records of their 340B operations to maintain eligibility in the 340B program.[32] HRSA has threatened to terminate covered entities for not maintaining auditable records that were not adequate to be audited.

WHAT DRUGS ARE ELIGIBLE AND AT WHAT PRICE?

For a drug to be covered by the Medicare and Medicaid programs, the manufacturer of the drug must enter into a pharmaceutical pricing agreement (PPA) with HHS that states it will provide drugs at prices not exceeding the 340B ceiling price to covered entities.[33] The Medicare and Medicaid programs are significant payers in the U.S. pharmaceutical market, so most drug manufacturers have executed PPAs with HHS to make their drugs more attractive to purchasers. The drugs subject to the 340B program and the discounts applicable to those drugs are discussed below.

Medicaid Definition of Covered Outpatient Drugs

- A manufacturer's obligation to extend 340B pricing to covered entities only applies to covered outpatient drugs.[34] The 340B statute defines the term *covered outpatient drug* by incorporating the definition from the Medicaid drug rebate statute.[35] The definition of covered outpatient drug includes prescription drugs, biological products other than vaccines, and insulin.[36] Excluded from the definition are drugs "provided as part of, or as incident to and in the same setting as" certain services (listed below), if Medicaid pays for the drug as part of the service and does not separately reimburse for the drug. The services listed in the statute are inpatient hospital services.

- Inpatient hospital services.

- Hospice services.

- Dental services (except that drugs for which the State plan authorizes direct reimbursement to the dispensing dentist are covered outpatient drugs).

- Physicians' services.

- Outpatient hospital services.

- Nursing facility services and services provided by an intermediate care facility for the mentally retarded.

- Other laboratory and x-ray services.

- Renal dialysis.[37]

CMS has adopted a regulatory definition that generally tracks the statute.[38]

Application of Covered Outpatient Drug Definition to 340B Program

As stated previously, the 340B statute incorporates the definition of covered outpatient drug from provisions in the Medicaid statute governing the drug rebate program. This definition states that drugs are excluded from the list based, partially, on whether Medicaid pays for them as part of a bundled service. This definition makes sense in the context of the Medicaid drug rebate program because the program only applies to Medicaid drugs, but it is difficult to apply in the 340B program because 340B drugs may be billed to and reimbursed by any payer, not just Medicaid. For any given drug, one payer might require that the drug be separately billed and reimbursed whereas another might choose to have the drug billed and paid for as part of a bundled service.

Currently, HRSA gives covered entities some discretion in determining whether a drug billed in a bundled manner is a covered outpatient drug for purposes of the 340B program. HRSA allows covered entities to develop their own policies, as long as they are "defensible, consistently applied, documented in policy/procedures, and auditable."[39] If a covered entity follows this guidance and determines that a drug is not a covered outpatient drug, it may purchase the drug through a GPO. Saline solutions, anesthesia gases, and contrast media are examples of drugs that hospitals often exclude from the definition of covered outpatient drug in their policies and procedures. HRSA proposed changes to its interpretation of covered outpatient drug definition so that fewer drugs would fall within the definition.[40] However, HRSA recently withdrew a final version of these changes.[41]

340B Price Calculations and Penny Pricing

The 340B statute establishes a maximum price, sometimes referred to as a *ceiling price*, that manufacturers may sell covered outpatient drugs to covered entities. The 340B ceiling price is calculated each quarter by subtracting the unit rebate amount (URA) from the average manufacturer price (AMP) for the smallest unit of measure based on pricing data from the immediately preceding quarter.[42] For new drugs, there are no sales data to determine the 340B ceiling price. As of April 2018, HRSA's policy is to require manufacturers of new drugs to estimate the 340B ceiling price for the first three quarters that a new covered outpatient drug is available for sale.[43] The statutory ceiling price calculation currently is required, beginning with the fourth quarter the drug is available for sale. The manufacturer also calculates the actual 340B ceiling price for the first three quarters the drug was available for sale and refunds or credits covered entities that purchased the covered outpatient drug above that price no later than the end of the fourth quarter after the drug is available for sale.

Beginning July 1, 2018, HRSA's policy for calculating 340B ceiling prices will change pursuant to new regulations.[44] Manufacturers will be required to use a standardized methodology to estimate the 340B ceiling price until AMP data are available to calculate an actual 340B ceiling price. The methodology for the estimated 340B ceiling price will be wholesale acquisition cost (WAC) minus the appropriate rebate percentage. Once the AMP is known, and no later than the fourth quarter that the drug is available, the manufacturer will be required to calculate the actual 340B ceiling price and offer repayment to the covered entity for the difference between the estimated and actual 340B ceiling price.

In some cases, the statutory 340B ceiling price calculation results in a price of $0.00. In these cases, HRSA instructs manufacturers to sell the covered outpatient drug at $0.01, which is known as the HRSA penny pricing policy.[45]

Orphan Drugs

Orphan drugs purchased by RRCs, SCHs, and cancer hospitals are statutorily excluded from the definition of a "covered outpatient drug" and therefore fall outside the scope of the 340B program.[46] An orphan drug is defined (by HHS) as one that treats a disease either affecting fewer than 200,000 people in the United States or more than 200,000, if there is no reasonable expectation that the costs of developing a drug for the condition would be recouped.[47]

Orphan drugs are often used to treat diseases other than the one for which the drug received its orphan designation. For this reason, HRSA decided to interpret the orphan drug exclusion narrowly so that it would only apply when a covered entity uses the drug to treat the condition covered by the orphan designation and not when the drug is used for other conditions.[48] HRSA's interpretation was challenged by pharmaceutical manufacturers, and a federal court held that the prohibition applies whether or not the covered entity is using the orphan drug for its orphan indication.[49] While the court decision clarified that manufacturers are never required to give 340B discounts on orphan drugs purchased by RRCs, SCHs, and cancer hospitals, manufacturers may opt to offer 340B discounts on a voluntary basis. CMS regulations provide that any discount offered to a 340B covered entity is excluded from the manufacturer's best price calculations, and CMS has stated that this exclusion applies to discounts on sales of orphan drugs to hospitals subject to the orphan drug exclusion.[50]

Covered Entity Requirements

Covered entities are subject to important statutory restrictions governing to whom they may legally transfer 340B drugs and how they bill such drugs to the Medicaid program. These restrictions, in turn, affect how covered entities manage their drug inventories, especially if they purchase and stock both 340B and non-340B drugs. These and other covered entity requirements are described below.

KEY POINT

Covered entities may not transfer 340B drugs to individuals who are not eligible to receive them and must comply with requirements to protect manufacturers from providing both a 340B discount and a rebate to the State Medicaid program. These restrictions affect how covered entities manage drug inventories.

Diversion

The 340B statute prohibits a covered entity from reselling or transferring 340B-discounted drugs to a person who is not "a patient of the entity."[51] This requirement is generally referred to as the *prohibition against diversion* or the *anti-diversion prohibition*. HRSA issued a notice on October 24, 1996 defining a *patient* for purposes of the 340B program.[52] According to that notice, an individual must satisfy three requirements to be eligible to receive the discounted drugs. All three of these requirements are applicable to grantees and FQHC look-alikes but only the first two are applicable to hospitals.[53] *First*, the covered entity must maintain records of the individual's healthcare. *Second*, the individual must be under the care of a physician or other healthcare professional who is employed by, under contract with, or in a referral relationship to the covered entity such that responsibility for the individual's care remains with the covered entity. *Third*, the individual must receive a healthcare service or range of services from the covered entity that is consistent with the service or range of services for which grant funding or FQHC look-alike status has been provided to the entity.[54] An individual is not considered a patient of the covered entity if the only service received by the individual from the covered entity is the dispensing of drug(s) for subsequent self-administration or administration in the home setting.[55]

Duplicate Discounts

The 340B statute states that covered entities may not submit a Medicaid fee-for-service claim for a 340B drug if a Medicaid agency will also be receiving a rebate on that drug.[56] This provision creates an obligation on covered entities to avoid what are known as **duplicate discounts**. In the ACA, Congress expanded the Medicaid drug rebate to include drugs covered by Medicaid managed care organizations (MCOs), and also provided that drug manufacturers would not be subject to duplicate discounts for these drugs. In contrast to Medicaid fee-for-service drugs, Congress placed the burden on state Medicaid agencies, rather than covered entities, to prevent duplicate discounts on MCO drugs.[57]

Carve In/Out Election and Use of Medicaid Exclusion File

In 1993, HRSA decided to give covered entities the option whether or not to purchase 340B drugs for Medicaid fee-for-service beneficiaries.[58] Covered entities that elect to use 340B drugs for Medicaid fee-for service beneficiaries are said to *carve in,* and covered entities that elect not to use 340B drugs for these beneficiaries are said to *carve out*. Covered entities are required to keep HRSA informed of their election. HRSA created the Medicaid Exclusion File (MEF) as a mechanism for documenting which covered entities carve in and which carve out. Covered entities that carve in are listed on the MEF, along with their Medicaid billing numbers and national provider identifier (NPI). The MEF alerts states and manufacturers that the covered entity uses 340B drugs for Medicaid beneficiaries. If a covered entity uses a different billing number for any child site, it may make a different election with regard to that child site. HRSA clarified in 2014 that the MEF does not apply to Medicaid MCO drugs.[59] Therefore, under HRSA policy, a covered entity may make a different carve in/out election with respect to Medicaid fee-for-service and MCO drugs.

State Medicaid Reimbursement and Billing Policies

Many state Medicaid agencies have adopted policies with respect to billing and reimbursement for 340B drugs. As stated previously, under HRSA policy, a covered entity may elect to carve out 340B for Medicaid fee-for-service beneficiaries, but carve in for Medicaid MCO beneficiaries, or vice versa. However, some state Medicaid agencies have adopted policies stating that a covered entity's election for both Medicaid fee-for-service and Medicaid MCO must be the same.[60] Other states direct covered entities to identify at the claim level when they are using 340B drugs for the Medicaid population. Although HRSA established the MEF to notify states and other interested parties about a covered entity's carve in/out election, these states require covered entities to go a step further and to apply a modifier on the Medicaid claim form when billing 340B drugs.[61] Typically, state Medicaid agencies require providers to use a *UD modifier* and retail pharmacies to include indicator "Ø8" on the claim to flag drugs that have been purchased at 340B prices.[62]

Some state Medicaid agencies also require covered entities to bill at actual acquisition cost (AAC) for 340B drugs, thereby passing the benefit of 340B pricing from the covered entity to the Medicaid agency.[63] Effective April 1, 2017, state Medicaid agencies are required under federal regulations to set a ceiling of AAC for all retail pharmacy drugs, including 340B drugs.[64] Covered entities concerned about the loss of Medicaid revenue as a result of the new AAC reimbursement rule also face the threat of Medicare cuts. CMS recently finalized a rule that will reduce reimbursement for 340B drugs reimbursed under Medicare Part B by close to 30%.[65]

Given the variability of state Medicaid agency requirements related to 340B billing and reimbursement, covered entities must keep informed of the policies for Medicaid programs to which they submit claims for 340B drugs.

Inventory Management—Implications for Diversion, Duplicate Discount, GPO, and Orphan Drug Prohibitions

Inventory management is a critical component of 340B program compliance. A covered entity must be able to track accurately its 340B drug inventory in order to comply with the diversion, duplicate discount, orphan drug, and GPO prohibitions. Covered entities have multiple options for maintaining and tracking their 340B drug inventories, including using a physical inventory, a virtual replenishment inventory, and/or a third-party vendor to track inventory.

Physically Segregated Inventory

A covered entity may manage its 340B inventory by maintaining physically separate inventories of 340B and non-340B drugs. Drugs needed for an eligible patient are taken from the 340B inventory, and drugs needed for an ineligible individual are taken from the non-340B inventory.

Maintaining physically segregated inventories presents challenges in many healthcare settings. The individual dispensing or administering the drug also must make auditable decisions in real time regarding whether an individual is eligible to receive 340B drugs, which can be difficult in mixed inpatient/outpatient areas or for covered entities that carve out Medicaid.

Nevertheless, physically segregated inventories might be suitable in settings where all individuals receiving treatment will be 340B-eligible outpatients. Also, some covered entities order expensive 340B drugs on an as-needed basis and physically segregate the product until it can be dispensed or administered to the patient or segregate 340B inventory that is ordered for a designated 340B-eligible patient.

Replenishment or Virtual Inventory

In a virtual inventory system, a single *neutral* inventory is maintained. Neutral inventory can be dispensed to any patient—340B-eligible or ineligible. Each drug that is dispensed is reviewed retrospectively, and the covered entity determines whether the drug was dispensed to a 340B-eligible patient or an ineligible individual.

The covered entity or contract pharmacy tracks the quantities of each drug that went to 340B-eligible patients by using what is often called an *accumulator*. When a full package size has been dispensed to 340B-eligible patients, it purchases replenishment product on its 340B account. Because the 340B drugs ordered in this manner replace drugs that were already dispensed, the ordered drugs virtually take the place of the dispensed drugs. The ordered drugs then become *neutral* inventory, and the dispensed drugs become the 340B drugs.

A virtual inventory system must ensure that the replenishment drug is the same as the drug originally dispensed. That means the replenishment drug must be the same active ingredient, same dosage, same route of administration, and same manufacturer as the original product. HRSA has issued diversion findings to covered entities that have not replenished the exact drug.[66]

To ensure that "mis-replenishment" does not occur, covered entities identify drugs for replenishment using the 11-digit National Drug Code (NDC). The first five digits are the labeler codes.[67] The next four digits are unique to an ingredient/dosage/route of administration combination. The last two digits designate the package size in which the drug is sold (i.e., 200 tablets versus 1000 tablets).

HRSA permits nine-digit replenishment "in exceptional circumstances" if the covered entity maintains auditable records demonstrating that the appropriate quantity was replenished from the correct manufacturer.[68] Drugs that share the same first nine NDC digits are identical except for the number of units included in the package, so the auditable records should show that the total number of units replenished equaled the quantity that the covered entity was entitled to replenish.

GPO Prohibition Considerations

For covered entities that are subject to the GPO prohibition, a virtual inventory system must track not only 340B-eligible dispensations but also 340B-ineligible outpatient dispensations. One example is dispensations the covered entity carved out to avoid Medicaid duplicate discount problems or those an in-house retail pharmacy customer who does not meet 340B patient definition requirements received. Any outpatient who does not or cannot receive 340B drugs must receive non-340B, non-GPO inventory. Typically, this inventory can be acquired through a WAC account that the covered entity sets up with its wholesaler or through a sub-WAC price file made available by the 340B prime vendor Apexus.[69] Drugs dispensed or administered to inpatients may be replenished with GPO inventory. Covered entities subject to the GPO prohibition must implement 340B utilization in all outpatient settings and be prepared to buy non-340B outpatient drugs on a WAC or Apexus sub-WAC account.

KEY POINT

For covered entities subject to the GPO prohibition, a virtual inventory system must track 340B-eligible dispensations AND 340B-ineligible dispensations to outpatients. The second category includes dispensations to Medicaid outpatients from covered entities that carve out or to outpatients who do not qualify as patients of the covered entity under HRSA guidance. The covered entity must purchase these drugs through a non-340B, non-GPO account, which is generally at WAC.

Additional Requirements

In addition to anti-diversion and duplicate discount requirements, covered entities are responsible for complying with the requirements listed below and may receive a HRSA audit finding if they do not comply.

HRSA Database Entries

Covered entities must ensure that their entries in the HRSA database are accurate and complete. If any data are inaccurate, including suite numbers for child sites, a covered entity will be cited for a database error in a HRSA audit. If a covered entity is listed on the HRSA database as carving out 340B drugs for Medicaid fee-for-service beneficiaries, but actually uses 340B drugs for Medicaid beneficiaries, it may be cited for a duplicate discount violation.

Orphan Drugs

The requirements related to orphan drugs are discussed above. Hospitals subject to the orphan drug requirement may be cited if they purchase one or more orphan drugs at a 340B price. However, if a manufacturer offers 340B pricing on its orphan drugs on a voluntary basis, hospitals are free to buy such drugs without violating 340B anti-diversion requirements.

Eligibility Requirements: Auditable Records and GPO Prohibition

Maintaining auditable records is a condition of eligibility for all covered entities. Compliance with the GPO prohibition is an eligibility criterion applicable to DSH, children's and cancer hospitals. These requirements are discussed in the Program Eligibility section above.

Contract Pharmacy Oversight

A covered entity is responsible for the 340B compliance of its contract pharmacies. If HRSA finds that a covered entity is not maintaining adequate oversight of a contract pharmacy, it will terminate the contract pharmacy registration. The requirements applicable to 340B contract pharmacy arrangements are discussed below.

Enforcement

There has been relatively little enforcement in the 340B program until a few years ago when HRSA began auditing covered entities for compliance with the 340B requirements described previously. The penalties for violating such requirements are generally well defined under the law and, if covered entities uncover a violation, they have a duty to disclose the noncompliance to HRSA. Covered entities also need to be mindful of compliance concerns outside the 340B program when operating their 340B pharmacy programs. Notwithstanding, until recently, HRSA has relied largely on self-policing and informal dispute resolution to enforce compliance within the 340B program.

Statutory Penalties for Covered Entities' Violations

The penalty for failing to comply with the anti-diversion and duplicate discount prohibitions are forfeiture of the discounts to the manufacturer.[70] If the violations of the diversion prohibition are done knowingly and intentionally, covered entities may be required to pay interest on the discounts refunded to manufacturers.[71] Termination of a covered entity from the program is allowed if there is evidence that diversion violations are not only knowing and intentional, but also systemic and egregious.[72] HRSA will terminate a covered entity that does not comply with eligibility requirements, including the GPO prohibition and duty to maintain auditable records.

Duty to Disclose

As previously stated, covered entities must attest during the recertification process that they will disclose to HRSA breaches of 340B eligibility and compliance requirements. When HRSA began the recertification process, the attestation stated that the covered entity would notify HRSA of any *material* breach of 340B program requirements. HRSA has implemented revised 340B registration and recertification forms that omit the word "material" in the statement requiring the covered entity to self-disclose to HRSA in the event of a covered entity's breach of 340B program requirements. The revised forms specify that the covered entity's authorizing official must certify the covered entity acknowledges its responsibility to contact the Office of Pharmacy Affairs (OPA) breach of 304B requirements or guidance by the covered entity (for more information, https://docs.340bpvp. com/documents/public/resourcecenter/HRSA_Recertification_Attestation_Language.pdf).

In public remarks at the 340B Coalition Conference in July 2016, however, the Director of HRSA's OPA clarified that self-disclosure of 340B program violations is required only when a *material* breach of compliance has occurred. This clarification comports with HRSA's web page on the self-disclosure process, which states that disclosure is required for material breaches.[73] It also comports with guidance on the Apexus web site recommending that covered entities establish a materiality standard for disclosing breaches and providing sample policies.[74]

KEY POINT

In the annual recertification process for the 340B program, the covered entity's authorizing official must certify that the covered entity complied with all 340B program requirements, rules, and guidance, and that it has self-disclosed any breaches (which OPA interprets to mean "material" breaches). A covered entity's oversight activities should provide documentation to substantiate this annual attestation requirement.

Compliance Concerns Outside of 340B Program

Federal and state laws outside the 340B program may be implicated in a covered entity's 340B program operations and arrangements. For example, federal law prohibits providing inducements to Medicare or Medicaid beneficiaries to procure healthcare items or services from a certain provider or pharmacy, from making payments to other persons or entities for referrals to the provider or pharmacy, and from submitting false claims for Medicare or Medicaid payment.[75] HRSA has stated that compliance with its requirements does not indicate that a covered entity or pharmacy is in compliance with these types of statutes, which are outside its oversight authority.[76] Covered entities and pharmacies should be mindful of these other federal and state requirements as they relate to their 340B program operations.

Dispute Resolution

HRSA has a history of addressing covered entity compliance issues informally and encouraging covered entities and manufacturers to settle their differences without government intervention. Towards that end, the agency issued voluntary dispute resolution guidelines in 1996 authorizing HRSA to adjudicate disputes, but only if the parties agree to participate in the process.[77] The process has been underutilized and widely viewed as ineffective due to its voluntary nature, prompting Congress to amend the 340B statute under the ACA and to direct HHS to establish a mandatory dispute resolution process through formal rulemaking.[78] A proposed rule implementing this statutory directive was published on August 12, 2016.[79] HRSA has since withdrawn the proposed rule.[80]

CONTRACT PHARMACIES

Covered entities typically provide 340B drugs to their patients in one of two ways—either they provide or administer the drug in an outpatient setting, or they dispense the drug from a retail pharmacy. Some covered entities contract with retail pharmacies to provide pharmacy services to the covered entities' patients. A *contract pharmacy* serves as an agent for the covered entity, typically dispensing the entity's 340B drugs, billing responsible payers, collecting reimbursement for such drugs, and maintaining 340B drug inventories.

Basis for Contract Pharmacies

HRSA has long recognized that covered entities have a right under state agency law to contract with a pharmacy to perform these services. In a 340B contract pharmacy arrangement, the pharmacy is the agent and the covered entity is the principal. In other words, the pharmacy acts on the covered entity's behalf pursuant to a contract that illustrates the parties' mutual assent to the arrangement. The contract pharmacy typically orders, receives, and dispenses 340B drugs, but only in its capacity as the covered entity's agent. Because a party's capacity to exercise rights and discharge responsibilities through an agent is rooted in common law,[81] HRSA did not consider its contract pharmacy guidelines to be anything more than an acknowledgment and application of a covered entity's pre-existing rights under state agency law. According to HRSA, "entities possess the right to hire retail pharmacies to act as their agents in providing pharmaceutical care to their patients [under state law] … even in the absence of Federal guidelines."[82]

KEY POINT

In a 340B contract pharmacy arrangement, the pharmacy is the agent and acts on the covered entity's behalf pursuant to a contract that complies with HRSA guidance. The contract outlines each party's responsibilities. HRSA contract pharmacy guidelines are clear that the covered entity is responsible for 340B program compliance.

Published Contract Pharmacy Guidance

HRSA has issued guidance on how contract pharmacy arrangements should be structured to ensure 340B program compliance. In 1996, HRSA described some "essential compliance elements" that contract pharmacy arrangements must address. At that time, HRSA limited each covered entity to one contract pharmacy.[83] Covered entities that desired to engage multiple contract pharmacies, or networks of covered entities that desired to jointly contract with one or more pharmacies, had to submit a demonstration proposal—an Alternative Methods Demonstration Project (AMDP)—to HRSA for approval. In 2010, HRSA replaced the 1996 guidelines, amending the essential compliance elements somewhat and specifying that each covered entity may enter into arrangements with multiple contract pharmacies.[84] Covered entities, therefore, no longer have to submit AMDPs and no longer need HRSA approval to establish multiple contract pharmacy arrangements.

Essential Compliance Elements

The essential compliance elements include the following:

- **Ship To, Bill To Arrangement**. The covered entity purchases, is billed for, and retains title to the 340B drugs, which are shipped to the contract pharmacy.
- **Comprehensive Pharmacy Services**. The arrangement provides comprehensive pharmacy services to patients.

- *Freedom of Choice*. The covered entity ensures that patients are free to choose their provider of pharmacy services.

- *Other Services.* The contract pharmacy may provide additional services, although access to 340B drugs is restricted to patients of the covered entity.

- *Adherence to All Applicable Laws.* The parties agree to adhere to all applicable federal, state, and local laws.

- *Reports.* The contract pharmacy will provide the covered entity with reports consistent with customary business practices.

- *Tracking System.* The contract pharmacy, with the assistance of the covered entity, will establish a tracking system suitable to prevent diversion of 340B drugs to individuals who are not patients.

- *Patient Verification.* The parties will develop a system to verify patient eligibility.

- *Duplicate Discounts.* The parties will not use 340B drugs to dispense fee-for-service Medicaid prescriptions unless the parties and the relevant state Medicaid agency have established an arrangement to prevent duplicate discounts that has been reported to HRSA. The arrangement must be reported to HRSA by both parties and be listed on the HRSA web site for others to note.

- *Maintaining Compliance.* The parties will identify the necessary information for the covered entity to meet its ongoing compliance obligations.

- *Outside Audits.* The parties understand that they are subject to audit by HRSA and/or participating drug manufacturers. The contract pharmacy will keep pertinent reimbursement accounts and dispensing records separate from its own operations. Pertinent records will be retained for a period that complies with state, federal, and local law.

- *Access to Agreement.* A copy of the agreement will be provided to HRSA upon the agency's request to the covered entity.[85]

Oversight

The contract pharmacy guidelines make abundantly clear that the covered entity is responsible for 340B program compliance in contract pharmacy arrangements.[86] If a covered entity chooses to use a contract pharmacy, HRSA expects it to conduct adequate oversight to ensure that the contract pharmacy is complying with the diversion and duplicate discount prohibitions. Although the guidelines permit the covered entity to determine "the exact method of ensuring compliance," HRSA has strongly indicated that an independent audit should be performed.[87] Third-party administrators that manage their contract pharmacy arrangements would not be considered an independent auditor.

Registration

HRSA requires all contract pharmacy arrangements to be registered with the agency.[88] Contract pharmacies may be registered online using HRSA's 340B database.[89] HRSA permits new contract pharmacy arrangements to be registered during the first 15 days of each calendar quarter.[90] If the registration is approved, the contract pharmacy may begin dispensing 340B drugs on behalf of the covered entity on the first day of the following calendar quarter.[91] HRSA requires that the parties have an executed agreement before the arrangement is registered. The registration information must be kept up to date. During recertification, the covered entity must review its registrations and attest to the continuing compliance of its contract pharmacies.

MANUFACTURER REQUIREMENTS

On occasions, manufacturers miscalculate the 340B ceiling price or otherwise overcharge covered entities for covered outpatient drugs that are subject to the 340B statute. The manufacturer sometimes detects these discrepancies, or they are the result of HRSA's investigation into issues raised by the covered entity. When HRSA or a manufacturer determines that overcharging has occurred, the manufacturer is required to post a public letter on the HRSA web site explaining the situation and the proposed remedy.[92]

The ACA required HRSA to implement changes to improve manufacturer compliance oversight. For example, the ACA directed HRSA to develop a system for verifying the 340B ceiling price charged to covered entities and to perform spot checks on the accuracy of prices charged.[93] Similarly, HRSA was directed to create a web portal for covered entities to look up the reported 340B ceiling price of a product.[94] HRSA was also directed to create a system for the refund of overcharges to covered entities and the recalculation of ceiling prices in the event of rebates and discounts to other purchasers that have the effect of lowering the 340B ceiling price.[95]

The ACA also authorizes HRSA to sanction manufacturers up to $5,000 for each instance of knowingly and intentionally overcharging a covered entity.[96] HRSA recently finalized regulations to implement those civil monetary penalties.[97] HRSA has delayed the effective date of that regulation. As of April 2018, the regulation is scheduled to go into effect on July 1, 2018.[98]

Manufacturers are also expected to maintain accurate 340B database entries, although HRSA does not have the authority to require them to do so. Nevertheless, HRSA strongly urges manufacturers to verify their database information because it is the source of data that covered entities would use to contact them regarding compliance issues, inquiries, and repayment.[99] The 340B statute requires drug manufacturers to offer a covered outpatient drug at 340B pricing "if such drug is made available to any other purchaser at any price."[100] HRSA has interpreted the "must offer" provision to mean that manufacturers may not discriminate against 340B covered entities when allocating drugs in a shortage or otherwise making products available to purchasers.[101] HRSA expects manufacturers to discuss allocation plans with it, but does not require manufacturers to do so.

AUDITS

The 340B statute gives both HRSA and drug manufacturers authority to audit covered entities.[102] Surprisingly, until 2012, the government had exercised this authority on only one occasion in connection with a hospital in western Pennsylvania, and manufacturers had never performed an audit.[103] Circumstances changed dramatically when, in 2011, the Government Accountability Office (GAO) published a report on the 340B program that found HRSA's oversight and enforcement of the 340B program to be inadequate, due in part to HRSA's over-reliance on covered entities' self-policing. The GAO report was mandated by Congress under the ACA.[104] Publication of the GAO report, in combination with political pressure from Congress, convinced HRSA to launch a major initiative to audit 340B covered entities.[105] Within a month of the report's publication, HRSA's Administrator announced that HRSA would begin auditing covered entities.[106] The audits commenced in January 2012 and are expected to continue indefinitely. Most audited covered entities are randomly selected, but a few are targeted.[107]

HRSA Audit Authority

The 340B statute gives HRSA the authority to audit covered entities with respect to the anti-diversion and duplicate discount provisions.[108] In reality, HRSA audits covered entities for compliance with all eligibility and 340B program requirements. HRSA is also empowered to audit manufacturers, although it has exercised that authority on only a few occasions.

HRSA Audit Process

HRSA may select a covered entity for audit based on a random selection process or on information that indicates the covered entity may have compliance issues. HRSA announces that a covered entity will be audited by sending it a letter. The HRSA auditor then arranges a call with the covered entity to discuss the logistics of the audit and sends a list of the documents that will be needed prior to audit. A HRSA audit usually covers a 6-month period in the 1-year period prior to the audit. The site visit normally lasts 1–3 days. As stated above, HRSA holds the covered entity responsible for any compliance issues at the covered entity's contract pharmacies, so prescriptions filled by a covered entity's contract pharmacies are audited.

Audit Reports and Disputes

HRSA issues an audit report several months after the on-site HRSA audit, which lists any violations the HRSA auditor found. The covered entity then has the option to dispute the findings within 30 days or to submit a corrective action plan to address the findings within 60 days. If the covered entity disputes the findings, HRSA will issue a letter with its determination with regard to the dispute as well as a second audit report that incorporates any changes it made from the original report. If HRSA does not reverse a finding, the covered entity must submit a corrective action plan within 60 days of receipt of the second letter. At one time, HRSA also required covered entities to draft an *open letter* to manufacturers that was posted on the HRSA web site, which listed the findings and offered to discuss the findings with any manufacturer that believed it was harmed by them but had not received repayment from the covered entity. Recently, HRSA announced it will no longer require covered entities to draft an open letter, but will instead list the findings on the HRSA database.

Manufacturer Audit Authority

Manufacturers may audit a covered entity with respect to compliance with the anti-diversion and duplicate discount requirements.[109] Notably, HRSA guidelines governing the manufacturer audit process confirm that manufacturers may only audit with respect to anti-diversion and duplicate discount requirements. These guidelines also state that the manufacturer must submit an audit work plan and request permission from HRSA to audit a covered entity based on "reasonable cause," indicating that the covered entity has violated a 340B program requirement.[110] If HRSA grants the manufacturer's request to audit, an independent auditor conducts the audit. The auditor prepares a report that is submitted to HRSA and the covered entity, and the covered entity has the opportunity to dispute the findings. If the manufacturer and covered entity disagree on the findings, they may enter into a voluntary dispute resolution process, but both parties have to agree to do so. Manufacturers do not have the authority to take action against a covered entity that it alleges violated a 340B program requirement. HRSA proposed regulations in 2016 to implement a mandatory dispute resolution process, which would give manufacturers the opportunity to present their arguments for a final decision from a dispute resolution panel, but has since withdrawn those proposed regulations.[111]

KEY POINT

HRSA guidelines governing the manufacturer audit process state that manufacturers may only audit for violations of the diversion and duplicate discount requirements. A manufacturer audit must be based on "reasonable cause" that the covered entity has violated one of these two requirements. The manufacturer must submit an audit work plan and request permission from HRSA to audit a covered entity.

HRSA Audits of Manufacturers

HRSA has the authority to audit manufacturers for compliance with 340B program requirements.[112] As of April 2018, HRSA has acknowledged only eleven audits of manufacturers, although it has stated informally that it plans to increase its oversight of manufacturers.

SUMMARY

This chapter examines the basis for current guidance and practices. There are numerous requirements and compliance issues for providers and manufacturers that choose to participate in the 340B program. Most of the 340B program's requirements are set forth in the 340B statute. Most of the instructions from HRSA that govern the 340B program are issued as guidance or communicated through HRSA's audit practices. Providers and manufacturers must struggle to discern their 340B compliance responsibilities and implement practices and operations consistent with 340B program requirements because the program's only legally binding requirements are found in the 340B statute, which is drafted in broad terms.

REFERENCES AND NOTES

1. The District Court for the District of Columbia determined that Congress gave HRSA rulemaking authority to issue regulations on three specific areas: (1) the establishment of an administrative dispute resolution process for the resolution of claims by manufacturers and covered entities, (2) regulatory issuance of standards and methodology for calculation of ceiling prices, and (3) establishment of standards for the imposition of monetary civil sanctions applicable to participating manufacturers. *Pharm. Research & Mrfs. of Am. v. HHS*, 43 F. Supp. 3d 28 (D.D.C. 2014). On January 5, 2017, HRSA issued a final rule on the calculation of ceiling prices and the imposition of monetary civil sanctions on manufacturers. *See* 340B Drug Pricing Program Ceiling Price and Manufacturer Civil Monetary Penalties Regulation, 82 Fed. Reg. 1,210 (January 5, 2017). HRSA delayed the effective date of the regulation four times. The regulation is scheduled to go into effect on July 1, 2018. 340B Drug Pricing Program Ceiling Price and Manufacturer Civil Monetary Penalties Regulation, 82 Fed. Reg. 22,893 (May 19, 2017).

2. 42 U.S.C. § 256b(a)(1).

3. *Id.* § 256b(a)(4)(A)-(L).

4. The ACA is the Patient Protection and Affordable Care Act, Pub. L. 111-148, 124 Stat. 119 (Mar. 23, 2010), as amended by the Health Care and Education and Education Reconciliation Act of 2010, 124 Stat. 1029 (March 25, 2010).

5. Note that, with respect to children's hospitals, Congress attempted to qualify this group as part of the Deficit Reduction Act of 2005, although they did not become eligible to register until HRSA issued guidance implementing the expansion in 2009. As a result, the ACA merely codified children's hospitals' pre-existing eligibility to participate in the program.

6. ACA, § 7101, 124 Stat. at 821-22.

7. This is not the same as the DSH patient percentage—a hospital must have a DSH patient percentage of .2733 to have a DSH adjustment percentage of at least 11.75% and a DSH patient percentage of .2277 to have a DSH adjustment percentage of at least 8%.

8. 42 U.S.C. § 256b(a)(4)(L)-(N).

9. *Id.*

10. *Univ. Med. Center of S. Nev. v. Shalala,* 173 F.3d 438 (D.C. Cir. 1999).

11. 42 U.S.C. § 256b(a)(4)(L)(i).

12. 59 Fed. Reg. 47,884, 47,885 (September 19, 1994).

13. 340B Hot Topics-HRSA Office of Pharmacy Affairs Update. HRSA Web site. http://www.hrsa.gov/opa/updates/august2014.html. August 4, 2014. Accessed October 10, 2017.

14. Disproportionate Share Hospitals. HRSA Web site. http://www.hrsa.gov/opa/eligibilityandregistration/hospitals/disproportionatesharehospitals/. Accessed October 10, 2017.

15. FAQ #1220, Apexus Web site. https://www.340bpvp.com/resourceCenter/faqSearch.html?category=content&Ntt=1220. Accessed October 10, 2017.

16. FAQs - 340B Program Eligibility, FAQ 6, HRSA Web site. http://www.hrsa.gov/opa/faqs/index.html. Accessed October 10, 2017.

17. Pub. L. No. 114-74, § 603(1), adding 42 U.S.C.§1395*l*(t)(1)(B)(v). Medicare defines "campus" as "the physical area immediately adjacent to the provider's main buildings, other areas and structures that are not strictly contiguous to the main buildings but are located within 250 yards of the main buildings, and any other areas determined on an individual case basis, by the CMS regional office, to be part of the provider's campus." 42 C.F.R. § 413.65(a)(2).

18. BBA 2015 at § 2)603), adding 42 U.S.C. § 1395*l*(t)(21)(A).

19. BBA 2015 at § 2)603), adding 42 U.S.C. § 1395*l*(t)(21)(B)(i)(II).

20. FQHCs and RHCs are exempted because Sec. 603 adopts the definition of "department of a provider" from the Medicare provider-based regulations. 42 C.F.R. § 413.65(a)(2).

21. Medicare Program: Hospital Outpatient Prospective Payment and Ambulatory Surgical Center Payment Systems and Quality Reporting Programs; Organ Procurement Organization Reporting and Communication; Transplant Outcome Measures and Documentation Requirements; Electronic Health Record (EHR) Incentive Programs; Establishment of Payment Rates Under Medicare Physician Fee Schedule for Nonexcepted Items and Services Furnished by an Off-Campus Provider-Based Department of a Hospital, 81 Fed. Reg. 79,562 (November 14, 2016).

22. Section 603 defines an "off-campus department of a provider" as a "department of a provider (as defined in 42 C.F.R. § 413.65(a)(2)) that is not located" on the campus of the main hospital or a remote location of the hospital. BBA 2015 at § 603(2)(b); 42 U.S.C. § 1395l(t)(21)(B)(i). Therefore, Section 603 acknowledges that all off-campus provider- based clinics are departments of the provider, despite the fact that some will not be reimbursed as such beginning January 1, 2017. *See also* 81 Fed. Reg. at 79,717-20, which states several times that 603 facilities ("non-exempted facilities") are provider-based departments.

23. 42 U.S.C. § 256b(a)(4)(L)(iii).

24. HRSA has stated that covered entities that cannot obtain 340B pricing from a manufacturer on a covered outpatient drug should notify HRSA. HRSA, HRSA, 340B Drug Pricing Program Notice, Release 2013-1 (February 7, 2013), "Statutory Prohibition on Group Purchasing Organization Participation."

25. *Id.*

26. *Id*

27. 42 U.S.C. § 256b(a)(4)(A)-(K).

28. FAQs - 340B Program Eligibility, FAQ 6, HRSA Web site. http://www.hrsa.gov/opa/faqs/index.html. Accessed October 10, 2017.

29. *Id.*

30. 42 U.S.C. § 256b(b)(2)(B)(i)(ii).

31. *See* section on Disclosure for additional information about disclosures.

32. The 340B statute states that covered entities must allow HRSA and drug manufacturers to audit the covered entity as a condition of eligibility. 42 U.S.C. § 256b(4) (incorporating the audit authority in section (5)). HRSA interprets this provision as requiring covered entities to maintain auditable records.

33. 42 U.S.C. § 256b(a)(1). See also Pharmaceutical Pricing Agreement, HRSA Web site. http://www.hrsa.gov/opa/manufacturers/pharmaceuticalpricingagreement.pdf. Accessed October 10, 2017.

34. 42 U.S.C. § 256b(a).

35. *Id.* § 256b(b)(1), incorporating *id.* § 1396r8-(k) by reference.

36. *Id.* § 1396r-8(k)(2).

37. *Id.* § 1396r-8(k)(3). The definition also excludes drugs or products for which the Food and Drug Administration does not require a National Drug Code (NDC) number, and those drugs and biological products that are "used for a medical indication that is not a medically accepted indication." *See id.* The exclusions are called the "limiting definition" in the statute. *Id.*

38. 42 C.F.R. § 447.502.

39. FAQ #1355, Apexus Web site. https://www.340bpvp.com/resourceCenter/faqSearch.html?category=-content&Ntt=1355. Accessed August 3, 2017.

40. 340B Drug Pricing Program Omnibus Guidance, 80 Fed. Reg. 52,300, 52,305-06 (August 28, 2015).

41. *See* 340B Program Omnibus Guidelines, Office of the Management and Budget, https://www.reginfo.gov/public/do/eAgendaViewRule?pubId=201704&RIN=0906-AB08. Accessed October 10, 2017.

42. 42 U.S.C. § 256b(a).

43. Notice Regarding Section 602 of the Veterans Health Care Act of 1992; New Drug Pricing, 60 Fed. Reg. 51,488 (October 2, 1995).

44. 340B Drug Pricing Program Ceiling Price and Manufacturer Civil Monetary Penalties Regulation, 82 Fed. Reg. 1,210, 1,217-20 (January 5, 2017).

45. *See* 340B Drug Pricing Program Ceiling Price and Manufacturer Civil Monetary Penalties Regulation, 82 Fed. Reg. 1,210, 1,215 (January 5, 2017).

46. 42 U.S.C. § 256b(e).

47. 21 U.S.C. § 360bb(a)(2).

48. Availability of Interpretive Rule: Implementation of the Exclusion of Orphan Drugs for Certain Covered Entities Under the 340B Program, 79 Fed. Reg. 42,801 (July 21, 2014).

49. *Pharmaceutical Research and Manuf. of Am. v. HHS*, —F.Supp.3d—, 2015 WL 5996374 (D.D.C. 2015). This lawsuit was the second lawsuit addressing the orphan drug prohibition. HRSA had originally published its policy as a regulation, but a federal court invalidated the regulation because it determined that the 340B statute did not give HRSA the authority to issue regulations related to the orphan drug prohibition. *Pharm. Research & Mfrs. of Am. v. HHS*, 43 F. Supp. 3d 28 (D.D.C. 2014). HRSA republished the policy as an interpretive rule, which prompted the second lawsuit.

50. 42 C.F.R. § 447.505(c)(2); 81 Fed. Reg. 5,170, 5,257 – 58 (February 1, 2016).

51. 42 U.S.C. § 256b(a)(5)(B).

52. *See* Notice Regarding Section 602 of the Veterans Health Care Act of 1992; Patient and Entity Eligibility, 61 Fed. Reg. 55,156 (October 24, 1996).

53. *Id*. at 55,157-58.

54. *Id*.

55. *Id*.

56. 42 U.S.C. § 256b(a)(5)(A)(i).

57. ACA, § 2501, 124 Stat. 119, 308-09. The ACA made multiple changes to the 340B statute, but the duplicate discount prohibition was not altered. *See, e.g., id.* §124 ,7101 Stat. 23-821 ,119.

58. Final Notice Regarding Section 602 of the Veterans Health Care Act of 1992; Duplicate Discounts and Rebates on Drug Purchases, 58 Fed. Reg. 34,058 (June 23, 1993).

59. HRSA, HRSA, 340B Drug Pricing Program Notice, Release 2014-1, p. 12 (December 12, 2014), "Clarification on Use of the Medicaid Exclusion File."

60. *See, e.g.* Iowa Department of Human Services Informational Letter no. 1638-MC (March 21, 2016). https://dhs.iowa.gov/sites/default/files/1638-MC_Update-340B_DrugPricing%20Program.pdf. Accessed October 10, 2017.

61. *See, e.g.* Medi-Cal Drug Rebate FAQs-Frequently Asked Questions. California Department of Health Care Services Web site. http://www.dhcs.ca.gov/provgovpart/Pages/DrugRebateFAQ.aspx. Accessed October 10, 2017.

62. *Id*.

63. *See, e.g.* Iowa Department of Human Services Informational Letter no. 1638-MC (March 21, 2016), https://dhs.iowa.gov/sites/default/files/1638-MC_Update-340B_DrugPricing%20Program.pdf. Accessed October 10, 2017.

64. Medicaid Program; Covered Outpatient Drugs, 81 Fed. Reg. 5,170, 5,174-76 (February 1, 2016); 42 C.F.R. §447.512(b).

65. *See* Medicare Program: Hospital Outpatient Prospective Payment and Ambulatory Surgical Center Payment Systems and Quality Reporting Programs, 82 Fed. Reg. 52,356 (November 13, 2017). The Medicare Payment Advisory Commission, commonly known as MedPAC, has recommended that

Congress reduce reimbursement for 340B drugs reimbursed under Medicare Part B. *See* MedPAC Report to Congress, Medicare Payment Policy, p. 56–58. MedPAC Web site. http://www.medpac.gov/docs/default-source/reports/march-2016-report-to-the-congress-medicare-payment-policy.pdf. March 2016. Accessed October 10, 2017.

66. As a technical matter, a misreplenishment does not necessarily mean that the covered entity diverted a 340B drug to an ineligible patient, but it does mean that a manufacturer provided a 340B discounted drug that may have been manufactured by another company.

67. In fact, some manufacturers have multiple labeler codes due to mergers and acquisitions or other restructuring.

68. FAQ #1222, Apexus Web site. https://www.340bpvp.com/resourceCenter/faqSearch.html?category=-content&Ntt=1222. Accessed October 10, 2017.

69. The Prime Vendor Program acts as a GPO, but HRSA has indicated that covered entities subject to the GPO prohibition may use it to acquire outpatient drugs. FAQs—GPO Prohibition, Question 13, HRSA Web site. http://www.hrsa.gov/opa/faqs/index.html. Accessed October 10, 2017.

70. 42 U.S.C. § 256b(a)(5)(D).

71. Patient Protection and Affordable Care Act, Pub. L. 111-148, § 7102(a), 124 Stat. 129, 823-27 (establishing 42 U.S.C. § 256b(d)(2)(B)(v)).

72. 42 U.S.C. § 256b(d)(2)(B)(v)(II).

73. Self-Disclosure Process. HRSA Web site. http://www.hrsa.gov/opa/selfdisclosures/selfdisclosure.html. Accessed August 3, 2017.

74. Establishing Material Breach Threshold Tool. Apexus Web site. https://docs.340bpvp.com/documents/public/resourcecenter/Establishing_Material_Breach_Threshold.pdf. March 9, 2016. Accessed October 10, 2017.

75. *Id.* § 1320a-7a(a)(5); *Id.* § 1320a-7b(b); 31 U.S.C. §§ 3729-3733.

76. *See, e.g.,* Notice Regarding 340B Drug Pricing Program – Contract Pharmacy Services, 75 Fed. Reg. 10,272, 10279 (March 5, 2010) (stating that compliance with contract pharmacy guidelines does not relieve a covered entity from responsibility to adhere to antikickback requirements).

77. Manufacturer Audit Guidelines and Dispute Resolution Process, 61 Fed. Reg. 65,406 (December 12, 1996).

78. ACA, § 7102, 124 Stat. at 826-27.

79. 340B Drug Pricing Program; Administrative Dispute Resolution, 81 Fed. Reg. 53,381 (August 12, 2016).

80. *See* 340B Drug Pricing Program; Administrative Dispute Resolution Process, Office of Management and Budget, https://www.reginfo.gov/public/do/eAgendaViewRule?pubId=201704&RIN=0906-AA90. Accessed October 10, 2017.

81. "Common law" is the name for the body of law the United States inherited from the United Kingdom at its formation, and the ways in which that body of law has been interpreted and molded since that time by judicial rulings and opinions. Common law often provides a set of principles that fill the gaps in formal, legislatively enacted, laws.

82. Final Notice Regarding Covered Entity Guidelines, 59 Fed. Reg. 25,110, 25,111 (May 13, 1994).

83. Notice Regarding Section 602 of the Veterans Health Care Act of 1992; Contract Pharmacy Services, 61 Fed. Reg. 43,449 (August 23, 1996).

84. Notice Regarding 340B Drug Pricing Program—Contract Pharmacy Services, 75 Fed. Reg. 10,272 (March 5, 2010).

85. *Id.* at 10,277-78.

86. *See, e.g., id.* at 10,278-79.

87. *See, e.g.,* HRSA Office of Pharmacy Affairs Update - Contract Pharmacy: Important Tips. HRSA Web site. http://www.hrsa.gov/opa/updates/2016/august.html. August 2016. Accessed August 3, 2017.

88. 75 Fed. Reg. at 10,278-79.

89. Notice Regarding Section 340B of the Public Health Service Act – Registration Period, 77 Fed. Reg. 43,342 (July 24, 2012).

90. *Id.* at 43,343.

91. *Id.*

92. HRSA Office of Pharmacy Update. HRSA Web site. http://www.hrsa.gov/opa/updates/update362014. html. March 6, 2014. Accessed October 10, 2017.

93. 42 U.S.C. § 256b(d)(1)(B)(i).

94. *Id.* § 256b(d)(1)(B)(iii).

95. *Id.* § 256b(d)(1)(B)(ii), (iv).

96. *Id.* § 256b(d)(1)(B)(vi).

97. 340B Drug Pricing Program Ceiling Price and Manufacturer Civil Monetary Penalties Regulation, 82 Fed. Reg. 1,210, 1,229-30 (January 5, 2017).

98. 340B Drug Pricing Program Ceiling Price and Manufacturer Civil Monetary Penalties Regulation, 82 Fed. Reg. 22,893 (May 19, 2017).

99. *See, e.g.,* HRSA Office of Pharmacy Affairs Update - 340B Pricing System: Manufacturers 340B Database Verification and Other Updates. HRSA Web site. http://www.hrsa.gov/opa/updates/2016/april. html. April 2016. Accessed October 10, 2017.

100. 42 U.S.C. § 256b(a)(1).

101. HRSA, HRSA, 340B Drug Pricing Program Notice, Release 2011-1.1 (May 23, 2012), "Clarification of Non-Discrimination Policy."

102. 42 U.S.C. § 256b(a)(5)(c).

103. In 2005, Aliquippa Community Hospital was accused of reselling drugs purchased through the 340B program to ineligible providers. See Letter from Mary Wakefield, Administrator, HRSA, to Sen. Charles Grassley at p. 6 (October 21, 2011).

104. ACA, § 7103, 124 Stat. at 827-28.

105. U.S. Government Accountability Office, Manufacturer Discount in the 340B Program Offer Benefits, but Federal Oversight is Needed, GAO-11-836, September 2011, available at http://www.gao.gov/new.items/d11836.pdf. Accessed October 10, 2017.

106. See Letter from Mary Wakefield, Administrator, HRSA, to Sen. Charles Grassley at p. 6 (October 21, 2011).

107. *Id.*

108. 42 U.S.C. § 256b(a)(5)(C).

109. *Id.*

110. Manufacturer Audit Guidelines and Dispute Resolution Process, 61 Fed. Reg. 65,406, 65,409 (December 12, 1996).

111. 340B Drug Pricing Program; Administrative Dispute Resolution, 81 Fed. Reg. 53,381 (August 12, 2016). *See also* 340B Drug Pricing Program; Administrative Dispute Resolution Process, Office of Management and Budget, https://www.reginfo.gov/public/do/eAgendaViewRule?pubId=201704&RIN=0906-AA90. Accessed October 10, 2017.

112. 42 U.S.C. § 256b(d)(1)(B)(v).

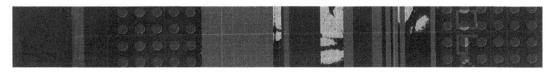

CHAPTER 4

The Basics of 340B Program Implementation

Christopher S. Shain, PharmD, BCPS and
Douglas J. Hosie, MBA, RPh

Implementing the 340B program in a hospital or health system is not for the faint of heart. The opportunity to reduce pharmaceutical acquisition expenses for eligible patients is essential to the programs and services provided to underinsured and uninsured patients. 340B program savings may also be critical to your organization's financial health. However, since its inception in 1992, the 340B program has grown in importance for safety net providers and has become substantially more complex to undertake. The 340B program's business, operational, and compliance requirements are laid on top of the already complex requirements to manage patient care and meet the requirements of other government programs, payers, and regulators. Meeting 340B program requirements demands significant planning and resources to manage well. The discipline of integrating 340B into a well-executed pharmacy and patient care program is both a challenge and a significant project.

Adding 340B to the mix in a complex health-system pharmacy may require a reassessment of current practices and policies while also requiring choices, rework, and development of policies, practices, and tools not typically considered within the bounds of 340B implementation. This chapter is designed to serve as a comprehensive guide to practical and operational 340B program implementation steps and strategies; in particular, leading up to software implementation. This guide can serve as a valuable reference for entities new to 340B as well as those continuing to manage the annual twists and turns that have become commonplace in the 340B world.

HOSPITAL PROGRAM ELIGIBILITY REQUIREMENTS

The requirements for hospital participation in the 340B program are outlined in detail on the Office of Pharmacy Affairs (OPA) web site.[1] Rather than restate in its entirety, the requirements (see **Table 4-1**) have been summarized for clarity in areas that hospitals commonly find confounding.

Participating 340B hospitals may be owned or operated by state or local government. Non-profit community hospitals may also participate in the 340B program if they have either been formally granted governmental powers or have a contract in place with state or local government to provide healthcare to low-income individuals not entitled to benefits under Medicare or Medicaid. If a government contract is required for participation in the program, the authorizing official (AO) should begin working toward this agreement as a first step. Without a contract, or if the discussions and negotiations result in a delay in contract signature from a government official, the hospital may miss the quarterly enrollment deadline leading to a full quarter delay in eligibility and resultant savings.

Table 4-1. Hospital Entity 340B Enrollment Requirements

Entity Type	Nonprofit/Government Relationship	DSH%[1]	GPO Prohibition	Orphan Drug Exclusion
Critical Access Hospitals	Yes	N/A	No	Yes
Rural Referral Centers	Yes	>8%	No	Yes
Sole Community Hospitals	Yes	>8%	No	Yes
Free-standing Cancer Hospitals	Yes	>11.75%*	Yes	Yes
DSHs	Yes	>11.75%	Yes	No
Children's Hospitals	Yes	>11.75%*	Yes	No

* Children's Hospitals and Free-Standing Cancer Hospitals that do not publish a DSH% as part of their MCR filing may use alternate calculations to support their meeting this requirement. Please see the full text for additional details.

DSH: disproportionate share hospitals DSH%: disproportionate share adjustment percentage

Hospitals commonly ask for a template or sample agreement to present to the government agency, but the Health Resources and Services Administration (HRSA) does not provide a sample. HRSA does not seek specific content or access to healthcare as outlined above, but it does require the authorizing official to certify that such an agreement is in place. OPA will contact the government official soon after registration to confirm the agreement. Samples of current contracts can be secured from peers. Although the details of the agreement are not dictated by OPA, upon registration, the covered entity will certify that the contract provides for "healthcare services to low income individuals who are not entitled to benefits under Title XVIII of the Social Security Act or eligible for assistance under the State plan of Title XIX of the Social Security Act."[2] Language proposed in the August 2015 340B Omnibus Guidance states that the government contract "should create enforceable expectations for the hospital for the provision of healthcare services, including the provision of direct medical care."[3] Hospitals should consider including enforceable expectations for the provision of care to avoid the need to modify contracts in the future. Examples of enforceable expectations may include financial or patient volume commitments but are not specified in detail and remain at the discretion of the contracting parties.

With the exception of critical access hospitals, hospital covered entities are required to exceed a minimum disproportionate share adjustment percentage (DSH%) on their most recently filed Medicare cost report (MCR). The requirements, by hospital type, are outlined in Table 4-1. For pharmacy leaders not familiar with the MCR, the DSH% calculation is found on line 33 of worksheet E, part A. For urban hospitals in excess of 100 patient beds that do not routinely include a DSH% calculation on their MCR (e.g., children's hospitals, free-standing cancer hospitals), a special alternate calculation may be used. This methodology requires the entity to demonstrate that net inpatient revenue from certain state and local sources for indigent care exceeds 30% of total inpatient revenue. Hospitals that qualify under this method are commonly referred to as *Pickle Hospitals* in reference to the Congressman who sponsored the applicable language.[4]

Children's hospitals have the most complex entry requirements concerning DSH%. If the children's hospital submits a MCR with a DSH% that exceeds 11.75%, it is accepted by OPA.

However, many children's hospitals do not include a DSH% as part of their cost report filing. If the children's hospital includes the components required to calculate a DSH% on worksheet S-3 of the MCR, OPA will calculate the applicable DSH% to verify eligibility. If the components are not available on worksheet S-3, children's hospitals have the opportunity to submit DSH% calculations verified by a credible, independent auditor for OPA's consideration. The various requirements and options for children's hospital 340B eligibility can be reviewed in final guidance published in the 2009 *Federal Register*.[5]

340B Savings Assessment

Subsequent chapters in this book will detail the financial management and tracking aspects of the 340B program. However, prospective 340B registrants often need a reasonable estimate of savings to begin contemplating expenses, operational requirements, regulatory risk, and additional full-time employees (FTEs) dedicated to 340B program management and oversight.

For the core hospital 340B program (not including a retail pharmacy or contract pharmacy network), the authors recommend a relatively simple initial calculation that serves most hospitals well. On line 73 of Worksheet C within the MCR, hospitals report inpatient and outpatient drug charges. Determine the percentage of outpatient drug charges in relationship to total charges. This percentage is a reasonable approximation of the fraction of core hospital drug purchases, which are dispensed or administered to outpatients associated with reimbursable departments on the MCR (i.e., exclude retail purchasing accounts and accounts serving outside departments that will not participate in 340B), that would be subject to 340B savings. Multiply the core hospital's total drug purchases by this percentage to determine the portion of drug expense to which 340B saving would apply. Apply an estimated 35-40% 340B savings rate to the outpatient portion of pharmaceutical expenses. This calculated savings should assist hospital leadership in understanding the magnitude of savings for the core hospital program. An important distinction must be made for rural hospitals and free-standing cancer centers because they are subject to the orphan drug restriction. Orphan medications may comprise a significant percentage of the outpatient drug charges and expense, making these calculations less reliable for hospitals subject to this program restriction. These hospitals may consider a more detailed dive into orphan drugs excluded from the program to gain similarly useful insight.

KEY POINT

A straightforward calculation of potential 340B savings can be done using Medicare cost report and drug purchase data. This estimate can assist in setting expectations and aligning decisions when entering the 340B program.

PREREGISTRATION DECISIONS

After hospitals have verified their 340B eligibility and determined the scope of savings opportunity, critical decisions must be made prior to program registration. Failure of the hospital's leadership to engage in the required assessments and ensuing discussions may have a deleterious impact on initial program performance and compliance. To that end, the hospital must choose an executive as the primary person responsible for the hospital's 340B program—the AO. The AO should be a hospital executive with the binding authority to sign government documents and authorize program registration who will have responsibility for 340B program integrity when the hospital enters the program.

What Are 340B Child Sites?

Child sites are simply outpatient departments, clinics, or other facilities that are registered for 340B participation and that sit outside the four walls of the primary (parent) hospital covered entity. Many hospital finance personnel may be familiar with "on campus" and "off campus" designations associated with Medicare's provider-based billing and reimbursement rules. OPA's use of *four walls* to distinguish the parent entity from child sites is not the same as the Centers for Medicare & Medicaid Services' (CMS) provider-based campus rules. Some hospitals struggle in determining the border of the four walls of the parent hospital as they find themselves in one large or a contiguous set of buildings, lobbies, atriums, and clinics. OPA, through their Prime Vendor partner Apexus, uses the language "outpatient clinics/departments within the four walls (i.e., same physical address) of the registered parent 340B hospital" in response to related frequently asked questions.[6] HRSA audits typically confirm that a reasonable interpretation of four walls, incorporating the physical address of the child site in comparison to the parent entity, is a useful guide.

Once a determination and listing of all potential child sites has been made, the hospital must determine the 340B eligibility of each site to prepare for registration. The MCR and a supporting trial balance with associated costs and revenue (charges) is the entity's primary guide. OPA requires that all child sites demonstrate costs (worksheet A of the MCR) and charges (worksheet C of the MCR) on a reimbursable line of the most recently filed MCR to confirm eligibility. This eligibility requirement applies to 340B drug purchases, drug administration, and prescribing by providers. In addition, OPA requires child sites to be registered at the department or clinic level, not just the physical structure's primary address. This detailed registration matrix can be particularly cumbersome for hospitals with a large number of clinics at one location or for health systems with more than one hospital location on a single MCR.

OPA provides the following clarification on their web site[1]:

> If an off-site location is actually a separate hospital or medical center, or even a small office with several services being provided, each clinic/department/service must be registered separately in the 340B program database. For example, if there is a single off-site location that provides radiology services, physical therapy services, and pediatric services, the covered entity should register each service individually to establish its eligibility for 340B drugs.

Entities may consider seeking outside counsel with 340B expertise when faced with unclear registration conditions and significant financial ramifications. For example, if a new hospital service line (e.g., pediatric infusion center) is being implemented on the main campus and is deemed within the four walls of the parent entity, 340B inventory can be used from the outset. However, if the new center is deemed outside the four walls, the hospital must wait for the new infusion center to appear on a filed MCR and then initiate the quarterly registration procedures for child sites. This may delay use of 340B inventory for the infusion center by 18 months or longer.

Group Purchasing Organization Prohibition

DSHs, free-standing cancer centers, and children's hospitals agree, as a requirement of participation, to not "obtain covered outpatient drugs through a group purchasing organization or other group purchasing arrangement."[7] Prior to OPA's February 2013 clarification,[7] the group purchasing organization (GPO) prohibition had modest compliance and financial impact on covered entities. Hospitals subject to the GPO prohibition purchased most or all non-340B inventory through a GPO account. OPA's current expectations as outlined in the clarification are detailed, specific, and create significant demands on hospitals' pharmacy revenue cycle and supply chain systems. Note that these requirements are specific to hospitals using a mixed *virtual inventory* of 340B and non-340B drugs, typically using 340B software. As a practical matter, few hospitals utilize duplicate inventories (and could not practically do so in mixed areas such as the emergency department and operating room). Tighter enforcement of the GPO prohibition is a primary impetus for wholesaler acquisition cost (WAC) account purchases. Hospitals that have not implemented the 340B program in a thorough and operationally sound manner may encounter significant WAC (full catalog list price) purchases with substantial negative financial consequences offsetting 340B program savings benefit.

The practical outcome for currently affected hospitals is a requirement to justify all GPO and 340B purchases. GPO inventory cannot be administered to hospital outpatients, only inpatients. The GPO prohibition creates a requirement that all pertinent hospital charges be captured and assigned as 340B or GPO inventories for replacement. In addition to traditional hospital GPO contracts, OPA considers distributor generics programs and health-system contracts negotiated on behalf of multiple hospitals—and any other agreement relying on sales aggregated across multiple providers—to be group purchasing arrangements. For this reason, inventory purchases that cannot be tracked and tied to an inpatient or 340B-eligible outpatient use must be purchased at an open market or full list price on a WAC account. The WAC account may only contain contract pricing secondary to direct agreements between the manufacturer and a single covered entity, or pricing available through the current 340B Prime Vendor Program™ managed by Apexus (which is exempt from the GPO prohibition). All other group purchasing contracts are excluded.

The financial impact of a significant portion of a hospital's inventory coming from WAC purchases can dramatically reduce the savings achieved through 340B purchases. Additional operational and financial ramifications of the GPO prohibition and WAC purchases are discussed throughout this chapter.

Orphan Drug Exclusion

Although the orphan drug exclusion will be covered in a chapter dedicated to rural hospitals, a brief discussion is warranted here. As part of the Health Care and Education Reconciliation Act, Congress altered the 340B program by excluding orphan drugs from the definition of covered outpatient drug, effectively removing them from the 340B program for hospital types outlined in Table 4-1.[8] The authors briefly note that the Pharmaceutical Research and Manufacturers of America (PhRMA) challenged the previously published OPA orphan drug regulations in court with the court ruling in PhRMA's favor by vacating OPA's orphan drug rule.[9] The end result is a comprehensive exclusion of orphan drugs from the definition of covered outpatient drug for affected entities, regardless of the patient's diagnosis or indication for treatment.

As affected hospitals prepare for 340B registration, ramifications of the orphan drug exclusion should be considered. As mentioned previously, the removal of orphan drugs from 340B purchases may significantly reduce the program's value for hospitals. Orphan drugs will also complicate ordering processes, 340B software management, and program integrity owing to some combination of the following:

- Software vendors may attempt to screen orphan drugs by the national drug code (NDC) for applicable customers based on a non-NDC specific list of orphan products produced quarterly by OPA from the master Food and Drug Administration (FDA) list.
- Distributors may proactively attempt to remove all orphan drug 340B prices from pertinent accounts for affected customers using the non-NDC list from OPA.
- Distributors may remove 340B prices from affected customer accounts at the request of orphan manufacturers. Manufacturers may be inconsistent in their identification of orphan drugs for rural hospitals and free-standing cancer centers.
- Some manufacturers are extending individual contract pricing on orphan products to rural hospitals and free-standing cancer centers and are allowing the contracts to be loaded to the 340B accounts. However, the prices are not official 340B prices but are considered individual agreements.

Covered entities should be prepared for additional work during program implementation dedicated to orphan drug setup and policy and procedure development. Affected hospitals should also consider the need for additional human resources to manage and self-audit orphan purchases as part of 340B program management. Entities should review orphan drug functionality and flexibility before making final 340B software decisions.

Retail Pharmacies, Repackagers, and Ship-to Addresses

Hospitals preparing for 340B registration must determine how owned retail pharmacies will participate in 340B. Although OPA's guidance in this area has not been entirely clear and complete regarding all possible options and scenarios, owned pharmacies generally fall into one of four categories.

1. *An outpatient pharmacy within the four walls of the parent 340B site*—For the pharmacy to receive 340B inventory directly, the address should be listed as a ship-to address on the OPA web site. Without this listing, distributors will be unable to set up accounts with the retail pharmacy shipping address. For entities subject to the GPO prohibition, the owned retail pharmacy as described here would apply and non-340B eligible purchases would be purchased at WAC.

2. *An owned outpatient pharmacy that operates from a location otherwise registered as a child site for clinics or other 340B-eligible activity taking place at that address*—In other words, the retail pharmacy exists at an off-site location that is registered to participate in 340B. In this scenario, OPA expects the entity to register the ship-to address under the child site and expects the pharmacy purchases to be subject to the GPO prohibition for affected hospitals.

3. *Hospital-owned outpatient pharmacies that sit outside the four walls and are not located at an address with registered child sites*—Although OPA guidance for this scenario has not been definitive, a frequently asked question (FAQ) from the 340B Prime Vendor indicates that entities can choose to exclude or incorporate these pharmacies into the 340B program.[10] Hospitals may choose to carve out and continue current purchasing practices in these retail pharmacies, especially if few 340B-eligible patients are expected. The entity may include the pharmacy by adding the retail pharmacy shipping address to the OPA web site. This would likely require observance of the GPO prohibition as "the GPO prohibition applies to covered entity sites which are registered" and that an "entity should not try to circumvent the GPO Prohibition by accessing GPO purchased drugs via an entity-owned pharmacy or contract pharmacy in a 340B registered location."[8]

4. *Pharmacies owned by the health system but not the actual covered entity*—If the pharmacy is not located at a 340B registered address, most health systems that wish to use 340B in this scenario register the pharmacy as a 340B contract pharmacy.

In addition to retail pharmacies, entities should add repackaging company addresses to the OPA web site, assuming 340B inventory will be included in the repackaging program. Multi-facility health systems that utilize a central redistribution model should add the center's shipping address to the OPA listing. Covered entities subject to the GPO prohibition cannot simply exclude these areas from 340B participation and continue supplying an all-GPO inventory to outpatient or mixed-use areas.

Medicaid Considerations and 340B Status

Hospitals new to 340B should begin planning their Medicaid inventory and billing decisions well before registration. From its inception, a central tenet of the 340B program has been the requirement to avoid duplicate discount violations.[11] Manufacturers that participate in a number of federal drug programs, including the Medicaid Drug Rebate Program and 340B, do so by signing a pharmaceutical pricing agreement (PPA) and are obligated to pay either state Medicaid agencies a rebate or provide a 340B discount to covered entities, but not both. Most hospitals have a critical decision regarding management of Medicaid billing early in their 340B participation. The decision can have significant business, compliance, and operational implications.

The decision is commonly described as Medicaid carve-in or Medicaid carve-out. Medicaid *carve-in* simply means that a hospital chooses to purchase drugs for eligible Medicaid outpatients at 340B pricing. Medicaid *carve-out* means that inventory delivered to Medicaid outpatients will not be purchased using 340B pricing, requiring non-contract WAC purchases for hospitals subject to the GPO prohibition. A small number of states, such as Illinois, have mandated that hospitals carve-in removing the decision from the covered entity.

Hospitals that choose to carve-in Medicaid are balancing various factors, including these critical considerations:

- Carve-in versus carve-out financial and operational impact.
- Handling of fee for service (FFS) Medicaid versus Medicaid managed care organizations (MCOs).
- Methods to manage retail prescriptions and physician-administered drugs.
- Traditional billing, claims modifiers, and actual acquisition cost (AAC) reimbursement.
- Standard Medicaid reimbursement versus reduced 340B reimbursement.
- Meeting the billing requirements of multiple state Medicaid agencies. It is the rare hospital that deals with a single state.

Carving-in Medicaid ensures that the entity is optimizing 340B purchases and savings. However, this may be offset by differential reimbursement to 340B providers and state requirements to bill and be reimbursed based on AAC. In addition, in a number of states, 340B retail claims and physician-administered drug billings require alterations to standard billing practices. For example, 340B hospitals carving-in Medicaid may be required to include UD modifiers on hospital outpatient claims while retail claims may require alterations to one or more National Council for Prescription Drug Programs (NCPDP) fields.

Although most retail pharmacy systems can accommodate the NCPDP field changes, changing Medicaid billing requirements for physician-administered drugs in the hospital outpatient setting may require extensive work with information technology and finance teams. If entities register for 340B as Medicaid carve-in, they must be prepared to bill according to each state's current requirements. As part of the Medicaid assessment, some hospitals may wish to manage Medicaid uniquely in their retail pharmacies in comparison to their hospital outpatient departments. If the retail pharmacy and hospital outpatient departments utilize separate National Provider Identifiers (NPIs) and Medicaid numbers, entities may choose to manage the two differently. Finally, choosing to carve-in Medicaid provides a 340B discount to the covered entity but should prevent the manufacturer from paying a Medicaid rebate.

The mechanism HRSA created to communicate FFS Medicaid carve in/carve out status among covered entities, manufacturers, and other 340B stakeholders is the Medicaid Exclusion File (MEF) found on the OPA web site.[12] When entities choose to carve-in Medicaid, they are required to publish the applicable NPIs and/or Medicaid provider numbers. This publication alerts Medicaid personnel and manufacturers that retail and hospital outpatient claims associated with these identifiers are not subject to rebate requests and payments. Any NPI not registered on the OPA web site is subject to Medicaid rebate requests and payments. In the rush to complete registration, hospital personnel outside Finance may ask for "the" entity's NPI, not understanding large health systems may use multiple NPIs and Medicaid provider numbers. Pharmacy, Finance, Compliance, and the AO should convene to determine all NPIs and Medicaid provider numbers that may be used to bill for inventory purchased at 340B prices if the entity chooses to carve-in some of or the entire 340B program. The information presented here is easy to apply when considering the entity's home state but does not clearly extend to the many hospitals whose geographical footprint crosses state boundaries.

The problem for most entities lies with the inflexible nature of the NPI, which is—by definition—a national identifier. For example, a covered entity may wish to carve-in 340B for their home state but may serve Medicaid patients from surrounding states for which it wishes to carve-out because of the cost and complexity of each state's unique billing requirements. In this scenario, covered entities may publish their NPI and home state Medicaid provider number on the MEF. In practice, this would likely result in avoidance of duplicate discounts for the home state but may cost the surrounding state rebates because the NPI is the primary identifier most states use to process rebate claims. Some entities try to prevent this conflict by just publishing Medicaid provider numbers for carve-in states; no NPIs. This is rarely a satisfactory solution because most hospitals are required to bill using their NPI; failing to publish it on the OPA web site will risk duplicate discount violations. For this reason, HRSA states the following on its web site:

> If covered entities decide to bill to Medicaid for drugs purchased under 340B with a Medicaid provider number/NPI, then ALL drugs billed to that number must be purchased under 340B and that Medicaid provider number/NPI must be listed in the HRSA Medicaid Exclusion File.[13]

The previous discussion supports the determination that, in its current iteration, the MEF does not account for the complex set of relationships and requirements across multiple state Medicaid agencies and covered entities concerning Medicaid billing. Hospitals may be successful in navigating these scenarios by communicating directly with Medicaid agencies.

Solutions to these difficult scenarios may involve separate NPI numbers for carve-in and carve-out states. Once again, this is likely impractical but could be explored by entities. Finally, covered entities should reach out to individual state Medicaid agencies to clarify carve-in versus carve-out status, billing requirements, and any impact on retail or hospital outpatient reimbursements. Entities must recognize that all 50 states (and the territories) are organized uniquely and have distinct 340B Medicaid billing requirements. Entities often don't know where to start when reaching out to state Medicaid agencies. Some reasonable starting points include colleagues in nearby 340B facilities, Medicaid contacts from hospital finance, 340B Prime Vendor, and the MDR Detailed State Contact Information document.[14]

Hospitals should not be surprised if they are required to speak to multiple personnel within Medicaid to gain a full understanding of the state's billing requirements. For example, varying offices and personnel may manage 340B policy, hospital billing, retail billing, MEF, and MDRP rebate management. Hospitals should not assume that these individuals have a working relationship or communication history related to 340B in the Medicaid office.

In summary, entities should work to limit the risk that their Medicaid registration status leads to the potential for duplicate discounts. Complex setups that include multiple NPIs and/or varying exclusion practices by state should be managed with clear communication between the hospital and all of the respective state Medicaid agencies.

With passage of the Affordable Care Act (ACA), Medicaid MCO drug claims became subject to manufacturer rebates as part of the Medicaid drug rebate program. Language was added that excluded 340B covered entities choosing to carve-in from this requirement. Although this provision was seen as a victory by 340B program advocates, the marketplace was not prepared to operationalize this new model, and HRSA did not clearly outline the participating parties' responsibilities (covered entities, contract pharmacies, state Medicaid agencies, Medicaid MCOs). OPA has publicly stated that Medicaid MCO drugs should be protected from duplicate discounts but also acknowledges that previous guidance and the MEF apply only to FFS Medicaid plans. In February 2016, CMS published final regulations concerning changes to the covered outpatient drug definition and average manufacturer price (AMP).[15] In this rule, CMS tasks state Medicaid agencies with creating a mechanism to identify and remove 340B claims from their Medicaid MCO plan data. States have until April 1, 2017 to submit new state plan amendments (SPAs) to CMS. SPAs contain significant detail regarding billing requirements for 340B covered entities and may outline the states' plans to manage Medicaid MCO rebates. Covered entities should review SPAs for all carve-in states and accommodate any new Medicaid billing requirements. Hospitals should communicate with all carve-in states regarding current policies surrounding rebate management of Medicaid MCO claims. Several states have incorporated MCO claims into their technical billing requirements and AAC billing requirements for Medicaid MCO claims. Many states with managed care rely on the MEF to screen MCO claims even though it was designed solely for FFS plans.

Although contract pharmacy relationships will be outlined in another chapter, it is worth noting that Medicaid requirements for contract pharmacy relationships have separate guidance. As the modern multiple contract pharmacy program arrived in March 2010, OPA published guidance stating that contract pharmacy arrangements must carve-out Medicaid unless the state and entity have an arrangement in place to protect against duplicate discounts:

> Neither party will use drugs purchased under section 340B to dispense Medicaid prescriptions, unless the covered entity, the contract pharmacy and the State Medicaid agency have established an arrangement to prevent duplicate discounts. Any such arrangement shall be reported to the OPA, HRSA, by the covered entity.[16]

340B Contract Pharmacy Enrollment

Upon execution of an agreement between a covered entity and a contract pharmacy, the parties are allowed to register a contract pharmacy relationship during the quarterly enrollment window. OPA provides a detailed enrollment guide for the on-line registration process. However, there are a few critical items that all entities should consider. First, the pharmacy address should be the exact address needed for distributors to provide deliveries as part of a ship-to bill-to arrangement. Although software vendors commonly serve as intermediaries between the two parties, the covered entity should ensure that the AO and contract pharmacy's primary contact are prepared to respond to HRSA as responses are required to authorize the agreement within 15 days of submission. Although the financial and operational details of the contract pharmacy agreement should be negotiated before registration, they are not a concern of HRSA. Important considerations for contract pharmacy will be discussed in Chapter 9.

By properly preparing for critical decisions prior to the OPA registration window, hospitals will be in a better position to complete registration, optimize program savings, and avoid business and compliance risk. OPA provides detailed hospital and contract pharmacy webinars and instruction manuals to guide entities through the on-line registration screens.

KEY POINT

A number of decisions and assessments regarding the 340B program should be understood and made prior to enrollment. These include a review of child sites, retail pharmacy and repackagers, Medicaid billing, and 340B program oversight.

340B PROGRAM OVERSIGHT

The 340B program is complex and requires customization in its design for each organization. The value of the program is significant but the oversight and auditing functions of the program can be overwhelming, especially for hospitals new to the program and for pharmacy leaders with 340B program accountability but with modest interest and support beyond pharmacy. Two primary phases of oversight for organizations pursuing 340B registration and implementation are an acute implementation phase and a sustained monitoring phase. Each has differing resource requirements. However, the most important link between both phases is a hospital or health-system executive champion and a pharmacy supply chain leader to direct a 340B oversight committee.

The executive champion, who may also be the AO, should be someone with authority and accountability in the organization's decision-making processes. This person should have the ability to speak to OPA on behalf of the covered entity, negotiate and approve contracts, and approve additional resources for 340B program management when required. Each organization's structure will dictate the most appropriate executive champion for 340B but is typically the chief financial officer (CFO), vice president of finance, vice president for supply chain, or other senior executive. The executive will champion the implementation project and create or allocate critical resources such as information technology (IT), 340B consultants, and external auditors. The executive's support will also be required for new positions and additional FTEs, such as a 340B program manager. Pharmacy supply chain leaders and the 340B executive champion should meet regularly and coordinate activities and assessments during the preregistration, implementation, and ongoing monitoring phases.

The 340B oversight committee has many roles and will change in membership over time depending on the stage of program implementation and maintenance. For example, during software implementation, an assigned project manager is an invaluable resource. Long term, the oversight committee's communication and cooperation will have a profound impact on the program's total value to the hospital/health system, program compliance, and audit preparedness. The committee should include expertise from the following areas:

- Pharmacy operations
- Pharmacy informatics
- Finance/reimbursement
- Information services
- Legal/compliance
- Internal audit
- Finance
- Executive champion

The expertise of the oversight committee should allow the team to focus and be accountable for the following:

- Audit plan development and execution, HRSA/OPA audit preparation, and review and response to 340B program gaps and violations noted by internal and external audits.
- Organizational changes impacting the MCR, 340B eligibility determinations, and OPA web site registration details.
- 340B software maintenance.
- 340B software and related data feed integrity.
- Retail pharmacy prescription capture of efficiency and compliance.
- 340B Contract Pharmacy relationships.
- Incorporation of new HRSA regulations or guidance.
- 340B policy and procedures oversight.
- Medicaid billing and avoidance of duplicate discounts.
- 340B financial impact reporting, including support of uninsured and indigent patients.

Many hospitals should consider additional dedicated resources to help manage 340B program activities. Although the requirements will vary for large versus small hospitals, individual facilities versus health systems, contract pharmacy versus no contract pharmacy, core program requirements exist for all facilities and require allocated resources. This should be considered when designing the position description and requirements. The 340B Prime Vendor makes job descriptions available on their web site.[17]

Dedicated 340B resources should be expected to manage the following:

- Coordinating CDM-NDC crosswalk maintenance.
- Coordinating drug record build and charge capture.
- Tracking direct and specialty 340B purchases that require manual intervention.
- Identifying and resolving software data discrepancies.
- Assisting with 340B internal audit activities.
- Serving as a 340B content expert.

PREPARING FOR SOFTWARE IMPLEMENTATION

All of the prior discussion in this chapter can be considered software implementation preparation. However, the focus becomes more technical in the period between OPA registration and the covered entity's start date in the 340B program. This 90-day interval is also commonly the initiation of software implementation. That timeframe is the focus of this section and encompasses a difficulty many hospitals encounter before achieving any savings.

Timing of Program Registration and Software Implementation

For hospitals subject to the GPO prohibition, reaching the quarterly start date for 340B participation while weeks or even months away from completion of 340B software implementation, can create significant financial losses before the first 340B purchase is made. The inability to track inpatient and outpatient charges and, therefore, justify 340B or GPO purchases forces hospitals to make some or all purchases on the WAC account. Entities are subject to the GPO prohibition on entry to the 340B program, not upon completion of software implementation. Although colleagues or software vendors may provide casual advice recommending that the hospital continue making full GPO inventory purchases until software implementation is complete, this is contrary to OPA guidance. Many hospitals consider this activity low risk because of the unlikely event of a HRSA audit soon after program entry, but the AO will be asked to attest, upon recertification, that the hospital is meeting and complying with all program requirements. Knowingly violating the GPO prohibition can be grounds for program dismissal by OPA.

Hospitals can employ strategies to minimize WAC purchases in this scenario. Some hospitals request a one calendar quarter delay in their 340B eligibility to permit software implementation and program set-up. If several weeks or months of WAC purchases are otherwise on the horizon, this option is reasonable. If the hospital expects completion of software implementation within a few weeks of the OPA start date, hospitals may choose to manage their inventory prior to their effective date, focusing on items that will cause the largest increases in WAC expense. When this strategy is employed, entities may also consider targeting purchases for select outpatient departments or clinics with only 340B eligible encounters. If hospitals can create a physically separate 340B inventory (and a distributor account) for these 340B eligible patient care areas, 340B savings can be achieved immediately. The resulting savings may offset the additional expense from WAC purchases and may lead to net savings from the program effective date. Many hospitals are unaware that they cannot continue making all GPO purchases without detailed virtual inventory tracking software in place for their patient care while awaiting completion of software implementation. Even though practitioners label certain areas of the hospital as *inpatient*, it is understood that many of these patients receive care as outpatients (e.g., observation, short stay) while on *inpatient* units.

KEY POINT

Plan for 340B activities during software implementation. Software implementation often involves more work and takes more time than planned. Map the pharmacy revenue cycle and supply chain and plan purchasing practices during implementation to minimize WAC spend and potential compliance risks.

Mapping the 340B Supply Chain

One of the most critical elements supporting a successful 340B software implementation can be managed immediately after 340B program registration. As discussed previously, 340B entities must align their MCR, OPA registration data, medication purchasing accounts, and intra-hospital supply chain. When OPA registration has been completed in alignment with the most recently filed MCR, the implementation team's focus should shift to creating a pharmacy supply chain that optimizes 340B savings and efficiency and promotes program compliance. In this section, we will use a fictional covered entity to describe common scenarios and discussions encountered by entities preparing for the 340B program.

The entity should start by physically mapping out the patient care and inventory storage areas. This may be done using detailed health-system physical plant maps or by sketching on a notepad. How many locations or pharmacies receive drug inventory, and where is it physically received? How many physical drug inventories exist (e.g., cabinets, satellites, surgical suites, infusion centers), and are they associated with one distributor account or distinct accounts? Covering all possible 340B set-up scenarios and inventory options is not possible in this chapter but is addressed in Chapter 6, the 340B Pharmacy Supply Chain. See **Figure 4-1** for relevant examples. Each of the scenarios should be looked at with two questions in mind. *First*, how is this area affected by drug purchasing and inventory management practices? *Second*, how will purchasing and inventory management decisions impact 340B software set-up? A quick orientation of the Sample Hospital campus includes:

- Main hospital building (i.e., four walls) containing a long-term acute care (LTAC) unit that is rented by an outside healthcare provider.

- A medical office building (MOB) at a separate physical address that contains private physician practices and a wound clinic recently registered as a child site on OPA.

- A surgical pavilion at a separate physical address that performs various outpatient surgeries and is registered as a child site but also houses a private rheumatology practice that includes a small infusion center.

- The central hospital pharmacy that purchases all medications on one GPO account and distributes medication to all units listed above.

- Sample Hospital that chose to carve-in Medicaid during registration.

Long-Term Acute Care Scenario

The LTAC patients are inpatients of another healthcare organization housed within Sample Hospital. However, as part of the contract, the central hospital pharmacy provides all inpatient medications for the unit via the main GPO account. This can continue as a 340B covered entity because there are no outpatients in the unit. Practically, however, Sample Hospital must decide how to manage this inventory in a 340B environment. Once 340B software is installed, all central pharmacy purchases will be replacement inventory whose purchases are based on historical inpatient and outpatient charges captured. The LTAC unit is not a hospital service, and no patient

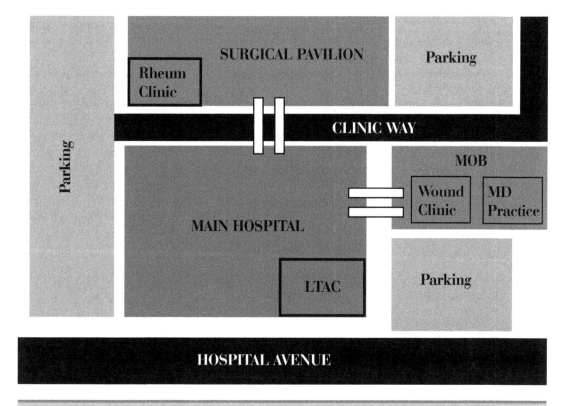

FIGURE 4-1. Sample Hospital Campus

charges are captured in the hospital financial systems. If the Sample Hospital continues supplying central inventory, replacement purchases will be made on the WAC account as the pharmacy will dispense/sell more inventory than can be accounted for with posted medication administration charges. The hospital may simply adjust the LTAC bill to account for WAC purchases and move forward. If this is not acceptable, the hospital could open a separate GPO account for the LTAC unit and maintain a physically separate GPO inventory just for LTAC inpatients. This may be cumbersome and may disrupt workflow in the pharmacy. Space permitting, the LTAC could begin purchasing their own inventory and bypass the central pharmacy entirely. Finally, the Sample Hospital could choose to carefully track all inventory (NDC-11 and applicable charge quantity) dispensed to the LTAC and manually load the data as a proxy for inpatient charges—many software vendors support these processes.

This scenario demonstrates how one small unit that was likely overlooked during 340B planning can lead to difficult discussions and supply chain decisions around 340B eligibility and perhaps significant cost in WAC purchases.

Medical Office Building

Sample Hospital determined that all patient encounters in the wound clinic are 340B-eligible encounters and registered the department as a child site with initial registration. Currently this inventory comes from the central pharmacy. Team discussions reveal that charge capture in the wound clinic is imperfect because single topical packages are used on multiple patients for treatment. The team understands that, with 340B software implementation, continuing to provide central pharmacy inventory to the wound clinic will limit 340B savings opportunities. Sample Hospital could choose to open a new 340B account with a ship-to address of the wound clinic child site for all inventory.

The private physician practices in the MOB receive small inventory supplies from the central pharmacy with vaccines as the dominant expense. Once again, any inventory sent to the private physician practices is unlikely to be associated with charge capture and will result in WAC purchases. Vaccines are not covered outpatient drugs and can be continually supplied to the physician practices at GPO. As part of the GPO prohibition discussed earlier,[7] OPA has provided a mechanism for non-340B departments outside the four walls to continue receiving GPO inventory. If Sample Hospital chooses, they may open a separate GPO account for the physician practice offices and maintain a separate inventory and could also consider medication delivery directly to the practices. Direct delivery to the practices is often impractical as physician practices require smaller quantities than are found in most commercial packages. This scenario also assumes that the physician practices are not reimbursable on the MCR, nor registered as child sites on the OPA web site. Finally, many hospitals continue providing vaccines at GPO pricing but absorb the incremental WAC expense from the small inventories supplied to most physician practices to minimize interruptions to workflow.

Surgical Pavilion

The surgical pavilion scenario is nearly identical to the wound clinic discussion. Operating room suites and anesthesia departments are commonly areas of incomplete charge capture. Many of the injectable drugs used in these areas are associated with significant increases in cost when moving from GPO purchases to WAC. Assuming all surgical pavilion patients have outpatient status and all providers meet the current employed, contracted, or credentialing standard, purchasing full 340B inventory on a separate account with separate inventory is an option. An inability to create a separate 340B inventory (e.g., routine small volumes of hospital inpatients transported to surgical pavilion, Medicaid carve-out) combined with poor charge capture can be costly. Sample Hospital's only recourse may be to improve charge capture with kits, additional operating room pharmacy technicians, or other technical or operational modifications.

In the current scenario, consider a private rheumatology practice that is not reimbursable on the MCR. 340B inventory cannot be used for infusion services within the practice. Depending on the drugs provided, there may be no WAC premium associated with expensive branded products supplied to the practice. If a significant WAC expense does exist, Sample Hospital could choose to manage a separate inventory and separate account for the rheumatology practice and supply GPO inventory.

Once all 340B supply chain decisions have been made, Sample Hospital must determine the impact on 340B software setup. In general, hospitals should only include departments and facilities in the eventual 340B data feeds (charges) that will drive inventory replenishment for purchasing accounts included in the split-billing process. For example, if in the scenario above Sample Hospital created a new 340B-only account for the surgical pavilion that supplied all of its inventory, the 340B data feed should not include charges from the surgical pavilion and the distributor account should not be integrated into the split-billing process. Sample Hospital has created a physically separate inventory for the surgical pavilion that does not rely on split-billing software. Including these outpatient charges will falsely elevate available 340B purchases because the separate purchase account should not be decrementing available quantities in the software. The same argument could be made if Sample Hospital chose to open a new GPO account to provide inventory for the physician practices. As no charges are entering the software from these practices, Sample Hospital should instruct the software vendor to exclude the purchase account from integration. The inventory is not coming from the central pharmacy that relies on the software to determine 340B, GPO, or WAC account usage.

SUMMARY

The many discussions and scenarios in this chapter should prepare you for 340B program registration leading up to software implementation. The authors cannot overemphasize the importance of a team approach in preparing for the 340B program. Pharmacy departments, in isolation, rarely have the full skillset required for all financial analyses, Medicaid billing modifications, and MCR determinations. In addition, the CE's legal and compliance departments should be invested in the program from the onset to promote program integrity. Finally, the AO will be expected to approve and authorize OPA submissions at least annually.

Pharmacy leadership should guide the organization through an evaluation of the current supply chain to identify compliance, operational, or financial gaps that may occur with 340B program implementation.

In Chapter 5, the authors take the next step and consider the full implications of software implementation. The material from Chapter 4 should allow hospitals and health systems to drive the implementation as opposed to being passive observers responding only to the software vendor's requests.

REFERENCES

1. 340B Drug Pricing Program Eligibility and Registration. Health Resources and Services Administration Web site. http://hrsa.gov/opa/eligibilityandregistration/index.html . Accessed October 11, 2017.

2. Department of Health and Human Services, Health Resources and Services Administration, Healthcare Systems Bureau. Office of Pharmacy Affairs (OPA) certification of contract between private, non-profit hospital and state/local government to provide healthcare services to low income individuals. https://www.hrsa.gov/sites/default/files/opa/files/hospitalreginfo.pdf. Accessed October 11, 2017.

3. Health Resources and Services Administration, HHS. 340B drug pricing program omnibus guidance. *Federal Register*. 2015;80(167):52300-52324.

4. Department of Health and Human Services, Centers for Medicare and Medicaid Services. *Medicare Disproportionate Share Hospital*. ICN 006741. https://www.cms.gov/Outreach-and-Education/Medicare-Learning-Network-MLN/MLNProducts/downloads/Disproportionate_Share_Hospital.pdf . Updated August 2016. Accessed October 11, 2017.

5. Health Resources and Services Administration, HHS. Notice regarding 340B drug pricing program – children's hospitals. *Federal Register*. 2009;74(168):45206-45211.

6. 340B Prime Vendor Program. Frequently Asked Question 1190. https://www.340bpvp.com/resourceCenter/faqSearch.html?category=content&Ntt=1190. Updated January 12, 2015. Accessed October 11, 2017.

7. Office of Pharmacy Affairs, Healthcare Systems Bureau, Health Resources and Services Administration, Department of Health and Human Services. *Statutory Prohibition on Group Purchasing Organization Participation*. Release 2013-1. https://www.hrsa.gov/sites/default/files/opa/programrequirements/policyreleases/prohibitionongpoparticipation020713.pdf . Published February 7, 2013. Accessed October 11, 2017.

8. Office of Pharmacy Affairs, Health Resources and Services Administration, Department of Health and Human Services. Section 340B Public Health Service Act. 2010. http://hrsa.gov/opa/programrequirements/phsactsection340b.pdf . Accessed October 11, 2017.

9. *Pharmaceutical Research and Manufacturers of America v. United States Department of Health and Human Services* (Civil Action 2013-1501). United State District Court for the District of Columbia. May 23, 2014. https://law.justia.com/cases/federal/district-courts/district-of-columbia/dcdce/1:2014cv01685/168424/29/. Accessed October 11, 2017.

10. 340B Prime Vendor Program. Frequently Asked Question 1298. https://www.340bpvp.com/resourceCenter/faqSearch.html?category=content&Ntt=1298. Updated November 10, 2014. Accessed October 11, 2017.

11. Office of Pharmacy Affairs, Healthcare Systems Bureau, Health Resources and Services Administration, Department of Health and Human Services. *Clarification on use of the Medicaid Exclusion Rule.* Release 2014-1. https://www.hrsa.gov/sites/default/files/opa/programrequirements/policyreleases/clarifica-tion-medicaid-exclusion.pdf Published December 12, 2014. Accessed October 11, 2017.

12. Health Resources and Services Administration, HHS. Final notice regarding section 602 of the Veteran's Healthcare Act of 1992 duplicate discounts and rebates on drug purchases. *Federal Register.* 1993;58(119):34058-34059.

13. Medicaid Exclusion File / Duplicate Discount Prohibition. Health Resources and Services Administration Web site. https://www.hrsa.gov/opa/program-requirements/medicaid-exclusion/index.html. Accessed October 11, 2017.

14. Medicaid.gov Web site. *MDR Detailed State Contact Information.* https://www.medicaid.gov/medic-aid-chip-program-information/by-topics/prescription-drugs/downloads/xxx-4-drugcon.pdf. Updated August 5, 2016. Accessed October 11, 2017.

15. Health Resources and Services Administration, HHS. Medicaid program; covered outpatient drug. *Federal Register.* 2016;81(20):5170-5357.

16. Health Resources and Services Administration, HHS. Notice regarding 340B drug pricing program – contract pharmacy services. *Federal Register.* 2010;75(43):10272-10279.

17. 340B Tools. Apexus Web site. https https://www.340bpvp.com/education/340b-tools/. Last Updated July 8, 2015. Accessed October 11, 2017.

CHAPTER 5

Christopher S. Shain, PharmD, BCPS and Gregg Niemiec, BS, RPh

Operations and Business Considerations in Implementing and Optimizing 340B Software:

340B Considerations in the Mixed-Use Pharmacy

Hospital covered entities (CEs) implementing 340B program software are compelled to balance operations with a focus on both compliance and drug savings. This balancing act commonly illuminates the intersection of pharmacy supply chain operations, drug charge capture, and hospital information system (HIS) data. Understanding the flow of data and the strengths and limitations of each dataset is critical to a successful and effective 340B software implementation. 340B software will, regardless of the selected vendor, heighten the requirement for accurate and comprehensive charge capture, drug formulary and chargemaster maintenance, and strategic drug purchasing. CEs must meet the challenge of supplying accurate and auditable transactional pharmacy data and must identify or hire skilled personnel to meet the complex business and compliance requirements of supply chain management in the 340B program.

Although relatively simple first-generation 340B software programs and rudimentary tracking systems (e.g., spreadsheets) were used to manage CEs' 340B programs prior to the current audit era, operational requirements, business risks, and audit preparedness demand more sophisticated 340B software functionality. This chapter highlights critical operational requirements and describes pharmacy operations and HIS requirements to support software implementation steps. It also provides a map of key personnel required to complete implementation and maintain 340B program software.

WHAT IS 340B SOFTWARE?

For the purposes of this chapter, the authors refer to 340B software (also known as *split billing* or *mixed-use* software) used in the non-retail hospital setting.

Fundamentally, mixed-use 340B software collects and collates drug charges and, based on hospital indicators, assigns drug utilization for eligible outpatients to 340B inventory replenishment. The software assigns inpatient charges to group purchasing (GPO) contracts. Replenishment purchases for 340B-ineligible outpatients (e.g., Medicaid carve-out), purchases stemming from untracked or unattributed inventory, and purchases for new inventory (e.g., new drugs or expanding inventory) are funneled to the non-contract wholesale acquisition cost (WAC) accounts.

Charge data, inpatient/outpatient indicators, and Medicaid status are provided to the software vendor through one or more data feeds. These data must be consistent with hospital clinical or financial systems and must support a Health Resources and Services Administration (HRSA) audit or other audits months or years in the future.

A fundamental step in implementing 340B software is building a *crosswalk* that converts drug charge quantities in the hospital's HIS into National Drug Code (NDC)-specific packages to be purchased from distributors or manufacturers for replenishment. Managing inventory replenishment, based on the charge assignment referenced above, is the culmination of the 340B data feed, crosswalk, and pharmacy supply chain integration in the software. Maintaining data integrity and the crosswalk relationships comprises a significant portion of the required 340B software and program maintenance going forward. Timely, complete, and accurate maintenance of 340B software and the associated data tables, purchasing accounts, and practices is crucial to achieve the greatest 340B savings value while remaining compliant. Lax or delayed maintenance is the most common reason for compliance lapses and savings loss.

KEY POINT

A well-executed software implementation requires planning and the engagement of sufficient resources and sponsorship. Extended or delayed implementation and poorly executed plans risk lost savings and may have 340B compliance implications.

A well-executed 340B software implementation project plan with full information technology (IT) support can be completed in approximately 120 days. If implementation is prolonged for months, it may be due to lack of an executive champion, the timing and focus of competing IT projects and support, irregularities in source data, or operational changes necessary to support compliant utilization of 340B drugs. CEs should check references for specific vendors to better gauge implementation time and resource requirements with a focus on the key elements of the project outlined below. To avoid significant delays, CEs should consider the following:

- Identify an engaged executive champion, often the Authorizing Official, to secure required IT resources and priority early in the project.

- Assign a professional project manager to coordinate multiple hospital departments, consultants, the 340B software vendor, and HIS specialists. Don't rely on the software vendor install team to manage the project independently.

The software implementation team should include, at various stages, an executive champion, pharmacy leadership and operations (e.g., informatics), finance (e.g., reimbursement, patient financial services), legal and/or compliance leadership, and IT. If available, CEs should consider assigning project management resources to the 340B software implementation project. In most organizations, pharmacy or supply chain leadership will have primary responsibility for 340B program management. As such, they should be intimately involved in the 340B software implementation project.

BILLING TRANSACTION FEEDS AS A SOURCE OF 340B DATA

Constructing billing transaction feeds for the 340B software vendor is a significant risk during 340B software implementation for several reasons:

- CEs and CE team members may be new to the 340B program. Moreover, 340B management personnel may have limited or no software implementation experience.

- Software vendors are focused on technical requirements—customers may unknowingly make technical decisions with 340B compliance and/or financial implications. Simply stated, the technical decisions may not achieve the policy or business goals of the CE without in-depth review and discussion of 340B program requirements.

- Many data elements to support 340B software function have multiple sources within HIS, each with relative strengths and weaknesses. The best source of data may rely on systems that are unfamiliar to the 340B project team.

- HIS data elements change over time with respect to a single dispensing or administration event.

Sources of Charge Data

An early, critical decision for a CE is the source of charge data for the 340B data feed to identify and quantify dispensing at the product level. The primary purpose of 340B software is to allow CEs to replenish inventory using the appropriate contract price (e.g., 340B, GPO, WAC). Inventory replenishment is based on dispensing activity and is typically managed as a perpetual inventory using drug charge capture and accumulation. The term *charge* is used broadly to represent evidence of drug dispensation or administration in a HIS. CEs must determine the optimal source of charge data, whether from pharmacy software or from the hospital financial system. The decision will have financial, operational, and compliance ramifications and is unique for each HIS vendor and may be influenced by local HIS setup and the CE's build choices. For example, pulling charge data from health-system pharmacy software may allow CEs to distinguish between inpatient and outpatient status at the time of dispense in a mixed-use area like the emergency department or operating suite. However, pulling these data from a financial system for a patient that is eventually admitted may reveal only inpatient (GPO) charges because most payers will not reimburse outpatient services for emergency department patients that are admitted. Another scenario stems from the common changes to patient status (inpatient versus outpatient) and payer status that occur during and, in the case of pending Medicaid, several weeks after the hospital encounter. A CE using financial systems charge data will likely find that, upon audit, the drug charge, patient status (inpatient versus outpatient), and payer status are better aligned when comparing the 340B data feed with currently displayed HIS information. For customers using pharmacy dispense data, it can be difficult to maintain consistency between the two sources because patient status and payer status are not commonly housed in the pharmacy system.

As an example, consider an observation patient in an acute care unit (340B eligible) administered (charged) one acetaminophen 325-mg tablet at 2200 hours on day 1 with a current payer status of uninsured. At midnight an automated program runs that creates a 340B data feed for day 1 charges, such that the acetaminophen dose enters the software as an outpatient 340B-eligible dispense. At 0800 hours on day 2 the ward clerk enters a change in patient status that includes an inpatient admission for the patient, effective at 2100 hours day 1. A new or revised acetaminophen charge is not created by this status change. How will the 340B software program accurately represent the administered acetaminophen dose as an inpatient GPO dispense? Further, assume that the facility in the example is carving-out Medicaid. One week after admission, with the support of patient financial services, the patient is enrolled in Medicaid and the hospital rebills the patient's claim to Medicaid. Based on a single flat file sent at the close of day 1, how will the 340B software identify the original outpatient charge as Medicaid and exclude it from 340B replenishment? These are the types of scenarios that should be explored with your 340B software vendor to determine the data source and associated policy and practices to support compliance. Many CEs fail to engage the vendor in this way and discover gaps in program savings or integrity well after implementation is completed and technical resources have moved to other hospital projects.

Other Possible Solution Scenarios

Although solutions to these and similar scenarios are dependent on the specific software functionality and the characteristics of the HIS, many hospitals use some combination of the following solutions:

- Admission, discharge, transfer (ADT) feeds that report all changes in patient and payer status and correct any patient- or payer-type data in the original daily feed.
- Rebilling patient claims to Medicaid that result in crediting of the original bill and rebilling with Medicaid payer status such that both transactions are sent to the 340B software.

Ultimately, the CE should create a data exchange between the HIS and 340B software vendor of a record of charge events that, when reviewed months later by an auditor, will show consistency regarding the drug and dose charged, the patient status (inpatient versus outpatient), and the payer status (e.g., Medicaid). **Table 5-1** outlines relevant points of discussion for any organization implementing 340B software.

Service location or department is another data element that should be evaluated by the 340B implementation team. The authors generally recommend against using location or department codes to discriminate between inpatient versus outpatient status. Consider that the requirement to differentiate inpatient versus outpatient charges in mixed-use departments is the primary force driving the necessity of 340B software. However, location filters may be useful and necessary to prevent charges from non-340B eligible departments from accumulating. Further, patient care locations that implement separate physical 340B or GPO inventories should be excluded from the 340B data feed and accumulations and purchasing data feeds.

KEY POINT

The pharmacy chargemaster and revenue cycle should be evaluated prior to starting 340B software implementation. The details of charge management and charge capture may require changes and updates for the 340B software to function properly.

Table 5-1. 340B Implementation Considerations

Data Source/Type	Considerations
Pharmacy Dispense	Flexibility with charge quantity (vial versus metric unit dispensed).
	Credits and other finance modifications typically not represented.
	Supplementation with ADT data may be necessary.
Finance Charge	Pre-HCPCS versus post-HCPCS charge quantity may impact waste capture.
	Charge codes may be filtered or aggregated in passage from pharmacy to financial systems.
	Direct access to nonpharmacy drug charges (e.g., radiology).
	Outpatient dispenses prior to admission identified as inpatient charges.

340B SOFTWARE CROSSWALK

The engine of 340B software is the *crosswalk*. Charge quantities from the data feed previously discussed must accumulate against a specific NDC for an amount equal to the full package purchased from the distributor or direct vendors. During software implementation, CEs must create relationships between charge codes and NDCs. Each relationship must include a conversion factor that ties the charge unit (e.g., mg, mL, vial, tab) to the quantity present in the package being purchased. CEs may point to their current pharmacy software formulary or drug dictionary as meeting the requirement for a 340B crosswalk. Although the pharmacy software formulary is an essential tool to be used in 340B software crosswalk production, it generally requires significant assessment and modification for 340B program management. For example, the primary NDC referenced in the formulary may not be the NDC currently being purchased or dispensed from inventory.

A portion of the modification will occur during the 340B crosswalk build, while some changes will fall under the long-term maintenance required for a compliant program. The following general steps for crosswalk build will assist in developing a complete crosswalk and are applicable to most HIS and 340B software vendor combinations:

1. Determine gaps in the current CDM dictionary as outlined by the 340B software vendor functionality. What items currently in inventory or recently purchased are not represented in the CDM dictionary?

2. Match each CDM code to a NDC from the current inventory or recent purchase history. Be certain that the "match" works in both directions; all charge codes should have a corresponding NDC, and all NDCs should have a corresponding charge code.

3. Determine the conversion factor for each CDM:NDC pairing in relation to the full package purchased from the distributor or manufacturer.

4. Identify charge codes or drug products that should be managed as exceptions by the 340B software.

Chargemaster Gaps

Before creating a crosswalk during 340B software implementation, the CE should determine if the current chargemaster has sufficient detail and granularity. Depending on the 340B software vendor's method for identifying a unique drug item, a CE may need to add charge codes for optimal 340B program performance. A lack of charge code granularity may affect the software's ability to accumulate charges for all NDCs. For example, suppose a CE has a single charge code for injectable glycopyrrolate but purchases and uses three distinct products: 1-mL, 2-mL, and 5-mL vials from multiple manufacturers. One CDM code cannot accurately represent the specific NDC from which each charge stems. Some software vendors may attempt to allocate charges proportionately based on recent purchases, but the specifics should be reviewed with the vendor until the CE feels comfortable with the processing and auditing of the transactions.

CDM granularity may also impact the software vendor's ability to maintain CDM:NDC crosswalk integrity. Legacy 340B software programs largely relied on CE personnel to manually update crosswalks with current NDCs. Second-generation 340B software systems can auto-update the crosswalk for CEs based on electronic data interchange (EDI) data for recent purchases or virtual inventory tracking. To identify similar products that may be substituted on the crosswalk, vendors generally use a combination of generic coding and/or package size to identify equivalent drugs. Once again, using the glycopyrrolate example, if the current crosswalk NDC is a 1-mL vial and the CE begins purchasing and dispensing 2-mL vials, the software can only update the crosswalk if it "sees" the 2-mL vial as an equivalent product and can match size/vial contents accordingly. If the software vendor uses a combination of generic code and package size to identify equivalent products, the 2-mL glycopyrrolate will not be auto-linked to the crosswalk for the 1-mL item. Charges will inappropriately continue to accumulate against the 1-mL vial, and future purchases of the 2-mL vial will be purchased at WAC (or purchased at GPO for rural hospitals not subject to the GPO prohibition) as there will be no accumulation associated with the 2-mL NDC. Many CEs complete 340B software implementation without understanding the details of the vendor's crosswalk management functionality. CEs should work to understand the technical details of crosswalk management and devote their resources accordingly.

Bar-code medication administration (BCMA) may change core 340B software functionality in the future. Customers with BCMA operations across all departments managed by 340B software could potentially bypass a CDM:NDC crosswalk by capturing the utilized NDC at the time of administration. At this time, most hospitals and health systems report product and department gaps in their BCMA operations that prevent them from abandoning crosswalk functionality. In addition, customers would still be required to create and maintain conversion factors referencing administration quantities and full package quantities. Managing this process outside of a traditional 340B crosswalk would be cumbersome because the number of NDCs managed may far exceed the number of charge codes.

Matching CDMs and NDCs

Because each manufacturer provides the 340B discount, HRSA directs that 340B replenishment be made for the actual NDC that was previously dispensed or administered. As charge quantities flow into the 340B software, they must be assigned to a specific NDC. The CE will work with the software vendor to create relationships between charge codes and the current inventory NDC. Because the initial crosswalk identifies current relationships, the software vendor should integrate it as soon as possible. A significant delay between the initial crosswalk build and subsequent activation can lead to inaccurate accumulations because purchasing patterns and NDCs in inventory change over time. Significant rework may be required to make the "aged" crosswalk current. As described in the previous section, CEs should clearly understand the vendor's crosswalk functionality before completing this step of implementation. Most 340B software vendors support multiple charge codes assigned to the same NDC. For example, a CE may dispense a 30-mL unit-dose cup of medication Z to adults under charge code 12345. The same CE may compound 5-mL pediatric oral syringes of medication Z using the 30-mL unit-dose cup as a source, charging the syringes with code 56789. In this scenario, both CDMs should be tied to the 30-mL unit-dose cup purchased from the distributor with a differing accumulation based on the amount dispensed.

CEs should work through all drug-related charge codes to complete the crosswalk build. A typical CE will encounter well over 1,000 charge codes to be matched. Most facilities will initiate the project with the current formulary (containing a link between CDM and primary NDC) and recent purchase history. The purchase history should include nonprimary distributor purchases. It is strongly recommended that personnel with pharmacy informatics expertise lead the crosswalk build project. With access to generic drug codes, manufacturer package sizes, and related drug database elements, pharmacy informatics experts can quickly establish reliable and consistent relationships between primary NDCs from the drug dictionary, chargemaster, and current inventory.

Crosswalk Conversion Factors

Once CDM:NDC matches are completed, customers can focus on the conversion ratios describing the number of billing units that must accumulate to account for the full package purchased from the distributor. Using the example of medication Z from the paragraph above, assume that an informatics expert has created a crosswalk relationship between CDM 12345 and the currently-utilized NDC for medication Z. When the CE charges the product, assume a charge quantity of "one" represents one 30-mL unit-dose cup. The CE purchases the product from the primary distributor in an overwrap package containing 25 cups. The 340B crosswalk conversion factor for this crosswalk relationship should be 25—in other words, 25 charges are required to account for a full overwrap package. The informatics expert also matches CDM 56789 to the currently-utilized NDC from medication Z. For the pediatric oral syringe, the CE charge quantity of "1" represents one 5-mL syringe. Therefore, six charges must accumulate for each 30-mL cup and 150 must accumulate (6 times 25) for the full overwrap package of 25 unit-dose cups. The 340B crosswalk conversion factor for this relationship should be set at 150.

The CE's use of the healthcare common procedure coding system (HCPCS) must be clearly understood during crosswalk completion, especially during the creation of conversion factors. Familiarity with the use of HCPCS in pharmacy dispensing or finance charge data fed into the 340B software is critical. If pharmacy dispense quantities are the source of 340B replenishment and are unaffected by HCPCS unit transitions from the finance department, then the methodologies already discussed should be sufficient to support accurate crosswalk development. If the charge quantities supporting 340B replenishment have been modified to account for HCPCS unit billing, personnel building the crosswalk must coordinate with the finance personnel to understand and align the specific charge codes affected. Finance can also verify the HCPCS units utilized at the time of crosswalk build. Personnel completing the crosswalk can find comprehensive HCPCS tables online; the CE should be aware that most hospitals do not incorporate the entire HCPCS dictionary.[1] Therefore, it is critical that CEs understand the local detail of their hospital-specific HCPCS usage during crosswalk development.

MEDICAID

Previous chapters of this book have outlined the importance of understanding the intertwining of Medicaid and 340B. In addition, the authors have tried to project the importance of making program decisions concerning Medicaid well before software implementation begins. However, ensuring that the software vendor correctly interprets the CE's decisions regarding 340B and Medicaid is the key element of effective software implementation.

In the mixed-use environment, the CE will be most concerned with hospital outpatient drugs administered to Medicaid patients. If the CE carves in Medicaid (i.e., uses 340B drugs to treat Medicaid patients), the software vendor has little additional work beyond ensuring that payer information is accurately captured for audit purposes. Carving-in Medicaid captures the eligible outpatient charges and replenishes inventory with 340B drug, resulting in the CE treating Medicaid patients identically to commercial patients. The software vendor has no need to filter or treat these charges uniquely.

CEs that choose to carve-out Medicaid need to ensure that software settings will screen 340B-eligible outpatient charges for Medicaid patients and prevent them from accumulating toward 340B inventory. The CE must work with the software vendor to ensure that charges for dispenses and administration of drugs paid by Medicaid plans, whether identified by name, code, or another method, are properly categorized. The CE should contact state Medicaid agencies to understand whether Medicaid managed care organization (MCO) plans should be included in the carve-out process. Correctly identifying the Medicaid plans for all states and distinguishing between Medicaid MCO and similarly named commercial plans will require expertise from finance or reimbursement departments.

When the software vendor has identified and managed the appropriate Medicaid plans, the CE must determine the details regarding which Medicaid plans will be filtered for the CE carving-out Medicaid. For example, some patients will be dually eligible for both Medicare and Medicaid. In many states, it is common practice for Medicaid plans to support patients by subsidizing co-pays or co-insurance when Medicaid is not the primary payer. When Medicaid provides any financial support for medication co-pay or co-insurance, the state becomes eligible for manufacturer rebates on the claims. In other words, it is possible for the state to collect rebates on crossover claims where Medicaid is not the primary payer.[2] The CE should ensure that the 340B software vendor is filtering all Medicaid charges that may result in rebate payments to the states, not only to patients with Medicaid as their primary payer.

Although not a core function of 340B split-billing software, many CEs that carve-in Medicaid find themselves—pursuant to state billing requirements—implementing new systems or procedures to manage billing modifiers and 340B-related costs on Medicaid bills. A detailed review of hospital and retail pharmacy billing practices is outside the scope of this chapter; entities should inquire about their 340B software vendor's capabilities regarding Medicaid billing.

FINAL IMPLEMENTATION STEPS AND OPTIMIZATION

As customers near the completion of software implementation, a sense of accomplishment is warranted. But it can lead to a lack of focus on the fine details where active management may be the difference between an average outcome versus exceptional implementation. In this section, we provide examples of these items and offer potential solutions when feasible.

Account Alignment

The final software configuration must align properly with the CE's current supply chain and inventory management. In other words, the software vendor's capture and utilization of charge data for split billing must align with the CE's account structure and inventory management. In the simplest terms, the charges fed into the 340B software for the accumulation of 340B packages should represent drugs administered from inventory purchases managed or split by the software. If cancer center inventory is managed as a separate physical 340B inventory on a unique purchasing account, then the charges associated with those administrations should not accumulate in the software. Capturing cancer center charges under this model would lead to an over-accumulation of 340B packages and overpurchase of 340B drugs with ensuing 340B drug diversion.

The reverse scenario leads to under-accumulation of 340B (and GPO under-accumulation for affected facilities) packages. If the central pharmacy supplies inventory to multiple drug cabinets for an outpatient surgical center across the street from the main hospital that is properly registered as a 340B child site, but the 340B software charge feed does not include charges from the surgical center, the CE will under-accumulate 340B-eligible dispenses. The end result will be additional WAC purchases that would have been justified on the 340B account with proper software setup.

CEs implementing 340B software should work diligently with finance and IT departments to understand the source and 340B relevance of all charge data reaching the software. Optimal 340B program performance is based on complete, comprehensive, and current capture of charges and the exclusion of areas and data streams that are not 340B-relevant.

KEY POINT

A pre-implementation review of all input should occur and include Finance, IT, and others supplying or managing data. Complete, comprehensive, correct, and sufficiently detailed information should be supplied to support proper results.

Covered Outpatient Drug Exceptions

Refer to previous chapters of this book for an expanded discussion on the covered outpatient drug definition (and its limiting definition) as defined in Section 1927(k) of the Social Security Act.[3] The definition becomes important during 340B program and software implementation for many CEs as they develop policies and procedures that carve-out certain drugs or classes of drugs from their program based on the limiting definition of covered outpatient drug. For example, many CEs, in concert with their legal and compliance departments, determine that inhaled gases do not meet the definition of a covered outpatient drug based on their administration as part of a procedure and their lack of direct reimbursement. If the items are not covered outpatient drugs by policy, they are not subject to the GPO prohibition and may be purchased on the GPO account without tracking charges. The CEs should also avoid 340B purchases for these items, and WAC purchases are unnecessary. Regardless of the specific items selected for the CE's exclusion, the purchases and software splitting must be properly managed in the software.

Most software vendors rely on the CE to identify the list of products for exclusion by NDC. Regular maintenance of the list of excluded NDCs is important. An incomplete or poorly maintained list of excluded NDCs can lead to purchases outside of the CE's policy framework (e.g., at 340B price) or lead to unnecessary WAC purchases. CEs should audit the NDC exclusion list soon after implementation and regularly thereafter to ensure that products are not being diverted to the 340B account or purchased at unnecessarily higher WAC prices.

One class of products that many CEs determine meets the limiting definition is radiographic contrast. This example demonstrates the importance of considering the financial ramifications of this policy decision. Many CEs subject to the GPO prohibition (rural hospitals will not access WAC pricing) will encounter five potential prices for radiographic contrast purchase:

1. 340B price (not all contrast manufacturers offer 340B pricing)
2. GPO price
3. WAC price
4. 340B prime vendor (Apexus) price (found on the 340B and/or WAC account)
5. Manufacturer direct price (often available through materials management or radiology departments)

The plethora of pricing options creates a complicated analysis. If the CE considers contrast a covered outpatient drug, the software should manage splitting across three accounts as with any other product. Depending on the CE's formulary, 340B pricing may not be available during the split because not all manufacturers offer 340B pricing for contrast agents. The price on the "340B" account may be a 340B prime vendor price in the absence of 340B pricing. Similarly, for a product purchased on the WAC account, relief in the form of prime vendor contract pricing may or may not be available, depending on the specific product purchased.

Finally, a direct price available from the manufacturer is an option that can be exercised without creating a 340B drug diversion or GPO prohibition issue. The CE should, however, understand HRSA's definition of a compliant "non-group purchasing/non-GPO" price. For a health system with more than one hospital, HRSA has stated that any system contract negotiated for a covered outpatient drug constitutes a group purchasing arrangement.[4,5] Therefore, some direct vendor prices should be viewed and managed as traditional GPO prices for 340B compliance and audit purposes. Individual contracts between the manufacturer and a CE meeting HRSA's guidance can offer pricing that avoids GPO prohibition issues.

To model the financial effects of a formulary and 340B eligibility decision for the CE, all of the pricing scenarios above must be combined with purchase history and utilization data that will project the percentage of inpatient and outpatient purchases if contrast media is included as a covered outpatient drug. For entities that exclude contrast media from their 340B program, the math is simpler because all purchases can be made on the GPO account or at a direct price from the manufacturer.

Supply Chain Technology Integration

Many health systems use additional supply chain technology (e.g., Lawson, PeopleSoft) for inventory and supply chain management beyond the pharmaceutical distributor ordering platform. All automation and software systems that affect inventory management should be assessed for 340B program impact during software implementation. Describing solutions for all available supply chain systems and 340B software vendors across all options is not feasible in this chapter. However, a summary of the systems and issues that most CEs find necessary to address during 340B software implementation include the following:

- *Controlled substance ordering system*—determine if the controlled substance ordering system (CSOS) will be integrated into the ordering and split billing process and what procedures are required to manage purchases and inventory for controlled substances across multiple accounts.

- *Carousel and cabinet automation*—determine if orders created by automation software will split properly with the 340B software and if the automation software will properly receive and allocate the electronic invoices. This evaluation should include an assessment of key carousel and cabinet features, including automated receiving and tracking and other supply chain data elements (e.g., carousel and cabinet location) by purchase order.

- *Secondary distributor and direct vendor ordering platforms*—determine if purchases from secondary vendors will properly split in the 340B software and if the software vendor receives the invoices such that package accumulations will be decremented appropriately.

- *Mobile ordering devices*—ensure that mobile vendor ordering devices will enter the ordering queue in such a way that 340B split-billing functionality is maintained.

In addition to the variety of software options that may play into each decision, the CE software implementation team should consider how manual workarounds and other settings will impact actual purchasing practices. Because multiple vendors are involved (e.g., 340B, supply chain, auto-mation) the specific scenarios presented by the move to address proper 340B procurement may not have been addressed in prior setups. Further, the respective "silo" of each vendor places the burden on the CE to assess, test, and manage the results of the integrated system. CEs are encour-aged to plan well, implement carefully, develop policies and practices to support compliance, and audit the resulting setups early after implementation and regularly thereafter.

340B Software Drug Catalogs

Understanding the importance of drug catalogs housed within the 340B software is a key compo-nent of program management. The drugs, prices, and other product characterizations found in the 340B software vendor's drug catalogs generally have a distributor catalog as their source and are maintained through EDI 832 file updates. A number of problems occur with various software vendor technologies as the result of inaccurate or incomplete catalog maintenance. The results of an incorrect or incomplete catalog entry may include the following:

- Inability to accumulate 340B charges to a purchased product in inventory because the drug and/or 340B price are not in the 340B software vendor drug catalog. This typically results in little or no 340B or GPO purchases and a high volume of WAC purchases for these products.

- Incorrect 340B savings reporting owing to absent, inaccurate, or dated drug prices in the software catalog. This occurs with greater frequency for specialty and other limited distri-bution drugs using a nonstandard ordering and supply chain.

- Inaccurate Medicaid billing when relying on vendor catalogs for actual acquisition cost.

CEs should inquire regarding the functionality of their 340B vendor catalogs and assess the impacts of absent or incorrect entries. CEs should expect routine catalog auto-updates as part of 340B software functionality. However, CEs should include routine drug catalog maintenance (e.g., update or correct missing prices; incorrect prices on specialty products; missing, incorrect, or incomplete product attributes) as part of their 340B program and software maintenance plan until they are comfortable that the vendor's process and performance are acceptable. Practices should include regular catalog audits on a monthly or quarterly basis and investigation of anomalous purchase patterns (e.g., higher than anticipated 340B, WAC, or GPO purchases that might result from catalog errors).

Crosswalk Management

For most CEs, a combination of buyers, 340B program managers, and informatics pharmacists are responsible for crosswalk maintenance. The specific requirements will depend on the software vendor's connectivity, analytics, and reporting. To minimize compliance risk exposure and to optimize savings capture, CEs should consider the following actions core to crosswalk management:

- Implement a streamlined process for requesting and creating new charge codes in coordination with hospital finance, reimbursement, and IT departments.
- Review and remedy any unmatched CDMs and NDCs by personnel with access to the dispensing or charging units and with access to pharmacy purchasing details. Monitor effectiveness of this effort through frequent software reports and purchasing performance.
- Pay particular attention to limited distribution drugs (specialty), drugs charged using HCPCS codes, compounded products, and drugs purchased from secondary distributors or manufacturers
- Identify products (NDCs) with unusually high 340B or GPO accumulations, indicating an improper conversion factor or other error during simple self-audits of the crosswalk.
- Ensure that pharmacy buyers are aware of the current NDC accumulations and understand the impact of switching NDCs on crosswalk maintenance. Generally, 340B program savings and maintenance requirements are optimized when buyers are thoughtful and exercise discretion in their buying patterns.

Health systems with multiple hospitals participating under one 340B identifier and a single 340B virtual inventory will require significant buyer training and coordination to promote operational efficiencies, optimized savings, and program integrity.

Purchasing in a 340B Environment

Purchasing decisions for pharmacy personnel increase in complexity with the 340B program. It is certainly true that 340B software alleviates much of the work required to manually split purchase orders across multiple accounts each day. However, buyers operating on auto-pilot may miss significant opportunities to optimize 340B program savings and enhance program integrity. Pharmacy buyers that review final purchase quantities after the split process can significantly reduce unnecessary WAC purchases by modifying daily purchases.

Assume seven packages of a product are being ordered and are expected to meet inventory demand for the week. After the split, the buyer notes that three packages are assigned to 340B, three packages to GPO, and one package to WAC. The buyer may note that the WAC price is significantly higher than either contract price and decides to modify the order quantity to six to avoid the WAC purchase, making a subsequent follow-up purchase when sufficient dispensations have accumulated to support a contract purchase—likely within a day or two in our example. Small interventions such as those outlined in this example can contribute significantly to program savings and efficiency over time.

Another straightforward intervention by buyers that can dramatically impact savings involves limited distribution items (i.e., specialty drugs). Some specialty items are available at 340B pricing through mainline distributor channels—others may only be available at 340B pricing through specialty distributors. A number of items will require direct orders from the manufacturer to obtain 340B pricing, while other items are so limited in distribution that they are not available to some hospital pharmacies. Pharmacy and supply chain leadership should help buyers prepare a specialty pharmacy purchasing playbook that outlines the procedures necessary to access each drug, including 340B pricing. Unfortunately, CEs may miss months of 340B savings opportunities owing to a lack of understanding of the scope of drug-specific details required to negotiate correct drug acquisition in the specialty channel. Finally, buyers should coordinate with the software vendor to understand how each of the alternative purchasing procedures will affect package accumulation tracking within the 340B software.

Another impact of the 340B program on medication purchasing is that it obscures the determination of the "best priced product." When facilities have a single purchasing account (GPO), identifying the preferred contract items for purchase is relatively simple. However, with 340B participation, purchases will be spread across two to three accounts with correspondingly different prices varying across multiple products. CEs may wish to identify preferred NDCs by calculating the best weighted price, comparing product purchase history across all accounts (340B, GPO, WAC—if indicated) by price. Although the mix of utilization is generally stable, prices across the three accounts can vary for a variety of business reasons. Repeating the analysis on a quarterly basis, generally aligned with 340B program price changes, is warranted.

WAC Expense Tracking

For CEs subject to the GPO prohibition, managing WAC expense will be a primary responsibility of the 340B manager position. Although tracking WAC expense in comparison to GPO and 340B purchases has some value, not all WAC purchases are made at a price higher than GPO price or even higher than 340B price due to market forces and the work of the 340B prime vendor and partners. The authors prefer tracking WAC premium as an index of effective purchasing. *WAC premium* can be defined as the additional expense incurred by making a WAC account purchase in comparison to the price that would have been paid on the GPO account. Broadly, this "premium" reflects the penalty paid over open-market pricing by a 340B-participating CE when various factors lead to a purchase that cannot be tied to a prior dispense. Determining the WAC premium simply requires re-pricing WAC purchases with GPO catalogue prices to determine the difference paid, or premium.

This WAC premium is differentiated from software settings, maintenance, and performance issue that might negatively impact 340B dispensation capture. CEs that identify the items contributing most to WAC premium and that address each of them on a monthly basis generally experience a much lower loss of their 340B program savings in the form of higher purchase prices. In addition to the program components previously discussed, the causes for WAC premium for many CEs may include the following:

- Items that are not covered outpatient drugs and medical supplies purchased at WAC when GPO contract pricing is available.
- Unintentional exclusion of departmental charge data from the 340B software data feeds.
- Inaccurate, incomplete, or outdated crosswalk information.
- Inaccurate or incomplete 340B software vendor drug catalog data.
- Medicaid carve-out dispensing and drug utilization.
- Incomplete charge capture associated with the operating room, anesthesia, floor stock, missing medications, and similar scenarios.
- Incomplete charge capture for multi-dose vials billed using HCPCS units.
- Undocumented medication waste or documented waste activities not transferred to 340B activities.
- Incomplete tracking of interdepartmental transfers or sales that do not result in a patient charge.
- Incomplete tracking of limited distribution items requiring special procedures to access 340B pricing.

- Lack of chargemaster granularity (e.g., 340B software may require vial size specific charge codes).

- Pharmacy order entry procedures that may not represent actual utilization and purchasing patterns (e.g., all rituximab dispensing may be entered using one vial strength, leading to all charges accumulating against one NDC).

Most sources of premium purchases are addressable through focused tracking, software setup and management, and practice and behavior changes achieved through training and follow up.

Because purchasing new drugs and increasing inventory levels will often lead to WAC purchases, CEs should not expect to completely eliminate WAC premium. However, tracking the data at least monthly and investigating the cause (using the list above) should allow CEs to achieve best practice management of WAC expense for their 340B program.

KEY POINT

Map all business processes that support 340B software functionality and adjust purchasing practices to ensure alignment. Employ software reports as a structured approach to track utilization and purchasing patterns and to ensure optimal 340B software management.

SUMMARY

340B program software implementation requires detailed project management, 340B program expertise, IT resources, and a vendor partner willing to provide transparency concerning the details of software functionality. The authors have attempted to provide a comprehensive guide to promote consideration of all points where hospital operations and 340B software intersect. When approached thoughtfully and with adequate resources, covered entities can enter the program with high efficiency and low program risk.

REFERENCES

1. Noridian Healthcare Solutions. Medicare Pricing, Data Analysis and Coding: 2016 NDC/HCPCS Crosswalk. https://www.dmepdac.com/crosswalk/2016.html. Accessed October 11, 2017.

2. Office of Inspector General. Department of Health and Human Services. States' collection of Medicaid rebates for physician-administered drugs. https://oig.hhs.gov/oei/reports/oei-03-09-00410.pdf. Published June 2011; accessed October 11, 2017.

3. Social Security Administration. Compilation of the Social Security Laws: Payment for Covered Outpatient Drugs. https://www.ssa.gov/OP_Home/ssact/title19/1927.htm. Accessed October 11, 2017.

4. U.S. Department of Health and Human Services. Health Resources and Services Administration. 340B Drug Pricing Program: FAQs. http://hrsa.gov/opa/faqs/index.html. Accessed October 11, 2017.

5. 340B Prime Vendor Program. 340B Drug Pricing Program FAQs. https://www.340bpvp.com/resourceCenter/faqSearch.html?category=content&Ntt=1187. Accessed October 11, 2017.

CHAPTER 6

340B Pharmacy Supply Chain

Lisa N. Schatz, PharmD, BCPS and
Steven Sundberg, PharmD

The pharmacy supply chain is complex in the best of times. Without 340B, the pharmacy supply chain requires diligence to keep the right amount of the right drug at the right price available for the right patient at the right time. When the requirements of the 340B program are added, standard supply chain practices must be enhanced to include elements that make supply chain practices compliant with 340B requirements. Because of the financial stakes involved, 340B compliance takes precedence over other processes for drug procurement and inventory management. The day-to-day execution of purchasing, receiving, and distributing medications with 340B in mind are pivotal activities that can either keep the covered entity compliant, or result in Health Resources and Services Administration (HRSA) audit citations and the potential loss of access to the 340B program.

Drug diversion is among the top three HRSA audit violations, ranking behind Office of Pharmacy Affairs (OPA) registration violations and duplicate discount violations. 340B drug diversion includes three types:

1. Purchasing and dispensing group purchasing organization (GPO) drugs for 340B-eligible outpatients; a violation of the GPO prohibition.[1]

2. Purchasing 340B drugs for unregistered areas outside the four walls of the registered covered entity.

3. Using 340B drugs to treat inpatients and nonqualified outpatients or to fill prescriptions for nonqualified Contract Pharmacy patients.

GPO PROHIBITION

Understanding the GPO prohibition statute, and where and how it applies, is a fundamental requirement to develop a compliant 340B pharmacy supply chain. The GPO prohibition was included in the original Veteran's Healthcare Act of 1992. Over the course of the program, HRSA issued several clarifications in the *Federal Register*.[2,3] Although generally well understood, variations in practice along with the growing complexity of the hospitals' application of the 340B program led the HRSA Office of Pharmacy Affairs to issue a 340B Drug Pricing Program Notice, Release No. 2013-1 effective August 2013.[4]

The statute states: Disproportionate share hospitals (DSH), children's hospitals, and free-standing cancer hospitals may not "obtain covered outpatient drugs through a group purchasing organization or other group purchasing arrangement." These entities must attest to compliance with this provision during their annual recertification. The statute further states: "If a covered entity subject to this prohibition participates in a GPO, the covered entity will no longer be an eligible covered entity and cannot purchase covered outpatient drugs at the section 340B discount prices." In other words, a covered entity that violates the GPO prohibition could be sanctioned or expelled from the program.

> Covered entities may also be subject to repayment to manufacturers for the time period for which the violation occurred. Covered entities removed from the 340B Program for GPO prohibition violations must demonstrate the ability to comply with the GPO prohibition to be considered eligible to reenter the 340B Program during the next regular enrollment period.[4]

340B grantee clinics and rural hospitals (critical access hospitals, rural referral centers, and sole community hospitals) are not subject to the GPO prohibition. A separate chapter outlines the unique elements that apply to this group. The principles and practices outlined in the remainder of this chapter, absent the specific references to the GPO prohibition, apply to all categories of covered entities.

Hospitals join group purchasing organizations to achieve discounts on drugs used to treat inpatients and outpatients that are not covered by the 340B program. To achieve discounts for both inpatients and 340B-eligible outpatients, hospitals must take precautions to avoid diversion across this boundary.

KEY POINT

Disproportionate share hospitals (DSH), children's hospitals, and free-standing cancer hospitals may not obtain outpatient drugs through a GPO or other GPO arrangement. A hospital's inventory and supply chain policies and practices should be designed to limit the risk of deliberate or inadvertent transfer of GPO-purchased drugs to outpatients.

DEFINING OUTPATIENT STATUS UNDER THE 340B PROGRAM

GPO-purchased drugs must be reserved exclusively for inpatients, and the GPO prohibition specifically states that the covered entity is prohibited from purchasing GPO medications for any of its eligible outpatient clinics. Therefore, it is imperative that the covered entity understand patient status in more detail and develop a practical method to identify exactly when a patient becomes an inpatient or an outpatient. A patient may convert from outpatient to inpatient at various points throughout a patient encounter. An emergency department patient may be admitted; a patient may be in "observation" status as an outpatient; a patient may be an outpatient for infusion therapy or for chemotherapy; and an outpatient having complications may be admitted as an inpatient for continuing treatment. All the internal stakeholders, including the 340B Steering Committee, must understand how to define inpatient versus outpatient status and develop technology and other processes that inform the procurement process.

For covered entities that have a retail pharmacy and/or participate in 340B contract pharmacy, it is important to identify and exclude outpatient encounters that would not directly result in a prescription being generated. For example, a visit for laboratory or radiology services would not typically be considered to generate a 340B-eligible prescription, thus should be separately considered as a type of outpatient status (i.e., these visit types should not feed into 340B software as a 340B qualified outpatient encounter).

KEY POINT

A covered entity subject to the GPO prohibition should develop practices to reliably and consistently identify inpatients and outpatients as outlined by the 340B statute.

PURCHASING AND INVENTORY MANAGEMENT IN A 340B PARTICIPATING HOSPITAL

Understanding Current Operations and Supply Chain

The best starting point to achieve an efficient and effective supply chain while ensuring compliance is to map all locations where 340B drugs will be used. 340B is not the only regulatory requirement to be met; state and federal law and regulations regarding medication handling, safety, and security must also be supported and maintained.

Start by reviewing all locations where drugs are currently ordered, delivered, and maintained to determine if a patient could ever be an outpatient in those locations. Include "inside" areas that are not typically registered with a supplier or the board of pharmacy (e.g., medication rooms in clinics and procedure areas).

Areas where inpatients and outpatients can both be treated are known as *mixed-use areas*. Medications in mixed-use areas may be managed using separate 340B and GPO inventories, but they are commonly managed using 340B split billing software to record use and manage a "virtually separate" inpatient and outpatient inventory. Patient charges are fed into a software accumulator that separates utilization into 340B qualified/outpatient, GPO/inpatient, and wholesale acquisition cost (WAC) categories. Medications are then purchased and replenished into a single, blended inventory, virtually allocated based on the accumulations within each accumulation "bucket." Subsequent purchases drain each respective accumulation, with offsetting patient charges adding to each accumulation. Most mixed-use areas are within the four walls of the covered entity, so proper identification of outpatients serves the dual purpose of properly (1) constructing the drug utilization data feed for the software accumulator and (2) identifying whether 340B drugs will be sent to that location as part of the supply chain operations.

Hospitals subject to the GPO prohibition must purchase drugs at the undiscounted WAC or list price in several circumstances (see section Managing WAC Purchases). Policy and practice choices can mitigate the addressable *purchase discount leak* that occurs when a hospital fails to maintain a tight perpetual inventory, incurring additional supply costs through lost 340B and GPO purchase opportunities. Tightly and completely tracked and managed dispensations lead to efficient capture of discounted purchasing opportunities.

Offsite pharmacy operations outside the four walls of the parent hospital, typically at a different physical address where 340B drugs will be used, must be registered with OPA as child site locations. For covered entities subject to the GPO prohibition, all registered locations (e.g., offsite child locations) are subject to the GPO prohibition and should be fully examined and catalogued.

KEY POINT

Map all locations where 340B drugs will be used. Pay particular attention to mixed-use areas where 340B-purchased drugs or GPO-purchased drugs must be tracked and managed in detail.

According to the 340B Drug Pricing Program Notice, Release No. 2013-1,[4] "certain off-site outpatient facilities of the hospital may use a GPO for covered outpatient drugs if those off-site outpatient facilities meet all of the following criteria:

1. Are located at a different physical address than the parent
2. Are *not registered* on the OPA 340B database as participating in the 340B Program
3. Purchase drugs through a separate pharmacy wholesaler account than the 340B participating parent; and
4. The hospital maintains records demonstrating that any covered outpatient drugs purchased through the GPO at these sites are not utilized or otherwise transferred to the parent hospital or any outpatient facilities registered on the OPA 340B database."

New off-site clinic areas must be reported on the Medicare cost report as a reimbursable location before being registered with OPA, thus GPO drugs may be used until registered if the above criteria are met. Otherwise non-GPO (WAC) purchases are required to replenish usage.

The gap or delay in enrolling new clinic or outpatient operations in 340B, as described above, can be a stumbling block for rapid, compliant access to 340B. It is important to plan and consider the 340B implications of new clinics, new outpatient care areas, and new outpatient service lines by making sure that the location is reimbursable, reported on the Medicare cost report, and registered with OPA before providing 340B medications.

Decide on Virtual or Physical Inventory

Following completion of the supply chain assessment, the covered entity has the opportunity to consider two methods to manage the 340B-compliant supply chain: virtual or physical inventory. In some instances, the selective use of both is well-advised.

A virtual inventory system is one where the covered entity's inventory is electronically tracked according to its usage. 340B, GPO- and WAC-purchased inventory is kept in a single comingled inventory. A *physical inventory system* is one where stock is kept in physically separate locations based on the usage and purchase type—340B or GPO for outpatient and inpatient areas and use, respectively.

A 340B software accumulator is used to achieve management of a virtual inventory, where all drug usage is categorized into the appropriate accumulator "buckets" according to the drug utilization by patient type (inpatient versus outpatient). This software is often referred to as *split-billing* software because the program splits medication usage and ordering by patient type and 340B eligibility. Replenished inventory in this method is considered *cured, neutral,* or *clean* and can be dispensed for any purpose, thus allowing for common inventory storage while maintaining 340B compliance. The advantage of a virtual inventory system is that the covered entity can manage operations efficiently without consideration of the purchase pedigree at the time of dispensing. Hospitals with extensive activity in mixed-use areas typically find this to be the only method suitable to achieve effective and efficient operations. The 340B software records all drug usage electronically, and it provides fully traceable records to demonstrate compliance upon audit.

KEY POINT

In a virtual 340B inventory system, replenished inventory is considered *cured, neutral,* or *clean* and can be dispensed for any purpose, thus allowing for common inventory storage while maintaining 340B compliance.

340B split-billing software is generally sold as a web-based subscription. Most commercially available software can accept a dispensing or charge transaction data feed from the hospital's electronic medical record or billing system. It takes time to build and test the accumulator drug utilization feed to ensure proper accounting for dispensing and the resulting accumulations. The software also utilizes standard electronic data interchange (EDI) messages from distributors to decrement accumulations with each purchase.

Once the covered entity has enrolled in the 340B program and is listed as active on the OPA web site, it is required to comply with the GPO exclusion prohibition and must maintain separate inventory or manage a virtual inventory purchasing either 340B drugs or WAC drugs for outpatient utilization and GPO for inpatient utilization. If the covered entity does not have the ability to track utilization according to 340B rules, purchases must be undiscounted WAC. Therefore, in planning for 340B, it is crucial to consider the time it will take to build the software and the data feed into the 340B implementation plan to ensure compliance at go-live. Any delay in the software go-live may result in a greater amount of WAC purchasing that will not be adjusted by accumulations and can be considered sunk costs.

Maintaining a separate physical inventory can be difficult. Manual tracking may miss some utilization and can be inaccurate and resource-intensive. Staff must assess and manage each prescription or dispensing activity to ensure compliance. On audit, it can be difficult to fully demonstrate compliance when manual methods are used.

A covered entity can choose to use a separate single-purpose (e.g., 340B only) physical inventory in areas that are always outpatient and eligible for 340B or conversely are exclusively inpatient for GPO purchases. In making this selection, the covered entity must be able to demonstrate that outpatients (or inpatients for GPO drugs) are the only patient category served at the location, and that the covered entity has elected to carve-in for Medicaid (e.g., an outpatient infusion center). Inventory must be purchased on a separate purchasing account. A best practice is to have the medications delivered in separate totes directly from the wholesaler or delivered to pharmacy and received in the 340B location, so the inventory is never co-mingled with the main pharmacy inventory.

POLICIES AND PROCEDURES

In April 2016, HRSA conducted a peer-to-peer webinar[5] reviewing how to write and implement policies matched to the required elements of the 340B program. Policies and procedures (P&P) should match operations. Apexus[6] and HRSA[7] have developed tools to self-audit policies and procedures to ensure they contain the required elements. (See also Chapter 7, 340B Policies and Procedures.) Most covered entities have an oversight committee and a process for P&P review. Participating in 340B may require more flexibility in the standard P&P review process, as it is important to adjust policies any time that there is a change in operational procedures. To set up the 340B program for success, be certain to only include achievable and easily executed items in the supply chain policies.

GETTING READY FOR 340B

Purchasing Account Set-Up

Once the mapping of operations is complete and all areas where 340B medications will be used are identified, an often overlooked step in preparing for 340B is reviewing the accounts on which medications are purchased. This step, although at first glance seemingly simple and a supply chain fundamental, if done properly can mean the difference in both achieving a compliant program and avoiding significant delays at the outset of 340B conversion.

Vendors cannot create 340B accounts until the covered entity is listed on the Office of Pharmacy Affairs Information System (OPAIS) and has a 340B identification number and Health Industry Number (HIN). A best practice is to initiate account set-up as soon as the covered entity is listed on the OPAIS. During the time between OPA registration submission until the covered entity is approved and listed on the OPAIS, the covered entity should review all existing wholesaler accounts and decide which (1) require additional WAC and 340B purchasing accounts and (2) should be sunset, and no longer used for purchasing. **Table 6-1** shows an example of the evaluative process for creating new accounts.

KEY POINT

> Take the time to review the account set-up to ensure all appropriate accounts, including direct purchase accounts, and all purchasers have access to the new accounts.

In the example in Table 6-1, the covered entity has six offsite child locations, of which two are mixed-use areas and four are 100% outpatient. Prior to participating in 340B, the covered entity had two GPO purchasing accounts. After mapping locations, it decided to create two new 340B and two new WAC accounts. One set of accounts was established to pair up with the existing GPO account for all of their mixed-use areas. The other pair of accounts would serve the 100% outpatient, offsite locations. It was also decided to sunset the Infusion Center's existing GPO account, as it would be served by the mixed-use group of accounts.

To assist in mapping operations, HRSA's peer-to-peer webinar in April 2016 included the tool, Mapping the 340B Drug Operations Environment, available on the Apexus web site.[8]

Direct Purchase Vendors

In addition to reviewing wholesaler accounts, many major direct vendors will also set up 340B and WAC purchase accounts. It is the responsibility of the covered entity to review all major direct vendors (intravenous [IV] Fluid Vendors, Blood/Plasma Vendors, and specialty drug vendors) and reach out to them for account set-up in a timely fashion. Most major direct vendors will also have electronic invoicing capability and electronic data interchange (EDI), which facilitates software accumulator tracking and adjustments.

For smaller direct vendors, particularly for medications used primarily or exclusively on an outpatient basis, the covered entity should reach out to the vendor to see if 340B and WAC accounts are available. For items that are primarily used on an outpatient basis where the vendor does not offer multiple account set-up, it may be important to get an individual contract with the vendor. Obtaining an individual contract that is covered entity-specific does not violate the GPO prohibition statute and, thus, would be considered a compliant process.

Repackaging pharmacies must offer the covered entity a trio of 340B, GPO, and WAC accounts.

Table 6-1. Example of the Evaluative Process for Creating New Accounts

Registration Name	Child Site Designation	Separate Physical Address	Current Wholesaler Acct	New Accounts Needed	Area Type	Comments
Covered Entity		Main Hospital Address	123456-GPO	123456 + New Account 340B1 + WAC1	Mixed Use	
Wound Care	A	Yes—offsite		New Acct 340B2 + WAC2	100% Outpatients	
Infusion Center	F	Yes—offsite	987654-GPO	123456 + New Account 340B1 + WAC1	Mixed Use	Sunset Account 987654
Operating Room (includes Outpatient Surgery)	D	Yes—offsite		123456 + New Account 340B1 + WAC1	Mixed Use	
Radiology Diagnostic (Breast Imaging)	E	Yes—offsite		New Acct 340B2 + WAC2	100% Outpatients	
Physical Therapy (Outpatient Therapy Services)	B	Yes—offsite		New Acct 340B2 + WAC2	100% Outpatients	
Physical Therapy (Location 2)	C	Yes—offsite		New Acct 340B2 + WAC2	100% Outpatients	

Vaccines

Many covered entities purchase vaccines directly from a vendor. Vaccines are not considered to be covered outpatient drugs. Covered entities can continue to purchase medications according to their usual and customary practices.

Managing the Distributor Partnership

A 340B participant can have a great partnership with their distributor if the participant understands the distributor's role and limitations. The requirement for creating new 340B accounts when the covered entity has a 340B ID and is listed on the OPAIS was reviewed earlier. Certain manufacturers also place ordering process restrictions for their medications, which the wholesaler must respect. Drugs that are freely ordered by a typical on-line process on a GPO account may require the purchaser to phone-in an order and have the medication drop-shipped as 340B.

Understanding when the distributor refreshes the GPO/WAC/340B catalogues is also important. Price changes that formerly took place every 3 years in a GPO-only environment now occur quarterly. It may be important to retrieve and store pricing catalogues every quarter, to appropriately calculate 340B savings. Many distributor account representatives are very knowledgeable in 340B and can provide assistance with ordering concerns or issues. Distributor account representatives may also include metrics in their quarterly business review. Keeping the lines of communication open is imperative.

Minimizing WAC Spend Prior to Go-Live

Up until the effective date on the OPAIS, a covered entity can purchase all medications under GPO contracts. The covered entity may not have visibility or access to 340B or WAC pricing prior to the effective date. However, it is prudent to ensure on-hand inventory prior to go-live is set to allow for the initial challenges of a decidedly more complex ordering process. A review and adjustment of key items in inventory prior to go-live can mitigate some of the initial WAC purchase burden, as 340B and GPO accumulations rise and permit replenishment using the appropriate account.

Orphan Drugs—A Consideration for Rural and Cancer Hospitals

The Orphan Drug Interpretive Rule available on the HRSA web site[9] was vacated by the U.S. District Court for the District of Columbia in October 2015. The rule applied to rural referral centers, sole community hospitals, critical access hospitals, and freestanding cancer hospital covered entities participating in the 340B program. The central tenets of the court ruling state that:

> the term "covered outpatient drug" does not include a drug designated by the Secretary under section 526 of the Federal Food, Drug, and Cosmetic Act for a rare disease or condition. Therefore, manufacturers are not required to provide these covered entities orphan drugs under the 340B Program. A manufacturer may, at its sole discretion, offer discounts on orphan drugs to these hospitals.[9]

After October 2015, purchasing of orphan drugs on individual contracts at or near 340B prices has been voluntarily extended by several manufacturers. As of April 2018, each manufacturer can determine how to handle orphan drugs. Chapter 11 covers additional supply chain considerations for hospitals subject to this provision.

MIXED-USE PURCHASING AND INVENTORY MODEL

Integrating Pharmacy Revenue Cycle with 340B Purchasing

One discipline that applies more forcefully to 340B covered entity hospitals is keeping a clean, current, and complete charge master. If a lax, undisciplined, or incomplete approach is taken with the pharmacy revenue cycle, the gaps will quickly be revealed in a 340B virtual inventory replacement model. Understanding how drugs get billed, whether charge-on-dispense or charge-on-administration, ultimately feeds utilization into the 340B software accumulator. All purchases must be supported by sufficient individual dispensations to equal a unit of purchase. All purchases must be defensible on audit; therefore, a clear and thorough understanding of how drug charging feeds an accumulator is imperative. Understanding whether the data feed to the accumulator comes from the pharmacy system or from the billing/charging system is also crucial. Understanding the handling of patient-specific medications, often charged on dispensation, impacts how drugs are accumulated especially when a full package size is dispensed.

340B Prime Vendor Program

The 340B Prime Vendor Program is a voluntary program by which HRSA contracts with a commercial provider to negotiate and serve as an interface between manufacturers and covered entities. Apexus is the current contractor. The 340B Prime Vendor web site states that "the primary goal of the 340B Prime Vendor Program is to improve access to affordable medications for covered entities and their patients. Over 25,000 safety-net providers are receiving additional savings on pharmaceuticals by participating in the Prime Vendor Program."[10] To participate in the program, a covered entity must apply for membership. This can be accomplished as soon as HRSA sets the effective date of 340B participation on the OPAIS. The Prime Vendor Program has been delegated the responsibility for HRSA-sponsored education and training, the 340B University, and other on-line education.

Pharmaceutical contracts negotiated by the Prime Vendor are exempt from the GPO prohibition and leverage "sub 340B" and "sub WAC" pricing for enrolled 340B participants.

First or Initial Purchases of a New National Drug Code Item

All initial purchases of a National Drug Code (NDC) by definition do not have utilization to support purchasing on either GPO or 340B accounts. Therefore, these initial purchases must be made on the WAC account. Subsequent purchases are based on utilization through software accumulations and can be replenished using the appropriate account.

Triggers to Buy

Many covered entities have established maximum and minimum inventory par levels. The discipline of setting a minimum par level, combined with an electronic inventory control system, is considered a best practice. Par levels can still be used within the 340B environment. A trigger to buy would be when the inventory dips below the minimum. In the 340B environment, this requires the purchaser to review the trigger determining whether accumulations permit purchasing on the 340B or GPO accounts before placing an order. This check is typically performed automatically by 340B accumulator software. If the drug is needed, and the accumulations do not yet amount to a full unit of sale, then the drug must be purchased on the WAC account.

Replenish to the 11-Digit NDC Level

340B requirements and guidance specify replacement of medications be NDC specific to the 11-digit NDC level. Apexus Frequently Asked Question (FAQ) 1222 states:[11]

> 340B covered entities should replenish at the 11-digit NDC level as standard practice. In exceptional circumstances, when 11-digit replenishment is not possible, a covered entity may replenish at the 9-digit NDC level if the covered entity maintains auditable records demonstrating that the appropriate amounts are replenished from the same manufacturer, regardless of the package size. 9-digit NDC replenishment should not be part of standard operations. A covered entity must maintain policies and procedures and auditable records which demonstrate a compliant replenishment model.

A circumstance that requires package replenishment at the 9-digit level requires documentation with the reason the covered entity chose 9-digit replenishment, when the replenishment occurred, with invoice retrieval capabilities. Inclusion of a policy statement concerning 11-digit replenishment in covered entity policies and procedures is recommended in the HRSA tool, Policy and Procedure Self-Audit Tool, available on the Apexus web site.[6]

> ## KEY POINT
>
> Replenish at the 11-digit NDC level and specify when 9-digit NDC level would be appropriate.

Integrating a 340B Software Accumulator into the Purchasing Process

Many distributor purchasing systems can receive an outbound direct data (EDI) feed from the 340B software accumulator. Utilizing this direct connection is a best practice. After order generation, there is generally a selection button that splits the order by distributing the purchase quantities over the accounts based on accumulations. If insufficient quantities are accumulated to cover the entire purchase, a WAC purchase is generated. WAC purchases should be reviewed prior to purchasing to determine how close the accumulations might be to a full unit of sale. Adding this due diligence to the buying process can minimize the amount of WAC expenditures by modifying purchase practices.

It is important to recognize that the accumulation buckets are not adjusted until the drug is received. Generating an order or a purchase order holds the accumulated dispenses supporting the purchases, but does not adjust the accumulation buckets. An inbound EDI data feed from the wholesaler or vendor records the invoice, date of purchase, and automatically deducts the quantities from the buckets. This process also permits shorts, outs, and other incomplete purchases to be correctly recorded. Without EDI, the purchaser will have to manually adjust the accumulator for each purchase.

Manual adjustments will be necessary for items purchased from direct vendors that do not support EDI. A best practice is to perform the manual adjustment at the time that the order is received from the vendor.

Managing Drug Wastage

Many facilities have a process to account for drug wastage resulting from prepared doses that are less than the total available dose in single-dose vials. Without a process to account for wastage, the covered entity may experience additional WAC purchases. The 340B accumulator software cannot record undocumented wastage.

Methods and mechanisms for documenting and billing for wastage are beyond the scope of this chapter. However, having a process to document wastage in the 340B environment allows for full single-dose vial sizes to be appropriately accounted for in the replenishment model. If the amount of wastage and the ability to document/bill becomes onerous, the covered entity may consider a separate physical inventory model. In such a model, where all patients are outpatients, accounting for wastage becomes of lesser importance. Technically, all drug use is 340B eligible.

CONTRACT MANAGEMENT

Group Purchasing Organization Contracts

Participating in a GPO affords savings by aggregating volume among hospitals and health systems nationwide. In 340B participating DSH, children's hospitals, and freestanding cancer hospitals' covered entities, use of medications purchased with a GPO-negotiated price is restricted to inpatients and to areas outside the four walls of the covered entity not registered as child sites by the GPO prohibition.

Some manufacturers may consider 340B volume with non-340B volume to calculate market share for market-share agreements. Each manufacturer handles GPO contracts differently. Some manufacturers require a Letter of Agreement (LOA) to be signed for participation in a GPO contract. As a covered entity moves into the 340B realm, it is important to review all previously signed LOAs for 340B implications.

Local Contracts

A covered entity can negotiate an individual contract with a manufacturer for pricing. As long as the contract is only for the individual covered entity, the drug products can be purchased on one account with no splitting, with the negotiated price attached to the product. Examples include contracting with compounding pharmacies. Including a statement in P&P about the locally negoti-ated vendor contracts, with vendor specification is a best practice.

If a local contract is negotiated for multiple facilities or an entire health system, the contract is considered a Group Purchasing arrangement and the GPO prohibition applies, thus splitting of utilization into 340B, WAC, and GPO buckets must occur.

Enhanced GPO Contracts

If a covered entity has negotiated an enhanced GPO contract, where the volume and discounts are above and beyond a standard GPO contract, the covered entity should estimate the 340B volume and determine if 340B volume is considered in the enhanced arrangement.

PURCHASING PRACTICES

A fundamental tenet of 340B participation is that purchasing and supporting records are auditable. This also pertains to supply chain practices. All 340B purchases should be traceable and point back to a 340B-qualified event. If a covered entity only purchases a specific drug on the GPO account and some use occurred in the outpatient setting, the covered entity has violated the GPO prohi-bition. If the covered entity carves out Medicaid, and shows no purchases of a drug used for a Medicaid patient on the non-340B account (only 340B purchases), the covered entity has violated the duplicate discount provision of the statute. If the covered entity only purchases controlled substances on the GPO account, it has violated the GPO exclusion rule. Multiple practices and convenience methods can lead a covered entity to a supply chain finding on HRSA audit. Supply chain policies should be applied to all purchases with the sole exception of medical necessity and/or instances where doing so would be a detriment to patient care.

Covered Outpatient Drugs

HRSA uses the standard definition of a covered outpatient drug (COD), as published in the Social Security Act Sᴇᴄ. 1927 [42 U.S.C. 1396r–8], to address drugs that are considered covered outpatient drugs under 340B.[12] The definition can be found in section (k) part (2) and includes prescription drugs, over-the-counters (OTCs) written on a prescription, biologicals, and FDA-approved insulins. Vaccines are specifically excluded from the definition of a COD in this section. CODs are also defined on the OPA web site.[13]

Limiting Definition of Covered Outpatient Drugs

The limiting definition of a COD can be found in Social Security Act Sᴇᴄ. 1927 [42 U.S.C. 1396r–8] (k) (3).[12] The limiting definition specifically excludes drugs for which there is no direct reimburse-ment, where the drug is included, or bundled into the reimbursement for the medical service. For example, drugs used for inpatients or hospice are not CODs.

The limiting definition can be used by the covered entity to clarify certain areas where 340B CODs can be challenging. Generally, anesthesia gases, large-volume parenterals, and radiologicals/contrast media meet the limiting definition. Contrast media and radiologicals are difficult to charge and track, making accounting for accumulations difficult. Large-volume parenterals are frequently not separately charged. The volume of anesthesia gases used during a surgical procedure is variable due to delivery at variable flow rates during a procedure. Application of the limiting definition provides the covered entity with the opportunity to exclude or consider excluding bundled drugs from the 340B program.

Determining Medications to Exclude from the 340B Supply Chain

340B statutes do not specify in detail which drugs can be excluded from the 340B program. If a covered entity selects certain drugs or a group of drugs to exclude from the 340B program, it should meet the limiting definition of CODs. Each covered entity should have a policy that specifically identifies which drugs, categories, or classes of drugs meet the limiting definition per SEC. 1927 [42 U.S.C. 1396r–8] (k) (3).[12]

If designated as meeting the limiting definition by the covered entity, anesthesia gases, contrast media, and large volume parenterals can be excluded from 340B purchasing. The 340B accumulation software should be set to permit full GPO purchasing.

Each CE should include a section in their P&P defining medications that meet the limiting definition of a COD. In common vernacular, these drugs are exempt from the GPO prohibition and would always be purchased using the GPO account. It is a best practice to include the medication categories or classes in the policy. However, specifying medications to the NDC level is typically part of the split-billing software set up. By indicating which medications are excluded, purchasing is always done with the GPO account.

Understanding the 340B Replenishment Model

340B purchasing uses a different model than traditional buying practices. 340B requires a true perpetual inventory tied to the type of usage. Each purchase must be auditable back to the utilization, which is generated from an encounter or provider visit where the patient and provider relationship meets the definition of 340B eligibility. Usage that does not meet the definition will need to be purchased on a GPO account (if inpatient) or WAC account. If the covered entity is subject to the GPO prohibition and has chosen carve-out status, all Medicaid utilizations must also be purchased on a WAC account. The covered entity is no longer able to buy-in large quantities of medications, as all purchases must be justified by utilization. After identifying a trigger to buy, the purchaser must review the utilization that has populated the accumulator buckets and purchase accordingly.

Generic Equivalence Versus 11-Digit NDC Replenishment

340B requires replenishment to the 11-digit NDC level to accomplish a 340B or GPO purchase. Drug unavailability of the accumulated NDC requires WAC purchase of an alternative, despite accumulations of the unavailable product (see First or Initial Purchases of a New National Drug Code Item above). If the covered entity needs the drug, there is no recourse other than buying what is available on the WAC account and beginning the accumulation process for that item. Covered entities not subject to the GPO prohibition must still account for class of trade and other requirements of their GPO contracts (e.g., the GPO contract may not apply to outpatient utilization, requiring a 340B or open market purchase).

Managing 340B Purchases Across the Enterprise

The 340B statute requires "all or nothing" participation. In other words, the covered entity cannot choose which outpatient areas within the four walls to include in the 340B program. By definition, all outpatient areas within the four walls are required to be included in the program. As such, the covered entity must decide how to track purchases so they trace back to an outpatient encounter that meets the definition of a 340B-eligible patient.

Managing GPO Private Label Medications

Many GPOs offer private label generic products, particularly injectables. Because GPO private label products are not available on the open market and typically do not have 340B or WAC prices, they are not generally considered substitutable using virtual inventory. If a private label GPO product in a virtual inventory may be inadvertently used for an outpatient in a mixed-use area, a best practice is to move entirely to a generically equivalent product that can be fully split and managed using 340B software. Often the same manufacturer offers a generically equivalent product that is not privately labeled. For the generically equivalent product when purchased only on the GPO account, a tactic that the covered entity can use is to approach their GPO and the manufacturer to obtain the GPO price for the alternative product. Many manufacturers and GPOs are willing to honor those discounts.

Managing WAC Purchases (There Will Always Be WAC Purchases)

In all instances, including 100% 340B areas, WAC purchases and replenishment may occur in the following five instances:

1. *Medicaid Carve-Out*

   If the facility has elected to carve-out Medicaid, then the CE must replenish medications used by those patients at a non-contract (WAC) price.

2. *New NDCs*

   A WAC purchase is required for a medication that has never been purchased or dispensed previously in a mixed-use virtual inventory environment.

3. *Lost Charges and Undocumented Injectable Waste*

   If an accumulator is populated from the covered entity billing system and any gaps exist in the revenue cycle process, there will be lost charges. If items or some part of utilization is not populating the accumulator when the need to purchase the drug arises, accumulation to complete the purchase may be insufficient. The only option for replenishment would be at WAC.

4. *Expired and Wasted Drugs*

   If medications have expired or the remainder of a vial or bottle has been wasted, there is typically no way to trace the amount of medications purchased on either the 340B or GPO purchase accounts. Therefore, the facility has no recourse except to purchase at WAC. Tracking expiration dates in crash carts and kits, rotating inventory to active usage to keep it fresh, and managing remotely stocked or infrequently used areas to minimize simultaneous expiration are important inventory management practices. For frequently expiring medications, some covered entities are able to trace the purchased amounts by NDC, by account, and then manually adjust the accumulator by percentages.

   EXAMPLE: If nine (9) medications expired, and three (3) were purchased on 340B, four (4) were purchased on GPO, the accumulator can be adjusted so as to not lose those seven (7) accumulations. The remaining two (2) were purchased on WAC and would be replenished on WAC.

5.   *340B-Ineligible Dispensations*

If an outpatient dispensation is not eligible for 340B replenishment (i.e., it takes place in an outpatient area or is ordered by a provider not meeting the 340B requirements), the covered entity must replace the drug at WAC.

Sub-WAC Pricing

The 340B Prime Vendor, Apexus, negotiates sub-340B prices with manufacturers on behalf of its members, much like a standard GPO. As an added value to Prime Vendor participating members, Apexus has negotiated a portfolio of sub-WAC priced products. The addition of sub-WAC prices to the supply chain provides options and choices especially when WAC is not a competitive price. WAC purchases do not require accumulations prior to purchase; thus, a covered entity can gauge when to judiciously purchase on the WAC account.

Purchasing Strategies When a Covered Entity Owns a Retail Pharmacy

A covered entity-owned retail pharmacy is generally listed on the OPA web site as a ship-to location. Retail pharmacies are not child-site locations and are not registered as such. In open retail pharmacies taking walk-in prescriptions, medication replenishment may require the use of an accumulator, especially when the logic to qualify patients requires the prescription to meet the parameters for 340B replenishment. Consideration must be given to whether the pharmacy is open to the public for non-340B traffic, or closed to serve only the patients seen by the covered entity. The set up required for covered entities that are Medicaid carve-out is different than for Medicaid carve-in.

For entities that are Medicaid carve-out, purchasing account set up would include a 340B account and a WAC or non-340B account. Replenishment using the 340B account would be for dispensations meeting the requirements of an eligible patient. All other purchases would be on the non-340B account, including Medicaid replenishment.

For entities that are Medicaid carve-in, the majority of purchases would be on the 340B account. Purchases not meeting the definition of an eligible patient would be purchased on the non-340B account. More complex situations (e.g., an open retail pharmacy in a covered entity carving out Medicaid) typically utilize 340B accumulator software to full account for eligibility and required purchasing and inventory management.

Controlled Substance Ordering

Purchasing of controlled substances has been on HRSA's audit radar as several covered entities violated the GPO exclusion rule by not fully undertaking the complex task of integrating controlled substance ordering software (CSOS) into their 340B software accumulator. If controlled substances are used during encounters that fit the patient definition, the covered entity must purchase the medications using the 340B account. It is a worthwhile effort to map how controlled substances are used throughout mixed-use areas and conduct tracers to demonstrate compliance. The covered entity is required to keep auditable records, so having documentation that utilization drives appropriate purchasing practices is a requirement. The challenge of meeting CSOS and 340B requirements should not be set aside.

KEY POINT

Because controlled substance utilization will occur in inpatient and outpatient areas, purchase controlled substances according to utilization and accumulations using your split-billing software to purchase on the appropriate account.

Receipt of Medications

340B does not impact standard processes for receiving medications. A best practice is to have a different person receive the medications than the person who placed the order. When checking in an order, you should match the quantity received against the invoice. Order discrepancies should be resolved immediately.

After medication receipt, the accumulator is adjusted via EDI. Purchases from each respective account are deducted from the appropriate bucket. Purchases from direct vendors without EDI capability should be manually adjusted in the accumulator. A description of how medications are received should be outlined in P&P.

Managing Drug Shortages

When managing drugs in short supply, the covered entity may be compelled to select an alternate product, with no prior accumulations. This means that the first purchase of the item must be at WAC. There are several strategies for minimizing WAC. If the WAC price is equal or lower than the 340B or GPO price, purchasing WAC has no downside. If the drug NDC is reviewed for replacement items with the same Generic Code Number (GCN), the transition in the accumulator software may be smoother than selecting a non-matching GCN. The accumulations will start over with the new NDC; however, the accumulations may be revitalized once the product becomes available.

Depending on the projected length of the shortage, the covered entity may want to purchase the smallest sizes available so it can accumulate quickly for useable package replenishment. That may not always be an option, certainly in these times of "get whatever is available" to meet the patient need. The pharmacy buyer, the 340B manager, and the clinical staff should all work together to develop strategies for drug procurement during times of drug shortage.

If the *only* source of drug is to purchase from a 340B account or GPO account to meet patient care needs, although in violation of the diversion/GPO exclusion statutes, it might be the only recourse. This practice is not recommended. However, HRSA *does* recognize that meeting patient care needs comes before statutory purchasing requirements. If this situation arises, document the reason for the purchase and keep the information on file for review during a HRSA audit.

There will always be *dead accumulations*—utilization that has partial package size accumulations. There may be no way to take full advantage of every accumulated dispensation. It is important to review the split-billing software accumulations and reports frequently to ensure that dead accumulations are kept to a minimum.

Apexus has prepared a whitepaper entitled "Strategies to Minimize Unnecessary WAC Exposure" outlining practical tips on the best practices in managing drug shortages and minimizing WAC spending.[14]

CENTRAL SUPPLY CENTERS AND 340B ORDERING

Many health systems have established a central supply center (CSC) as a way to leverage the cost savings opportunities from economies of scale. These include purchasing, packaging, movement of partial packages, and even specialty packaging, compounding, and IV medication preparation. Health-system member hospitals that are 340B participants present a number of complex requirements to aggregating volume while remaining compliant with 340B requirements. Enrolling 340B facilities in a CSC can be done in a compliant manner; however, considerations for a successful CSC outcome are numerous. Each must be solved in a logical sequence so that every step of the process remains compliant.

KEY POINT

Inventory that is replenished after being tracked through split-billing software is neutral or cleared and can be used anywhere in the covered entity.

Using a physical inventory-only method can be accomplished in a compliant manner, but it does not allow for co-mingling of CSC inventory; therefore, it may not be the most economical approach. A best practice is to have a virtual inventory split-billing system at the covered entity that has a "bill to-ship to" relationship with the CSC. Accumulations for each CE feed into their own separate accumulators, allowing visibility into the amounts to purchase for each 340B facility, facilitating the CSC purchasing and replenishment process.

An electronic perpetual inventory system at the CSC is an important prerequisite. Having the capabilities of the perpetual inventory extend to each of the covered entities is also a key consideration. Visibility into the inventory/split-billing feed at the local covered entity and at the CSC is important to provide transparency in the replenishment of automated dispensing devices or robot dispensing systems.

Setting up a sub-inventory or virtual inventory for each covered entity within the perpetual inventory at the CSC is one of the most significant considerations for maintaining compliance. Selection of a formulary of manageable products (a limited number of NDCs) for replenishment directly from the CSC by consensus of all system hospitals, not just the 340B facilities, is also a best practice. Finally, build a granular tracking mechanism and practices to allow for demonstration of replenishing inventory only from the virtual inventory purchased by the covered entity. Traceable records must be built into any CSC replenishment model.

KEY POINTS

Set up a virtual inventory at the CSC

Create a set of manageable NDCs across all hospitals

Replenish CE 340B inventory only from the virtual inventory of that covered entity

Case Study
Managing 340B through a Centralized Repackaging Center— Suburban Healthcare System

BACKGROUND

Suburban Healthcare System (SHS) is a large integrated health system spreading across the suburbs and exurbs of a major city, including 12 acute care hospitals and a multi-campus children's hospital, comprising over 3,500 inpatient beds. The SHS Central Services Center Pharmacy (CSC) opened in 2014 to provide centralized repackaging and compounding services to SHS inpatient pharmacies. The CSC utilizes a central inventory management platform, including two medication carousels to manage and track inventory. The system-wide perpetual inventory software system provides the backbone to allow inventory visibility, medication order management, and financial tracking across the SHS inpatient pharmacy network by linking the software system within each inpatient pharmacy.

The initial focus for the CSC was to provide packaging for the two hospitals with centralized robotic filling, with expansion to the provision of unit dose repackaging to non-robot sites of care over the following year. Currently the SHS CSC provides repackaging services to all of the system's inpatient pharmacies including three hospitals that participate in the 340B program, totaling over 500,000 doses monthly.

PREPARING FOR 340B

The CSC began servicing the system's 340B hospitals in late 2015. In researching the approach that other CSC facilities had taken, two models were identified. First, opt out of providing services to 340B facilities; or second, require the 340B facilities to purchase their own inventory using the processes outlined above to split purchases, ship it to the repackaging center where the individual hospital inventory would be sequestered, repackaged, and returned to the 340B facility. Neither of these solutions was considered viable, so a third approach was undertaken.

The initial step in planning was to create a defined CSC replenishment formulary of approximately 300 items that had 340B contract pricing. The next challenge was to determine a methodology to purchase and track medications delivered to 340B and non-340B hospitals in a manner that would ensure compliance with 340B program statutory requirements. To that end, the CSC was registered on the OPA web site as a "ship to" location for each of the covered entities. This allowed for the creation of CSC "Child" purchasing accounts by the distributor for each 340B hospital. The creation of accounts allowed the CSC to purchase inventory under the appropriate account type for the covered entity (WAC, GPO, or 340B) that would then be billed to the hospital but shipped to the CSC. Tracking of the 340B sites CSC inventory was accomplished using a virtual inventory in the CSC inventory management software.

Once the inventory ordering and tracking processes were defined, purchases of medications were made for each 340B site under the appropriate account using automated splitting software to "fill" each site's virtual inventory accumulations in the local 340B software. The virtual inventory maximum and par (average) levels were established based in each site's utilization, as well as the CSC package size for each NDC to be delivered.

CSC 340B WORKFLOW

The CSC fills medication orders for each SHS inpatient pharmacy Monday through Friday. Orders are created each morning within the CSC's inventory management system, filled from repackaged CSC inventory, placed in site-specific totes, and delivered by a contracted courier service. Totes are delivered same day on Mondays and Fridays and overnight for next day delivery Tuesday through Thursday. Each day following order fulfillment, CSC staff repackages depleted inventory back to established MAX levels. Inventory for the 340B sites once purchased and accounted for in the site-specific virtual inventory is blended with the CSC physical inventory; therefore, tracking of quantities sent to the 340B sites is critical.

Each day following order fulfillment, the CSC's inventory management system-generated shipping manifest for the 340B sites is used to decrement quantities sent from each covered entity's virtual inventory "bank." Once the bank for a particular NDC reaches the set PAR level, the medication is reordered from the wholesaler under the site-specific CSC child account using automated split-billing software to ensure purchases are made based on available accumulations. Inventory received daily from the wholesaler for each 340B site is first incremented into the site-specific virtual inventory "bank," then subsequently incremented into the CSC physical inventory.

Although this presents additional steps in the CSC workflow, the process serves to allow the CSC to provide repackaged medications from a single physical inventory to both 340B and non-340B inpatient pharmacies while tracking the inventory from each covered entity virtually. Because each dose replenished to the covered entities can be traced back to a utilization/accumulation, SHS has been able to maintain compliance with the 340B program requirements.

Centralized repackaging operations are becoming an increasingly common approach for large hospital networks to drive savings through efficient utilization of costly packaging equipment and personnel and to drive formulary standardization to ensure best acquisition price.

A CSC can also address costly low unit-of-use medications by purchasing in small quantities and sharing them across many facilities, among other benefits. Our experience at the SHS CSC pharmacy has clearly demonstrated that these benefits can be extended to 340B hospitals in a blended 340B and non-340B network, while maintaining compliance with 340B program requirements.

SUMMARY

Although 340B creates challenges to the pharmacy supply chain, a thoughtful study of the 340B statute and guidance can support 340B-compliant, efficient purchasing practices. The use of 340B software not only permits management of complex, mixed-use inventory and purchasing at a local site, but it can also foster effective use of centralized supply centers.

REFERENCES

1. Veterans Healthcare Act of 1992, Public Law 102-585. Section 602, section 340B. https://www.gpo.gov/fdsys/pkg/STATUTE-106/pdf/STATUTE-106-Pg4943.pdf. Accessed September 7, 2016.

2. U.S. Public Health Services. Final Notice Regarding Section 602 of the Veterans Health Care Act of 1992 Entity Guidelines. http://www.hrsa.gov/opa/programrequirements/federalregisternotices/entityguidelines051394.pdf. Accessed September 7, 2016.

3. U.S. Department of Health And Human Services, Health Resources and Services Administration Notice Regarding 340B Drug Pricing Program—Children's Hospitals https://www.gpo.gov/fdsys/pkg/FR-2009-09-01/pdf/E9-21109.pdf. Accessed September 7, 2016.

4. U.S. Department of Health and Human Services, Health Resources and Services Administration, 340B Drug Pricing Program Notice, Statutory Prohibition on Group Purchasing Prohibition. http://www.hrsa.gov/opa/programrequirements/policyreleases/prohibitionongpoparticipation020713.pdf. Accessed August 10, 2016.

5. Health Resources and Services Administration, Office of Pharmacy Affairs, 340B Peer-to-Peer Program, Self-Audit Series: Defining your 340B Drug Operations Environment in Required Policies and Procedures. https://hrsa.connectsolutions.com/p6ca520km6r/. Accessed August 10, 2016.

6. Apexus. 340B Tools. Policy and Procedure Self-Audit Tool. https://www.apexus.com/solutions/education/pvp-education/340b-tools. Accessed September 7, 2016.

7. Health Resources and Services Administration, Office of Pharmacy Affairs, 340B Peer-to-Peer Program, Self-Audit Series: 340B Policies and Procedures. http://peertopeer340b.com/Videos/2016/20/PDF/Table%20-%20P&P%20for%20OPA%20Monthly%20Update.pdf. Accessed September 12, 2016.

8. Apexus. 340B Tools. Mapping the 340B Drug Operations Environment. https://www.apexus.com/solutions/education/pvp-education/340b-tools. Accessed August 10, 2016.

9. Health Resources and Services Administration. Orphan Drug Exclusion. http://www.hrsa.gov/opa/programrequirements/orphandrugexclusion. Accessed August 10, 2016.

10. 340B Prime Vendor Program. www.340Bpvp.com. Accessed August 12, 2016.

11. 340B Prime Vendor Program, Frequently Asked Questions, #1222, Can an entity ever replenish at the 9-digit NDC level? https://www.340bpvp.com/resource-center/faqs. Accessed August 12, 2016.

12. Social Security. Compilation of the Social Security Laws. Payment for Covered Outpatient Drugs. https://www.ssa.gov/OP_Home/ssact/title19/1927.htm. Accessed August 12, 2016.

13. Health Resources and Services Administration, 340B Drug Pricing Program. Eligibility & Registration. Eligible Drugs. http://www.hrsa.gov/opa/eligibilityandregistration/index.html. Accessed August 12, 2016.

14. Apexus. Strategies to Minimize WAC Exposure. https://docs.340bpvp.com/documents/public/resourcecenter/340b_minimize_wac_exposure.pdf. Accessed August 12, 2016.

CHAPTER 7

340B Policies and Procedures

Lisa N Schatz, PharmD, BCPS and
Fern Paul-Aviles, PharmD, MS, BCPS

Policies and procedures (P&Ps) govern how a covered entity's 340B program is conducted. It is imperative that the written P&Ps reflect actual practice, because there are many ways to conduct a compliant 340B program in the context of patient care delivery and pharmacy practice in large and complex hospitals. Policy and procedure review is part of the Health Resources and Services Administration (HRSA) audit process with comparisons to the 340B statute, 340B guidance documents, and best practices. Writing and following P&Ps, while conceptually simple, can be a difficult task due to the complexity of the 340B program. It is worth the time and effort to think through 340B processes, even using a process flow diagram, as a preliminary step in drafting P&Ps. When referring to these guidelines in this chapter, the actual policies when written may be more encompassing or more restrictive depending on the covered entity.

The 340B policies and procedures should follow the institution-wide format for P&Ps, including references, pertinent definitions, and review and approval dates. Policies should also consider the broader patient care, regulatory, and other institutional prerogatives.

Several resources are available that support the development of P&Ps so it is not necessary to completely start fresh. HRSA has conducted a peer-to-peer webinar to discuss areas that should be contained in the program P&Ps.[1] Additionally, to assist with appropriate P&P content, Apexus has published sample P&Ps and a set of downloadable tools outlining proper content and compliant 340B operations, available on the Apexus web site.[2,3]

In constructing policies, the topics in the Apexus sample P&Ps should be included aside from ensuring that all 17 areas recommended by HRSA are covered in adequate detail. Topics covered in the Apexus sample P&Ps include the following definitions:

- Patient eligibility
- Enrollment
- Prevention of duplicate discount
- Education and competency
- Inventory management
- Contract pharmacy operations, oversight, and monitoring
- Noncompliance and material breach
- Program compliance that contains an audit plan

Table 7-1 provides a more comprehensive list of topics. The tool in **Table 7-2**, adapted from a HRSA document, lists the 17 elements HRSA recommends. Not all elements apply to every

Table 7-1. Example of Policy and Procedure[3,4]

POLICY TOPIC

- Background on the 340B Program
- Definitions
- References
- Covered Entity Eligibility
- 340B Program Enrollment, Recertification, and Change Requests
- Patient Eligibility/Definition
- Prevention of Duplicate Discounts
- 340B Program Roles and Responsibilities
- 340B Program Education and Competency
- Inventory Management
- Contract Pharmacy Operations
- 340B Non-Compliance/Material Breach
- 340B Program Compliance
- Contract Pharmacy Oversight and Monitoring
- Prime Vendor Program (PVP) Enrollment and Updates
- Suggested Appendices

Source: Adapted with permission from sample P&P courtesy of Apexus LLC, Irving, Texas.

covered entity; therefore, the covered entity should review the list for their entity type, contract pharmacy participation, and physical versus virtual inventory.

The Apexus tools include sample P&Ps for disproportionate share hospitals (DSHs) and community health centers.[3,4]

KEY POINT

Ensure that all HRSA-recommended areas are included in P&Ps.

The samples should be used as a starting point, and the P&Ps should be customized to your institutional P&P format. Copying and pasting the Apexus sample policies is not recommended, as it will indicate that the 340B program team has neither given much thought as to how the program is conducted nor devised policies to reflect specific operational practice variations. Further, template policies may conflict with regular practices and activities at the covered entity.

It is important to keep P&Ps accurate and up-to-date. A covered entity should have a formal process for P&P review for all policies, not just 340B policies. A covered entity may need a more flexible, separate process for 340B P&P review on a more frequent basis, so that policies and procedures are an accurate reflection of current practices. Because of the intensive scrutiny of the 340B program and the more flexible and current nature of 340B guidance, 340B program managers at the covered entity may need to employ more diligence than is normally necessary to ensure that policies are amended, edited, and approved in a timely fashion. 340B program leaders are encouraged to stay current with HRSA audit practices and with changing guidance and frequently asked questions (FAQs) on the HRSA and Apexus/340B Prime Vendor web site as sources for continuing review and updates.

Table 7-2. 17 Elements to Self-Audit Policies and Procedures

Policies and Procedures to Describe Covered Entity's Process for:	Policy Topic	Policy Section	Comments
1. Registration/ recertification and ensuring that the 340B database is up-to-date and accurate for parent, applicable off-site outpatient facilities, and contract pharmacies (including the frequency regular reviews are performed, how this review is documented, and timely update of 340B database records).	OPA registration	340B enrollment, recertification, change requests	
2. Determining what sites are eligible (i.e., reimbursable on the CE's most recently filed Medicare Cost Report, approved service sites on the grant, located within the 4 walls of the parent entity or registered on the 340B database).	OPA registration	340B enrollment, recertification, change requests	
3. Procurement, including the identification of all accounts used for purchasing medications (including for parent entity, off-site outpatient locations, and contract pharmacies, if applicable).	Supply chain	340B procurement, inventory management, dispensing	Procurement accounts for CPs needed
4. Prevention of GPO violations, including self-negotiated contracts for individual entities and integrated delivery networks.	Supply chain	Mixed-use areas	
5. Identification of any exclusions to the definition of covered outpatient drugs (i.e., bundled drugs or inpatient drugs).	Exclusions	Definitions Covered outpatient drugs	Are there any drugs that are only purchased on the non-340B accounts?
6. Conducting oversight of its CP(s) by performing internal audits and external/independent audits (e.g., methodology, frequency).	CP Oversight	Monitoring and reporting	Section needs what is audited, frequency of audit, and how reported
7. Tracking and accounting for all 340B drugs in a physical inventory, from receipt to dispensation/administration of the medication, including periodic inventory counts and reconciliation with inventory system.	Inventory management	340B procurement, inventory management, dispensing	Include documentation of tracers for provider administered medications
8. Tracking and accounting for all 340B drugs via accumulation in a virtual replenishment model from receipt to dispensation/administration of the medication.	Split-billing software	Split-billing software	Detail how usage is accumulated
9. Handling the situation where the CE does NOT use an 11-digit to 11-digit NDC match process (such as seen with a CDM and NDC crosswalk) for handling this situation and maintaining auditable records to demonstrate proper accumulation in a replenishment model, if applicable.	Split-billing software	Split-billing software	Call out specific replacement to the 11-digit NDC

Table 7-2. continued

10. Prevention of diversion at CE by confirming the following: site eligibility location, referral/responsibility of care remained with CE, medical/patient health record, patient eligibility (including status change), provider eligibility (relationship and how changes in provider eligibility are handled within CE), service in the scope of grant (if applicable/non-hospital).	Dispensation eligibility	340B Policy Statements Locations Responsibility of care Referrals Record of care	Agreement with state/local government, MCR worksheets, or scope of grant
11. Prevention of diversion at CE—monitoring the 340B split-billing software (e.g., frequency).	Split-billing software	Diversion	Purchases should be trackable; include tracers
12. Prevention of diversion at contract pharmacy by confirming the following: site eligibility location, referral/responsibility of care remained with CE, medical/patient health record, patient eligibility (including status change), provider eligibility (relationship including how changes in provider eligibility are handled within CE), service in the scope of grant (if applicable/non-hospital).	CP	CP Rx eligibility List of patients List of providers Eligible locations	Include tracers
13. Prevention of diversion at contract pharmacy(ies)—monitoring the 340B split-billing software (e.g., frequency).	CP	CP split-billing software	Tracers needed
14. Complying with orphan drug exclusion (only applicable to SCHs, RRCs, CAHs, CANs and their contract pharmacies).	Orphan drugs	Orphan drugs	Include for applicable CE
15. Prevention of duplicate discounts at CE and off-site outpatient facilities (e.g., physician administration; outpatient prescriptions; billing multiple state Medicaid agencies, if applicable), including the frequency regular reviews are performed, how this review is documented, and timely update of the MEF.	Medicaid	Definitions	Include policies for all state Medicaid agencies in service area
16. Prevention of duplicate discounts at CPs for outpatient prescriptions.	CP	Medicaid at CP	Include state Medicaid agencies in service area
17. When and how CE would self-disclose and CEs definition of noncompliance material breach.	Material breach	Material breach	Include guidelines to use in determining material breach

CAHs: critical access hospitals, CANs: freestanding cancer hospitals, CDM: charge description master, CE: covered entity, CP: contract pharmacy, GPO: group purchasing organization, MCR: Medicare cost report, MEF: Medicaid exclusion file, NDC: national drug code, OPA: Office of Pharmacy Affairs, RRCs: rural referral centers, SCHs: sole community hospitals

Source: Seventeen elements used with permission from Allison Gross, Health Resources and Services Administration, Office of Pharmacy Affairs. February 2016 Update. http://www.hrsa.gov/opa/updates/2016/february.html. 340B Policies and Procedures http://peertopeer340b.com/Videos/2016/20/PDF/Table%20-%20P&P%20for%20OPA%20Monthly%20Update.pdf. Accessed September 14, 2016.

> # KEY POINT
>
> Keep P&P accurate and up-to-date. Follow HRSA, Apexus (340B Prime Vendor), and other notices as sources of current information.

The 340B program is fundamentally a drug-pricing and purchasing program, and many elements of 340B-related policies are specific and unique to pharmacy operations. However, a number of operations or practices that occur outside the pharmacy department may impact 340B program compliance, such as patient registration and revenue cycle processes (e.g., generation of UD modifiers in billing notices for prevention of Medicaid duplicate discounts). In instances where the impact and practice is in a different department than pharmacy, policies governing those practices should be addressed in each affected department's policies or standard operating procedures, or in an institutional or corporate policy that governs all departments.

340B PROGRAM POLICIES

Eligibility

The covered entity should refer to the statute 42 U.S. Code §256b (a)(4) section(A) through (K) for covered entities other than hospitals, and sections (L), (M), (N), or (O) for the definition of how hospitals meets the statute.[5] The Apexus tool, Hospital Eligibility Criteria, can be used as a reference to assist the covered entity in determining how they meet the statute.[6] Include a section in one of the initial policies that states how the covered entity meets the definition. Document the section of the statutory definition of a covered entity that fits your institution.

If the covered entity no longer meets eligibility requirements, such as a disproportionate share percentage dropping below the threshold, the covered entity is required to notify HRSA immediately and cease participating in the 340B program. A statement to that effect should be included in the P&Ps.

Office of Pharmacy Affairs Registration and Recertification

Office of Pharmacy Affairs (OPA) registration errors are among the top three findings on HRSA audit. It is important that the covered entity document how frequently to undertake the due diligence to delineate all areas of service where 340B activities take place and define the process of checking the 340B database to ensure it is up-to-date.

The database review process should be documented in a P&P. The aspects of accurate registration to check include the parent site, all registered child sites and their suite numbers, all other nonregistered outpatient facilities that are newly provider-based but not yet 340B-eligible, and all registered contract pharmacies (CPs). CP registration must be an exact match to the list on the covered entity's pharmacy services agreement. For hospital mixed-use areas and in-house retail pharmacies that carve-in Medicaid, the national provider identifier (NPI) and state Medicaid numbers must be listed on the OPA database in the Medicaid exclusion file when registering the parent entity and each child site. Establish in the policy whether the Medicaid numbers will be listed for only the hospital's home state, surrounding states, or all states for which a claim has been generated.

A best practice is to include review of the OPA web site in the 340B audit plan and conduct the review immediately prior to the annual recertification period opening, plus making appropriate changes as they occur throughout the year. Most changes can be made on line when they occur and do not need to wait for the open registration period. Many covered entities review and update the CP list quarterly, primarily for economic and service area reasons; however, the review serves the additional purpose to keep the OPA registered locations current. CP review processes should be described in a P&P.

KEY POINT

Make changes to the hospital's OPA web site listing as they occur. Include a review of the hospital's OPA web site listing in the P&P for annual self-auditing.

The overall OPA registration and review P&P should include a description of the process for reviewing all areas of service where outpatient 340B-eligible activities take place, and address how each area is determined to be eligible to participate in the 340B program:

- The location is within the four walls of the CE and does not need to be separately registered in the OPA Information System (OPAIS).

- The location is outside the four walls of the CE and is listed as a reimbursable outpatient location on the Medicare cost report (hospitals). Note that merged former hospital facilities that are child sites of a parent hospital must have each outpatient area registered on the OPAIS.

- The location is an approved service site listed on the HRSA grant (grantees).

Locations determined to be eligible and using 340B drugs should be correctly registered on the 340B database (hospitals and grantees).

Patient Definition

Although not part of the 17 recommended aspects to include in P&Ps, the Apexus sample P&Ps includes an example policy that defines the patient of a 340B-covered entity. It is important for the covered entity to define and document how patient eligibility is determined.[7,8] Because the patient definition is the statutory underpinning of the 340B program under which all operations must operate to be compliant, it is important for each covered entity to understand their operations well enough to define appropriate 340B dispensations using patient eligibility as a benchmark.

The main principles of the definition of a 340B-eligible patient include providing care in an outpatient area; maintaining a relationship with the individual, including a record of care; receiving care from a provider who is employed, contracted, or is consulted via a referral relationship while the covered entity maintains responsibility for care; and receiving care that is consistent with the grant funding (grantees only).

In all 340B service areas, it is important to understand how a patient meets this definition. In each service area, the process for identifying an eligible patient should be clear and documented. In mixed-use areas, patient changes in status from inpatient to outpatient status (or the inverse), should be outlined; methods to identify an eligible provider should be understood. A description of areas registered and listed on the OPAIS should also be addressed. In retail pharmacies owned by the covered entity, a process for identifying an eligible patient presenting a prescription for 340B dispensation should also be documented. Covered entity retail pharmacies using a 340B software provider to screen and categorize patients should document the elements evaluated by the software logic to determine eligibility, and not merely state that software is used. All pharmacies contracted to provide 340B dispensations on behalf of the covered entity should have a documented process for identifying eligible patients and for specifying identification elements and methods used for patient, provider, and prescription identification.

In all three of these service types—mixed-use, covered entity-owned retail pharmacy, and CPs—covered entities are required to have auditable processes in place that ensure compliance with the 340B patient definition. A best practice for a covered entity is to describe how a prescription or dispensation is qualified for 340B and define all "qualification filters" by policy. Documentation in the procedures should include how the dispensation flows through the qualification filters by service location, patient status, patient health record, entity-provider relationship, scope of grant, and Medicaid status to demonstrate how the patient definition is met and diversion is avoided.

EXAMPLE

A particular area of vulnerability for hospitals in identifying a 340B-eligible dispense in a mixed-use area is a patient's transition from outpatient to inpatient care. Generally, hospitals participating in the 340B program may categorize a patient as *outpatient* using one of four methodologies: (1) the patient's location at the time of dispensing/charging; (2) the patient's location at the time of administration of the medication; (3) the status of the patient by the time the final bill is generated; or 4) patient status at midnight, for the entirety of the preceding 24 h. The 340B program managers and the writer of the P&P must identify which method is used to define a 340B-eligible dispense and document it in the P&P.

Potential wording in a policy addressing 340B qualification in a mixed-use area might read as follows:

(1)   The query selection criteria will be the "service date patient type, which reflects the patient's registration type at the time the drug was **dispensed and charged** from the pharmacy computer system or automated dispensing cabinet.

    (a)   Later reclassifications for billing purposes or due to registration errors will not alter the patient type at the time of charge, which will be used to determine 340B qualification."

Although a HRSA auditor might not note the absence of this item in a P&P, ignorance of or inattention to this element may lead to inconsistent qualification of 340B patients and a finding of diversion if the covered entity's software is not set up consistent with the hospital's definition of an eligible dispensation.

PURCHASING AND INVENTORY MANAGEMENT POLICIES

Group Purchasing Organization Prohibition Requirement

The group purchasing organization (GPO) prohibition applies to DSHs, children's hospitals, and freestanding cancer hospitals. These three covered entity types must attest to compliance with this provision during their annual recertification and must have procedures in place to ensure that covered outpatient drugs are not obtained through a GPO or a GPO-like arrangement. Violation of the prohibition may result in expulsion from the 340B program. It is important to document by policy *when* and *where* medications purchased through a GPO will be used.

KEY POINT

For applicable covered entities, specifying practices to mitigate the risk of violating the GPO prohibition in P&Ps is a best practice.

Covered Outpatient Drug Exceptions

HRSA uses the definition of a *covered outpatient drug*, as published in the Social Security Act SEC. 1927 [42 U.S.C. 1396r–8].[9] The definition can be found in section (k) part (2)[9] and includes prescription drugs, over-the-counter (OTC) drugs written on a prescription, biologicals, and FDA-approved insulins. Vaccines are specifically excluded from the definition of a covered outpatient drug in this section. With the exception of these specifically-identified covered outpatient drugs, HRSA has instructed that hospitals may define what they consider as covered outpatient drugs and must apply the definition consistently. See Apexus FAQ 1355.[10] P&Ps should define how a drug is determined to be a covered outpatient drug. The covered outpatient drug definition may be addressed in a section of the policy devoted to definitions.

The limiting definition of a covered outpatient drug can be found in section (k) part (3).[9] This definition specifically refers to what is commonly known as *bundled* drugs where reimbursement is bundled for the service and not directly for the drug.

The 340B statute does not specifically define when a drug meets the limiting definition of a covered outpatient drug, but allows the covered entity to specify which medications in the covered entity's setting meet the limiting definition. Generally, anesthesia gases, large-volume parenterals, and radiologicals/contrast media meet the limiting definition and are excluded from 340B program consideration. Each covered entity should have a policy that specifically calls out which classes of drugs meet the limiting definition as per SEC. 1927 [42 U.S.C. 1396r–8] (k) (3)[9] and how it was determined.

KEY POINT

Develop a policy that specifies which drugs meet the limiting definition of an outpatient drug.

Orphan Drug Exclusion for Expansion Entities

An *orphan drug* is defined as a drug that has been designated by Health and Human Services (HHS) as one that treats a disease either affecting fewer than 200,000 people in the United States or more than 200,000, if there is no reasonable expectation that the costs of developing a drug for the condition would be recouped. The 340B statute exempts these orphan drugs from the definition of covered outpatient drug for the Expansion Entities: for sole community hospitals, rural referral centers, critical access hospitals, and freestanding cancer hospitals.[11]

As outlined in Chapter 3, HRSA promulgated a rule outlining the scope of the orphan drug exclusion that was subsequently challenged by the Pharmaceutical Research and Manufacturers of America (PhRMA). The District Court vacated the HRSA Orphan Drug Rule in October 2015. As a result, sole community hospitals, rural referral centers, critical access hospitals, and freestanding cancer hospitals must complete a section in their policies that outlines compliance with the orphan drug exclusion with limited direct guidance. A straightforward way to address this is to extend the covered outpatient drug policy outlined above to include the covered entity's identified orphan drugs. The policy should also address the resources and references used to identify an orphan drug. The OPA list from the HRSA web site[12] and the U.S. Food and Drug administration (FDA) web site[13] are primary sources.

KEY POINT

For applicable covered entities, management of the Orphan Drug Exclusion should be included in the P&Ps that address the limiting definition of covered outpatient drugs.

Virtual or Physical Inventory Decisions

Understanding the requirements to prevent violations of the GPO prohibition impacts how a covered entity structures their existing supply chain to become 340B compliant. Designing compliant operations begins with deciding how to handle inventory and working backward to the purchasing process; and then writing and implementing the policy and procedure framework to support the selected option.

The use of the *physical inventory method* requires the physical space and a dedicated location to separate each inventory, and separate 340B and GPO purchasing accounts. A covered entity using a physical inventory model may decide that certain areas within the four walls and certain registered child locations always provide care that meets the 340B patient definition. In other words, the patients served in those areas are always 340B-eligible and, therefore, may always keep a solely 340B medication inventory. A less commonly used but viable option for an area that would be considered "GPO Only," such as an intensive care unit that only cares for inpatients, can be handled in the same manner if properly isolated. In the instances outlined above, a separate 340B and GPO purchase account is required. The purchasing policy for 340B-only or GPO-only areas should describe the decision points that lead to a separate physical inventory supported by a separate 340B account.

In the 340B program context, the term *mixed-use* is used to identify areas where both inpatients and outpatients receive care. An example would be a hospital inpatient nursing unit, which cares for patients under observation—classified as an outpatient status, or an operating room suite that supports both inpatient and outpatient procedures drawing from a single inventory. Typically, hospital mixed-use areas are served by the main or inpatient hospital pharmacy. Writing policies for these areas requires a detailed understanding and mapping of hospital pharmacy operations.

Before writing policies for mixed-use locations, decisions regarding purchasing and inventory management should be considered. A best practice is to track usage with a virtual inventory supported by 340B split-billing software.

The virtual inventory model is also known as a *replenishment model*, and it requires that the initial purchase of a product at the 11-digit National Drug Code (NDC) level be made on a WAC account. Because the virtual inventory accumulator splits dispensations into 340B, GPO, and WAC buckets based on data from the hospital's electronic medical records (EMR) and patient billing systems, the split-billing software serves as a key safeguard against violations of the GPO prohibition. A trio of purchasing accounts (340B, GPO, and WAC) should be created to support split-billing purchasing practices. See Chapter 6, 340B Pharmacy Supply Chain, for a discussion of mapping operations and account set-up. The 340B split-billing functions are generally similar across the various vendors in the marketplace, and a detailed discussion of setup is not appropriate here. However, the mapping of the patient care data supporting differentiating inpatients, outpatients, and other elements of 340B eligibility remains a key starting point for proper setup of 340B split-billing systems. Supply chain and operations policies or practices should support and be supportive of the technology backbone that determines and allocates compliant purchasing.

Deciding which accounts are needed is dependent on the type of facility (i.e., subject to the GPO prohibition and requires a WAC account) and how inventory will be handled. Documenting the preliminary decisions on drug handling and inventory management will help design and keep supply chain operations compliant. The P&P should describe the decision in general terms referring to mixed-use areas and dedicated 100% 340B locations, rather than the individual departments or locations, as these may change over time and the policy statement will be out-of-date. Best practices include building and maintaining a regularly updated appendix or table of accounts and locations with setup details. Be certain that the updates to the table are reflected in the distributor account setup details and in software settings and tables. Additionally, a full review should be undertaken prior to each annual HRSA recertification.

EXAMPLE

Hospital A, a 340B DSH hospital, owns Location B, a facility across town that was formerly a hospital and is now a 100% outpatient treatment center. Location B is suitably reported on Hospital A's Medicare cost report and properly enrolled as a 340B child site. Hospital A also owns 340B-eligible provider-based physician practices located across the city in various locations. At the parent Hospital A location, there are inpatient services, dedicated outpatient areas, and mixed-use areas.

During set-up, it was decided that Hospital A would have a trio of accounts for all mixed-use areas, using a virtual inventory model. Because the 340B patient definition is always met at Location B, it utilizes a separate single 340B account and a separate physical inventory. It was decided that all dedicated outpatient areas and physician practices would be supplied from Location B.

Documentation of the separate physical inventory supply chain operations going forward is kept via spreadsheet detailing which locations are supplied from Location B. Specifically, all operations at Location B, all 340B-eligible provider-based physician offices in various locations, and all dedicated 340B outpatient areas at Hospital A are supplied from Location B. See **Table 7-3** for a depiction of this scenario. A description of replenishment practices for the hospital mixed-use areas and the separate inventory model should be included in Hospital A & B's P&Ps.

Table 7-3. Complex Replenishment Documentation

Location	Service Types	Source of Replenishment
Hospital A	Inpatients	Hospital A—from accumulations in the split-billing software
Hospital A	Mixed-use outpatients	Hospital A—from accumulations in the split-billing software
Hospital A	Dedicated outpatients	Location B
Location B	Dedicated outpatients	Location B
Provider-based physician practices	Dedicated outpatients	Location B

Describe Accounts

The Apexus 340B Program Policy and Procedure Self-Audit Tool (https://docs.340bpvp.com/documents/.../Policy_and_Procedure_Self-Audit_Tool.doc) recommends identification of all accounts used for purchasing at the parent, off-site child locations, and contract pharmacies. Defining which accounts, by type, will be used to purchase medications in all settings will help the covered entity remain compliant, especially when more than one person purchases medications. Having a *job-aid* that lists the vendor, account type, account numbers, phone numbers, and which items are purchased on the account by item number will assist pharmacy buyers in understanding and documenting the procedure for how the covered entity purchases medications. The P&P can refer to the job aid, rather than having details of buying practices in the P&P. Processes can be changed more frequently on the job aid, allowing the P&Ps to remain up-to-date.

KEY POINT

Having a job aid that can be updated as buying practices change can keep P&Ps up-to-date.

DEFINING COMPLIANT BUYING PROCEDURES

Describe Buying Processes for Mixed-Use Areas (Virtual Inventory Model)

For covered entities that use split-billing software, policies should define how the accumulator tracks utilization and describe the areas where dispensations are recorded and tracked in the accumulator. In other words, describe how the data are fed into the accumulator and the logic used to define an inpatient versus an outpatient. Documenting which areas are charge-on-dispense versus charge-on-administration will help provide a framework that is auditable. It may be important for the covered entity to list the charge-on-dispense areas in the policy if those are the exceptions, and note that the remaining areas are charge-on-administration. Outpatient dispensations, as defined by charges, will flow into the 340B bucket. Inpatient usages will flow into the GPO bucket, and outpatient uses that do not meet the 340B patient definition will flow into the WAC accumulator (e.g., Medicaid carve-out). The P&P should include documentation of how the covered entity prevents diversion by reviewing available accumulations prior to purchasing. Documentation of how the covered entity purchases medication to comply with the GPO prohibition should also be included in the P&P.

Describe Buying Process for 100% 340B Areas (Physical Inventory Model)

In areas where a physical inventory model is used, more traditional supply chain practices for buying and inventory management can be used and should be documented in a P&P. Documentation of the purchasing process should be detailed enough to explain how a covered entity determines the trigger to buy, whether it is inventory management by par-level or a "want book." Usually a covered entity will have a 340B purchasing account and a WAC or non-340B purchasing account, in the case of a covered entity not subject to the GPO prohibition rule. The covered entity should define when each account should be used and document this in the P&P.

Regardless of virtual or physical inventory, include a statement in the P&P whether the covered entity is buying at the 11-digit NDC level, and when 9-digit NDC replenishment may be used. The documentation should specifically call out the term *11-digit NDC level* replenishment. Note, though, that 11-digit replenishment is required only when using a virtual inventory system; if the hospital is purchasing directly on a 340B account for areas where 100% of the patients are 340B-eligible, 340B purchases can be made prospectively (prior to dispensing) and an initial purchase at WAC price is not necessary.

Obtaining Drugs from Other Hospitals or Other Pharmacies

Not infrequently, a hospital may discover that a drug is needed urgently for patient care reasons, but that it is not in the hospital's inventory. In those cases, it is customary to reach out to other hospitals in their own health system, or to other hospitals or retail pharmacies in their community. With the passage of the Drug Supply Chain Security Act (DSCSA)[14] and the increased emphasis on compliance with the 340B program, obtaining drugs from another pharmacy poses compliance risks that did not exist previously. To assist pharmacy buyers and other staff with 340B compliance, a policy, and a job aid, addressing acquisition of drugs from other pharmacies should be created. The policy must take into consideration the prohibition on diversion of 340B drugs (e.g., supplying 340B drugs to 340B-ineligible areas or hospitals) and the prohibition on using drugs purchased at GPO pricing in 340B-registered areas. The policy should address the following possible solutions to obtaining a drug (keeping in mind the GPO prohibition and the prohibition on diversion of 340B drugs):

- *Borrow-replace*. The hospital needing the drug may choose to order a replacement supply of the drug as soon as possible and return it to the loaning entity.
- *Selling the drug*. The hospital needing the drug may purchase the drug from the seller, usually at the WAC (non-contracted) price. Bear in mind that even if two hospitals are both 340B-eligible, the loaning hospital cannot sell or transfer 340B-priced drugs to another 340B-covered entity unless they are both part of the *same* covered entity.

- *Do not borrow, loan, or sell any drugs.* For compliance reasons, this would be the ideal solution, but for urgent patient care situations not borrowing or purchasing drugs from another pharmacy may not always be possible.

The policy should address transfer of drugs between the following types of 340B areas:

- 340B mixed-use areas
- 100% 340B-eligible areas keeping a separate (100% 340B-priced) inventory
- Non-340B-eligible hospitals

Additional consideration should be given to whether transfer of drugs will occur between hospitals or pharmacies that are not part of the same ownership structure, which means that the DSCSA requirements will apply.

Managing Direct Purchases

Most covered entities have a single main drug wholesaler, an intravenous (IV) solutions distributor, and a variety of smaller vendors from which specific medications are purchased. It is important to determine which vendors support 340B accounts and set up accounts at the start of participation in the 340B program. Larger vendors offer electronic data interchange (EDI), which will send electronic invoices that update a split-billing accumulator with purchases. In the case where a vendor does not provide EDI updating of the mixed-use accumulator, a manual process may be required. The manual process for updating the accumulator for direct purchases and any other required adjustments should be documented in a P&P.

In the cases where compounding pharmacies do not offer any negotiated pricing, the pricing can be considered equivalent to a WAC price and only one account is necessary. The hospital should identify in its P&P or an appendix which vendors offer only non-contracted pricing.

KEY POINT

Specify how purchases for physical inventory, virtual inventory, borrow-loan, and direct purchases will be made in the P&Ps.

Describe Virtual or Physical Inventory

Once medication on-order arrives, the process for receipt of medication should be documented. Most likely, the process for checking the invoice against the received medications will be identical regardless of the account type. The receiving procedure can be documented in the general pharmacy P&Ps and need not be a separate 340B policy. Recommended elements include receipt of medications, separation of duties between ordering and receiving, inventory count frequency, inventory count reconciliation, and documentation and resolution of variances. Having defined procedures is important in the physical inventory environment, particularly in areas deemed 100% 340B. Inventory segregation and replenishment processes should be described in detail. The process for inventory true-up by cycle counts or other periodic inventory validation methods should also be described in the P&P.

Procedures for the virtual inventory should include a description of how the software accumulator receives and tracks utilization, how the accumulator is used by the buyer to allocate purchases to each account, how the accumulations are adjusted when an order is received, and when to perform a manual adjustment. Permission for manual adjustments and documentation of adjustments should also be addressed. The effort spent to document how the data flow into the split-billing software and how the split-billing software processes dispensations into accumulations is critical to satisfy the requirement of auditable records. This documentation is also useful as the covered entities' IT systems, care areas, and practices change over time.

CONTRACT PHARMACY POLICIES

Lack of CP oversight is one of the most common findings of non-compliance in HRSA audits. The full responsibility for maintaining a compliant CP network remains with the covered entity. A covered entity with CP relationships should have documented P&Ps that the covered entity actively uses to maintain a compliant CP network.[15] Include these elements in the contract pharmacy P&P:

1. *Maintain a CP Pharmacy Service Agreement*

   Prior to initiating services with a CP, the covered entity must secure a signed agreement with the CP, commonly known as the pharmacy services agreement (PSA). The PSA must be signed and executed prior to registering the participants with OPA. The PSA must list all participating pharmacy locations in the PSA, with a store identifier and correct address. The PSA must include a statement that the CP must maintain auditable records. A statement discussing the requirements of a PSA should be in the CP P&P.

2. *CP Listings on the Office of Pharmacy Affairs Information System (OPAIS)*

   The CE should have a policy addressing review of the accuracy of the CP listings on the OPAIS. The active listings must match the PSA exactly. If the covered entity has a process to review the economic and operational viability of individual pharmacies and decides that a certain pharmacy should no longer be in the network, the covered entity must have the PSA amended to remove the location and submit the termination notice online through the OPAIS, following the standard OPA process.[16] The frequency of the review should be specified in the P&P and be performed annually at a minimum, with attention to the OPA recertification deadline.

3. *Prevention of Diversion of 340B Drugs*

   The responsibility for proper CP network management lies with the covered entity, and as such it should have an understanding and documentation of how prescription eligibility is determined and the practices and policies in place to prevent diversion, duplicate discount, and general business challenges (e.g., true-ups of "dead" partial accumulations, reversals of prescriptions found ineligible, refunds of fees for "rewinds" and returns, inclusion or exclusion of prescriptions). Policies should be reflective of the PSA provisions as described above. It is incumbent on the covered entity to understand how the 340B software logic identifies 340B-eligible patients and prescriptions, manages eligible locations, and how it and the CP maintain accurate and up-to-date provider lists and associated software settings and rules. A statement discussing the 340B-eligibility process and how the CP maintains auditable records should be included in the P&Ps.

   Each individual CP location must be in the PSA and listed with an effective date on the OPA web site before it is used for 340B purposes. Noncompliance with this requirement would be considered diversion and requires the covered entity to self-disclose the violation. CP locations can be listed in a more readily updated appendix of the PSA.

   The covered entity should have an audit plan to review CP eligibility processes to ensure no diversion has taken place. The detailed audit plan may be specified in the CP P&Ps, or in the overall 340B program audit plan. A schedule for CP audit frequency should also be specified. The current recommendation by the OPA is for the covered entity to commission an annual audit by an independent outside auditor. The P&Ps should address whether a hospital's internal audit team may be considered "independent" (which may depend on the organizational structure at the covered entity). Future OPA statements, FAQs, and any proposed statutory changes to the 340B program may lead covered entities to reconsider the scope, depth, frequency, and process for CP auditing.

4. *Prevention of Duplicate Discounts*

    CPs are required to carve-out Medicaid fee-for-service patient prescriptions unless an arrangement has been made with the state Medicaid agency and reported to HRSA.[17-19] A statement of how traditional Medicaid prescriptions will be handled should be in the CP P&Ps. The complexities of prescription claims should also be understood and addressed in P&P and program set-up. Bank Identification Number/ Processor Control Number (BIN/ PCN) number assignments for commercial and managed Medicaid plans are often indistinguishable at the claim level. The covered entity should have a statement concerning how managed Medicaid claims are handled in the CP P&Ps.

    The P&Ps should also address how claim transactions are processed to ensure no duplicate discounts (Medicaid) occur and how to prevent 340B drug diversion.

5. *Purchasing and Inventory Management*

    The 340B inventory at a CP remains the property of the covered entity. The P&Ps should have documentation that the inventory ownership remains with the CE and how inventory true-up or reconciliation will take place. The P&Ps should document the replenishment process via a "bill-to ship-to" arrangement.

    HRSA has provided guidance to maintain a CP network that includes required elements.[20]

KEY POINT

Comprehensive P&Ps for managing a compliant CP network is a best practice.

POLICIES FOR AUDITING

Auditing of the 340B program, internally by the covered entity and externally as discussed above, is an important component of overall program management. A best practice for a 340B program is to have policies that delineate internal systems and process controls ensuring program compliance. Monitoring program requirements through auditable records is a fundamental compliance practice. It is also a best practice to have a defined schedule that specifies which program elements will be reviewed and the extent and nature of records reviewed, including the frequency of audits. Internal and external audits are also best practices. Include a description of what will be audited and the frequency of audit.

Self-Audits (Internal)

Auditing the OPA registration listings and a comparison to the OPA web listing and hospital's Medicare cost report should be done on an annual basis and performed prior to the annual recertification. Changes and updates to child sites should be reviewed with Finance to ensure that all locations are appropriately accounted for on the Medicare cost report and listed accurately on the OPA web site. CP listings should be included in the self-audit and may be reviewed more frequently throughout the year.

Mixed-use areas should be monitored on a regular schedule. In the virtual inventory environment, a review of the frequency of auditing aspects of the split-billing software should be specified in the P&Ps. At a minimum the policy should specify annual audits, with audits following any significant operational, technology, or regulatory changes. Typical audit elements should include monitoring the accuracy of the background database that supports output from the electronic health record translated to dispensing accumulations. Audit policies should also address follow-up on accumulation anomalies and any subsequent corrective actions. An important audit element is the use of tracers to review accumulations coincident with patient status to confirm that diversion is not occurring.

In areas where patient care and dispensations are 100% 340B that use a separate physical inventory, audit practices should include monitoring to ensure all dispensations meet the 340B eligibility criteria. Inventory true-up and other monthly account-close activities can also be documented and used as an audit element. Ensuring compliance with Medicaid carve-in/carve-out status should be included as an audit element to prevent duplicate discounts or diversion.

Prescription transactions in covered entity-owned retail pharmacies should be tracked back to a qualifying 340B encounter, and the prescriber's status as an employed or contracted prescriber should be validated. Retail encounter tracer audit frequency should be specified in the P&Ps.

Review of CP prescription qualification logic should be included as part of the audit process. Tracers that track a prescription back to a qualified encounter should be included. Frequency of CP tracers should be specified in the P&Ps. If the CE chooses Medicaid carve-in status, auditing of Medicaid provider numbers and NPI numbers should be part of the auditing schedule. If the CE chooses Medicaid carve-out status or has a CP network, auditing of Medicaid claims to ensure no diversion or duplicate discounts occurred should be part of the auditing schedule.

KEY POINT

Include a schedule of what will be audited and with what frequency in the self-audit P&Ps.

External Audits

Contracting with an outside firm to perform a top-to-bottom assessment of the 340B program is also a best practice. If the external auditor can review the program as if they were conducting a HRSA audit, the covered entity can also get an unbiased view of program vulnerabilities. All aspects of the covered entity's program including mixed-use, 100% 340B locations, off-site clinics, physician-administered drugs, covered entity-owned retail pharmacies, and CPs should be audited. Specifying that an external audit will be performed and what will be audited should be included in the audit P&Ps. Covered entities should seek 340B-specific audit client references due to the unique nature of 340B program transactions and processes.

KEY POINT

Specify in the P&Ps that an annual external audit will be done; include retail pharmacies owned by the 340B covered entity and the 340B CP network, if utilized.

340B OVERSIGHT COMMITTEE POLICIES

Proper 340B program management includes involvement of leadership, operational, compliance, and other authorities that have responsibilities for various aspects of the program or related programs (e.g., Medicare, Medicaid billing). A 340B Oversight Committee should provide this broad and varied oversight. Policies should be developed to address committee composition, its role in program management, the frequency of meetings, and standing agenda. Executive oversight of the 340B Committee is critical owing to the regulatory, compliance, and reporting obligations inherent with the 340B program. If the Oversight Committee is a health-system wide committee where the system includes multiple covered entities, it should be comprised of representatives from each covered entity. Suggested 340B Oversight Committee composition includes the following primary members or departments and functions:

- Pharmacy Services
- Director(s) of Pharmacy as listed on the OPA web site
- 340B Program Manager
- Pharmacy Informatics
- Information Technology/Systems
- Hospital Compliance/Counsel
- Internal Audit
- Director of Finance (or other authorizing official as listed on the OPA web site)
- Hospital Administrator
- Federally Qualified Healthcare Center (FQHC) Administrator (if applicable)
- Executive Sponsor
- Authorizing Official

When program violations occur, HRSA expects an officer of the organization (preferably the Authorizing Official) to make reporting decisions and self-disclosure.

KEY POINT

Establishing a well-informed and thoughtfully composed Oversight Committee with clear duties and responsibilities in the P&Ps is a best practice.

DEFINING MATERIAL BREACH AND SELF-DISCLOSURE POLICIES

Background

In an Apexus document that provides covered entities with further guidance on material breach, the background information below is important to reference and understand.[21] Any type of program violation may meet the definition of material breach by virtue of its serious and systemic nature of the violation, its size and scope, or a combination. Each covered entity may define material breach for their 340B program and should include the definition and process for self-disclosure in policies and procedures:

> Upon annual recertification, each covered entity's authorizing official must attest that "the covered entity acknowledges its responsibility to contact HRSA as soon as reasonably possible if there is any ... material breach by the covered entity of any of the foregoing [aspects of 340B compliance]." In this context, *material breach* refers to an instance of noncompliance with any of the 340B program requirements. To increase program transparency among all stakeholders and ensure that covered entities can rely on a reasonable threshold **to guide consistent and effective self-disclosure decision-making**, **it is recommended that covered entities define "material breach" for their organizations**

and establish a process for self-disclosure in their policies and procedures. A breach of 340B compliance requirements include any adverse event that results in diversion and/or duplicate discounts. For example, the following events are considered adverse: a facility that uses the 340B Program while not being eligible, a facility providing 340B drugs to ineligible patients, 340B drugs missing in a facility's inventory, and a facility billing for 340B drugs contrary to an organization's MEF [Medicaid Exclusion File] status *(emphasis added)*.[21]

At the time of this writing, the current version of hospital 340B program recertification has the word "material" removed from the attestation. However, HRSA has continued to state that the intent of OPA is for covered entities to self-report only breaches that rise to the level of materiality.

Material Breach Policies

Every 340B-covered entity needs a P&P to address when the CE commits a "material breach." The 340B Program Oversight Committee should define what constitutes a material breach as a policy statement. This is an expectation of OPA upon audit. An active and vigorous self-audit process will often reveal program vulnerabilities and possible program violations. The Oversight Committee may review and gather facts, determine the extent of the materiality of the event, and make a recommendation to the authorizing official or health-system executive with 340B oversight. The executive may seek legal counsel in determining whether the event meets the definition of material breach and should be reported to HRSA as a self-disclosure with a corrective action plan.

Events that do not meet the definition of materiality may be handled internally and may still require process improvement, as they may highlight areas of program vulnerability. They may also obligate the covered entity to repay a manufacturer or work with commercial or government payers and contract pharmacies to remedy the breach. Obligations to repay unearned 340B discount exist regardless of the materiality of a breach, and the covered entity's policies and processes surrounding repayment should be addressed in the P&P. A best practice is to define a threshold for material breach and to have the 340B Program Oversight Committee make the final determination of materiality on a case-by-case basis after all investigation and fact-gathering have been completed.

An Apexus tool is available to assist the covered entity in designing a material breach threshold to include in a P&P.[21] Pertinent suggested definitions of threshold indicators for material breach from the Apexus tool:

1. X% of total 340B purchases or impact to any one manufacturer.
2. $X (fixed amount), based upon total outpatient or 340B spend, or impact to any one manufacturer.
3. X% of total 340B inventory (units).
4. X% of audit sample.
5. X% of prescription volume/prescription sample.
6. Will not self-correct within x months.[21]

The covered entity's P&Ps should also address several issues surrounding breaches that are unique to contract pharmacy relationships:

- Make it clear that the contract pharmacy must report all breaches; the covered entity should make the determination of materiality.
- Specify that CPs may not rectify breaches of 340B without notifying the covered entity.

Set a required time-period within which the contract pharmacy must report the breach to the covered entity. The policy discussing material breach should also address the CE's process for manufacturer repayment, including the following elements:

- Time span for notification of the manufacturer after the breach is detected and/or quantified.
- Source of manufacturer contact information.
- Elements included in a corrective action plan.
- Number and frequency of attempts to contact the manufacturer and if no response is received, the timespan after which the matter will be considered closed.

KEY POINT

Develop specific guidelines to define a material breach in the P&Ps.

POLICIES FOR BILLING, MEDICAID, AND PREVENTING DUPLICATE DISCOUNTS

To ensure compliance with the statutory requirement of prohibition of duplicate discounts, the covered entity should develop policies that comply with proper patient identification and Medicaid billing.

Upon registration with OPA, each covered entity is required to attest whether they will purchase, dispense, and bill Medicaid for 340B-priced drugs. If the answer is "yes," the covered entity is considered Medicaid carve-in for 340B program purposes. All Medicaid provider numbers or NPI numbers are required to be listed on the OPA web site in a database known as the Medicaid Exclusion File (MEF). If the covered entity has chosen carve-in status, an examination of all states (beyond the covered entity's home state) where the covered entity has the potential to bill Medicaid must be completed to ensure full compliance. Each state may require different processes for the covered entity to notify Medicaid that the drug was purchased at 340B price. It is the responsibility of the covered entity to determine what those processes are (e.g., UD modifiers for medical claims, indication of 340B-acquired drugs in designated fields for retail pharmacy claims) and implement them in their billing process. Physician-administered drugs (i.e., drugs administered in physician offices) and retail pharmacy claims may have different billing requirement for Medicaid carve-in (e.g., actual acquisition cost or using a quarterly or annual settlement process).

For Medicaid carve-out, where the facility will not purchase, dispense, and bill Medicaid for 340B-priced drugs, the facility should define how Medicaid plans are identified and excluded from 340B drug replenishment. Plans with Managed Medicaid should be identified by BIN/PCN. When the BIN/PCN is identical for Commercial Insurance and Managed Medicaid, the covered entity should have a process in place and documentation of how it will handle those transactions to remain compliant and ensure no diversion or duplicate discount takes place. Identification of other state Medicaid plans from outside the covered entity's home state should be part of the carve-out process documentation. The facility should have a process to identify and adjust accumulations of Medicaid-pending dispensations. Documentation of plan identification and handling of Medicaid pending status should be included in the billing P&Ps.

KEY POINT

Have specific guidelines in the P&Ps for proper Medicaid management, regardless of Medicaid carve-in or carve-out status.

CPs are required to carve-out fee for service or traditional Medicaid. Documentation of how the CP will handle Medicaid claims should be in the CP P&Ps. Include a statement in the P&P that defines the process for Managed Medicaid claims for the CP.

POLICY AND PROCEDURE MAINTENANCE

Many 340B-covered entities have a formal and protracted process for P&P review and approval. The 340B environment is always in a state of flux, thus, a more fluid review process may be required. As processes change, P&Ps should be adjusted to reflect the current procedures. Covered entities should be aware that procedural changes that do not match policies can be a red flag to HRSA that the CE is not managing the program appropriately. Make sure that policies reflect current actual practices and are reviewed at least annually to keep pace with 340B program actual practices. P&P upkeep is an important task for proper compliant 340B program management.

KEY POINT

Make sure that policies reflect current actual practices and are reviewed at least annually to keep pace with 340B program actual practices.

Finally, it is incumbent on the 340B Program Oversight Committee and pharmacy leadership to keep up with the latest information provided by HRSA, through 340B University live and on-line, and with active participation in various advocacy groups. Keeping up ensures that the 340B program is compliant, and policies are reflective of current 340B practices.

SUMMARY

P&Ps govern how the 340B program is conducted and should contain the 17 elements recommended by HRSA. Keep P&P accurate and up-to-date. Follow HRSA, 340B Prime Vendor, and other notices as sources of current information. Include a statement in the policies that ensures OPA registration information is accurate. Have a section on definitions that includes the Patient Definition. For applicable covered entities, specifying practices to mitigate the risk of violating the GPO prohibition in P&Ps is a best practice. For applicable covered entities, management of the Orphan Drug Exclusion should be included in the P&Ps that address the limiting definition of covered outpatient drugs. Specify in the P&Ps how purchases for physical inventory, virtual inventory, borrow-loan, and direct purchases will be made. Comprehensive P&Ps for managing a compliant CP network is a best practice. Include a schedule of what will be audited and with what frequency in the self-audit P&Ps. Establishing a well-informed and thoughtfully composed oversight committee with clear duties and responsibilities in the P&Ps is a best practice. Develop specific guidelines to define a material breach in the P&Ps. Have specific guidelines in the P&Ps for proper Medicaid management, regardless of Medicaid carve-in or carve-out status. Above all, make sure that policies reflect current actual practices and are reviewed at least annually to keep pace with 340B program actual practices.

REFERENCES

1.   Health Resources and Services Administration, Office of Pharmacy Affairs, 340B Peer-to-Peer Program, Self-Audit Series: Defining your 340B Drug Operations Environment in Required Policies and Procedures. https://hrsa.connectsolutions.com/p6ca520km6r/. Accessed October 14, 2017.

2. Apexus. 340B Tools. DSH Sample Policy and Procedure Manual. https://docs.340bpvp.com/documents/public/resourcecenter/DSH_PolicyManual.docx. Accessed October 14, 2017.

3. Apexus. 340B Tools. 340B Program Policy and Procedure Self-Audit Tool. https://www.340bpvp.com/education/340b-tools/. Accessed October 14, 2017.

4. Apexus 340B Tools. CHC Sample Policy and Procedure Manual. https://docs.340bpvp.com/documents/public/resourcecenter/CHC_PolicyManual.docx. Accessed October 14, 2017.

5. Cornell University Law School. Legal Information Institute. 42 US Code §256b Limitations of prices of drugs purchased by Covered Entities. https://www.law.cornell.edu/uscode/text/42/256b. Accessed October 14, 2017.

6. Apexus. 340B Tools. https://docs.340bpvp.com/documents/public/resourcecenter/Hospital_Eligibility_Criteria.pdf. October 14, 2017.

7. Health Resources and Services Administration. 340B Drug Pricing Program. https://www.hrsa.gov/opa/eligibility-and-registration/index.html. Accessed October 14, 2017.

8. 340Bpvp. Resource Center. Frequently Asked Questions. https://www.340bpvp.com/resource-center/faqs/patient-definition/. Accessed October 14, 2017.

9. Social Security. Compilation of the Social Security Laws. Payment for Covered Outpatient Drugs. https://www.ssa.gov/OP_Home/ssact/title19/1927.htm. Accessed October 14, 2017.

10. Apexus. FAQ. Consistent application of the limiting definition of a Covered Outpatient Drug. https://www.340bpvp.com/resourceCenter/faqSearch.html?category=content&Ntt=1355. Accessed October 14, 2017.

11. Health Resources and Services Administration. Orphan Drug Exclusion. https://www.hrsa.gov/opa/program-requirements/orphan-drug-exclusion/index.html /. Accessed October 14, 2017.

12. Health Resources and Services Administration. Orphan Drug Exclusion. https://www.hrsa.gov/sites/default/files/hrsa/opa/programrequirements/orphandrugexclusion/orphandruglist092017.xlsx. Accessed October 14, 2017.

13. U.S. Department of Health and Human Services. National Institutes of Health. National Center for Advancing Translational Sciences. Genetic and Rare Disease Information Center. https://rarediseases.info.nih.gov/diseases/fda-orphan-drugs/a. Accessed October 2017.

14. FDA. DSCSA Guidance Documents. http://www.fda.gov/Drugs/DrugSafety/DrugIntegrityandSupplyChainSecurity/DrugSupplyChainSecurityAct/ucm382022.htm. Accessed October 14, 2017.

15. Federal Register. Volume 75, Number 43, Friday March 5, 2010. HRSA Notice regarding 340B Pricing Program - Contract Pharmacies https://www.gpo.gov/fdsys/pkg/FR-2010-03-05/pdf/2010-4755.pdf. Accessed October 14, 2017.

16. Health Resources and Services Administration. Office of Pharmacy Affairs. 340B Database. Change Request. https://www.hrsa.gov/opa/340b-opais/index.html. Accessed October 14, 2017.

17. Health Resources and Services Administration. Office of Pharmacy Affairs. 340B Pricing Program Updates. http://www.hrsa.gov/opa/updates/2016/august.html. Accessed October 14, 2017.

18. Federal Register. Vol 75, No.43. Friday March 5, 2010. Notices. Department of Health and Human Services. Health Resources and Services Administration. Notice Regarding 340B Drug Pricing Program—Contract Pharmacy Services. https://www.gpo.gov/fdsys/pkg/FR-2010-03-05/pdf/2010-4755.pdf. Accessed October 14, 2017.

19. Federal Register. Vol 75, No.43. Friday March 5, 2010. Notices. Department of Health and Human Services. Health Resources and Services Administration. Notice Regarding 340B Drug Pricing Program—Contract Pharmacy Services. C. Contract Pharmacy Service Mechanism (3) (i) https://www.gpo.gov/fdsys/pkg/FR-2010-03-05/pdf/2010-4755.pdf. Accessed October 14, 2017.

20. Health Resources and Services Administration. Office of Pharmacy Affairs. 340B Pricing Program. Contract Pharmacy Oversight. http://www.hrsa.gov/opa/updates/contractpharmacy02052014.html. Accessed October 14, 2017.

21. 340Bpvp. Resources. Documents. Establishing Material Breach Threshold Tool. https://docs.340bpvp.com/documents/public/resourcecenter/Establishing_Material_Breach_Threshold.pdf. Accessed October 14, 2017.

CHAPTER 8

*Kevin A. Scheckelhoff, MBA, RPh and
Heather Easterling, MBA, PharmD*

340B Considerations in Retail and Specialty Pharmacy

BACKGROUND

As the U.S. healthcare system continues to evolve and as care transitions from the inpatient to ambulatory setting, health systems frequently consider operating specialty pharmacy and/or retail pharmacies. Ambulatory pharmacy business lines can create unique opportunities and challenges for 340B-covered entities. When 340B drug pricing can be applied to retail and specialty prescriptions, there is a material financial benefit due to the lower cost of goods sold. However, the 340B program's complex regulatory and guidance structure requires adequate resources to ensure compliance and protect the covered entity's qualification status across the enterprise. Based on the compliance risk associated with 340B, a thoughtful strategy for retail and specialty pharmacy programs should be developed and utilized when implementing these services.

The focus of this chapter is to provide an understanding of 340B in the context of an overall strategy for retail and specialty pharmacy services, to build a patient care and business model that uses 340B appropriately, and to provide a discussion of regulatory considerations and financial reporting.

RETAIL/SPECIALTY STRATEGY AND MISSION

A 340B-covered entity's mission in creating a retail or specialty pharmacy service is typically multi-fold. An ambulatory pharmacy can provide a unique, aligned set of services, leveraging the health system's larger patient care resources; it can also serve as a convenient location for patients and employees to obtain prescriptions. When a covered entity fills its own patients' prescriptions and manages the associated clinical, compliance, and quality activities, the organization gains access to a valuable pool of patient data that provides insights into drug-related quality indicators such as compliance and outcomes. With the cost benefits brought by 340B, an ambulatory pharmacy service line can generate a revenue stream to offset the uncompensated or undercompensated care that the organization provides and extend key pharmacy and patient care services to the uninsured and underinsured. Important considerations for optimizing the 340B program elements, specific to a retail and specialty pharmacy strategy, may include acute care discharge prescriptions and prescriptions generated from 340B-eligible ambulatory clinics of the covered entity.

Employee prescriptions might provide an opportunity in that the covered entity may have some ability (as the drug benefit sponsor) to influence where employees have prescriptions filled. However, to qualify for 340B coverage, an employee prescription must meet the same 340B qualification criteria as any other patient.

An organization's administrative, pharmacy, and compliance leadership team needs to assess the potential for 340B-qualifying prescriptions that will be generated, along with the offsetting non-340B prescriptions, to determine if retail pharmacy services are operationally and financially feasible. Specialty pharmacy services, including prior authorization activities, compliance management and monitoring, medication assistance, and other clinical and patient support services, may help to bring additional prescription volume into the traditional retail pharmacy program. However, the associated additional cost, resources, and expertise required should be evaluated in detail.

PATIENT CARE MODEL DESIGN

Supporting retail and specialty pharmacy services require a team of qualified professional personnel. Beyond the obvious pharmacists and technicians to support the operational aspects of filling and dispensing prescriptions, the endeavor requires prior authorization and medication assistance technicians, business office personnel to handle billing follow-up, auditing personnel for 340B compliance, information systems support, mail order services, and clinical pharmacists to serve as liaisons to the various clinical areas targeted by the specialty pharmacy business.

The hiring and training of prior authorization technicians and medication assistance technicians to help all of the medical center's patients is an important investment. The efforts of these individuals may not always result in a prescription fill generated for the institution. This may be due to being locked out of a pharmacy network by the patient's third-party payer, by a pharmacy benefit manager (PBM), or by a medication supplier. It may also be a patient's choice to take a prescription and related care to another provider. The staff of technicians should support a unified intake and approval process for prescribers so all patients are served at the highest level of care and so that the prescribers can rapidly, reliably, and consistently enroll patients and transition care. In any health-system retail pharmacy model, there is always a subset of patients who cannot or will not have their prescriptions filled at the organization's ambulatory pharmacy.

Specialist pharmacy clinicians and technicians are generally assigned to ambulatory areas, in particular, care areas providing clinical services that have medication-intensive patients. An organization can assess patient care, provider, and claims data to determine the services and clinics generating the highest volumes of specialty medications and evaluate the potential for 340B qualification. A targeted assessment and strategy based in these clinics can create the critical mass required to implement services and the corresponding revenue, which will support growth as the service matures and grows. The role of care area-based clinicians is to monitor patients, plan therapy, and facilitate the necessary resources and authorizations to ensure appropriate patient care success. This team can also support medication therapy compliance programs and resolve logistical, behavioral, cost, and other issues for patients to ensure reliable access to medications.

Specialty pharmacy requires information technology (IT) support to attain the proficient use of the electronic medical records system, pharmacy and medical claims systems, and retail and specialty pharmacy business information systems and automation. Case management software systems can support pharmacy personnel in monitoring side effects, managing recurring refill notices, establishing a mechanism for documenting interventions, and creating reports to demonstrate outcomes associated with specialty drug therapy. An organization entering the specialty pharmacy setting will need to determine whether to build or buy a pharmacy-specific case management system to monitor patients.

As an organization assesses its patient demographics and service model, mail service pharmacy should also be considered. The logistics of mail service pharmacy include developing a partnership with a delivery service, contracting with a mail order supply vendor, and planning for cold chain deliveries and other special handling requirements.

BUSINESS MODEL: CORPORATE STRUCTURE

Many covered entities are a component of a larger, regional health-system corporate structure. Where such a structure exists, the health system has several options to position retail and specialty pharmacy operations. Pharmacies owned by the covered entity and located inside a disproportionate share hospital (DSH), a children's hospital (PED), or freestanding cancer hospital (CAN) physical address or listed as a child site are not-for-profit by definition and subject to current group purchasing organization (GPO) prohibition guidance.[1] Within this structure, prescriptions fall into one of two categories: (1) 340B-eligible based on patient Health Resources and Services Administration (HRSA) definition criteria[2] where drugs purchased at 340B price may be utilized; or (2) 340B-ineligible where drugs must be purchased from a non-GPO wholesaler acquisition cost (WAC) account. The term *WAC account* is an incomplete description of the pricing available to a covered entity subject to the GPO prohibition, as this account may contain 340B prime vendor contracts and individual covered entity contracts along with non-contract WAC pricing. The 340B account may also contain sub-Public Health Service (PHS) prime vendor contracts as well as 340B pricing.

A health system may elect to position one or more pharmacies within a corporate structure that is not tied to the 340B-covered entity. This structure can be for-profit or not-for-profit depending on the organization's preferences. The separate corporate entity can then establish 340B contract pharmacy relationships with covered entities in the health system as well as with non-related covered entities. In this structure, prescriptions fall into one of two categories: (1) shared 340B-eligible prescriptions where revenues, dispensing, and other fees and drug replenishment are processed under a contract pharmacy agreement's terms between the pharmacy and covered entity; or (2) 340B-ineligible prescriptions where drugs are purchased from the retail pharmacy's buying account separate from the 340B relationship. More complex structures require more sophisticated contracting and financial reporting with auditable tracking of the 340B relationship for both parties. When the contract pharmacy model is utilized, the covered entity—not the contract pharmacy—will realize the majority of savings associated with 340B pricing. Associated payroll, drug purchases, and operating expenses should be clearly assigned and reported through the contract pharmacy. Transactions between related parties should be at fair market rates or under terms approved by a health-system compliance officer. Pharmacy ownership and corporate structure decisions should be made with the advice and oversight of the organization's legal counsel and compliance office.

Figure 8-1 represents a health-system structure example: this system is structured with a corporate umbrella that owns a number of corporate entities, including a 340B-eligible covered entity DSH. The system has the option to locate one or more pharmacies within its for-profit business unit (business unit A) or structure pharmacies within the DSH corporation (business unit B). Pharmacy A would have the option to become a contract pharmacy for the DSH should that entity choose to pursue this option. One advantage of this model is that the for-profit organization can utilize unique pharmacist and technician job descriptions as well as compensation guidelines and staffing models appropriate for the service line and not be forced to utilize hospital benchmarks.

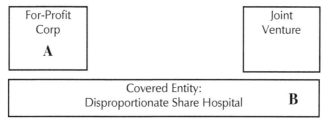

Umbrella Health System Corporation

| For-Profit Corp **A** | | Joint Venture |

| Covered Entity: Disproportionate Share Hospital   **B** |

FIGURE 8-1. Corporate Structure Examples

BUSINESS MODEL: ORGANIZATIONAL STRUCTURE

As previously discussed, retail and specialty pharmacy services require infrastructure and resources. Most of the personnel—the business office (as the organization determines), the 340B program staff, and pharmacy personnel—will likely be the responsibility of the pharmacy department. To ensure program integrity, internal and external auditors reporting outside of the pharmacy team are important members of the overall 340B team.

When a covered entity owns a retail/specialty pharmacy or contracts for pharmacy services, there are additional 340B program compliance risks. Having the support and involvement of corporate officers and administrators is important; a constructive way to obtain that support is to incorporate those leaders into a 340B steering committee. Potential 340B committee participants might include the following:

- 340B program manager
- Ambulatory pharmacy manager
- Chief compliance officer
- Chief financial officer
- Chief strategy officer
- Director of pharmacy services
- General counsel
- Pharmacy business manager
- Reimbursement specialist
- Representative from the internal audit team
- Representative from patient accounting
- Representative from information systems

BUSINESS PLANNING FOR NEW OR EXPANDING RETAIL/ SPECIALTY PHARMACY SERVICES

Thoughtful business planning is a key success factor when creating new retail or specialty service lines and can also be applied to the expansion of existing programs. Because the retail pharmacy is rarely a core competency of a health system, the planning process can facilitate discussion and establish reasonable expectations across the organization. Key elements of a retail pharmacy financial forecast are listed in **Table 8-1**.

KEY POINT

Effective business planning can facilitate the assessment of business risk when opening or expanding non-core competency services such as retail pharmacy.

Net Revenue

Retail pharmacy often allows the immediate identification of net revenue when a prescription is paid for in cash or is adjudicated electronically with a third-party payer. However, one must take into account that adjudicated prescriptions can be reversed and payment amounts adjusted after the fact. Third-party payments should be reconciled against prescription sales transactions to vali-

Table 8-1. Financial Forecast Elements

Net revenue
- Prescription mix
- Payer mix
- Volume estimates

Staffing/labor costs
- Prescription fulfillment
- Clinical oversight
- Patient communications
- Delivery programs
- 340B quality and compliance
- Revenue cycle

Operating expenses
- Shipping
- Rent
- Accreditation
- Fees
- Utilities
- Insurance

Cost of goods sold
- 340B eligible sales
- 340B non-eligible sales

Infrastructure requirements
- Floor space
- Information systems and other capital assets
- Construction/renovation costs

date that full payment was actually received and, if not, what additional information or action item is required to obtain the balance due under the provider agreement.

Specialty prescriptions dispensed to patients are typically covered by a prescription benefit. In some circumstances (i.e., an injectable or infusion drug), a specialty drug may be covered by a patient's medical benefit; such a plan may require a claims submission process as opposed to adjudication. Prior authorization submissions or telephone contacts are frequently required to verify insurance coverage at the initiation of specialty therapy. Medical claim-based prescriptions usually result in the creation of gross and net revenue values depending on the contracted or negotiated rate of reimbursement with the third-party payer. The net revenue forecast can be developed by using a conservative estimate of the pharmacy's capture rate for outpatient prescriptions generated within the health system.

A best-case scenario is when the health system utilizes the electronic medical record (EMR) to generate e-prescriptions as well as printed prescriptions that are provided to patients as a hard copy (i.e., there is minimal or no use of hand-written prescriptions). A 6- or 12-month history can be extracted from such an EMR system to detail:

1. Prescription count and capture rate by location by prescriber
2. Prescription drug product mix
3. Payer mix by type
4. Patient-designated pharmacy location for e-prescriptions
5. 340B eligibility

KEY POINT

Electronic medical record data can provide detailed insights into the number and type of prescriptions generated by a health system.

Utilizing Encounter Data

Where comprehensive EMR prescription detail is not available, an alternate method to determine total prescription potential utilizes encounter data from the health system's outpatient clinics and discharge statistics for emergency department(s) and hospital inpatients. These reports can provide an indication of the number of patients in (or returning to) the home environment as well as this population's payer mix.

Prescription mix can be estimated by evaluating utilization data from various sources: e-prescribing systems often allow generic product identifier (GPI) level data analysis as do some EMR medication reconciliation documentation systems. Other sources of prescription data include employee drug utilization histories obtained from the health system's PBM (if self-insured) and contract pharmacy 340B prescription transaction files. These utilization histories can provide insights into local prescribing patterns, reimbursement rates, and health system-specific prescribing (matching prescribing physicians with health-system affiliated physicians). If the covered entity is engaged in a 340B contract pharmacy relationship, shared transactions reported from the 340B software or program administrator are particularly valuable because they are covered entity-specific and provide insights into the 340B eligible/ineligible ratio, market reimbursement rates, and prescription mix at the national drug code (NDC) level.

The utilization and EMR data can be used to develop average revenue per prescription estimates by site of care. Organizing by location also facilitates estimating 340B eligibility percentages and prescription category impact. Emergency department and urgent care prescriptions are predominantly generic drugs prescribed for a limited time with minimal or no refills. Acute care discharges tend to include branded drugs and refills as a function of patient acuity and chronic disease diagnosis. Traditional ambulatory clinics are similar to acute discharges with the addition of some specialty drugs. Designated specialty clinics (e.g., oncology, hepatology) are frequently the primary source of specialty prescriptions and generate brand and generic prescriptions as well. **Exhibit 8-1** shows an example of a retail/specialty financial forecast template.

Medicaid Assumptions

The covered entity will be required to commit to utilizing 340B-purchased drugs on qualified Medicaid prescriptions (carve-in) or not (carve-out). This decision is usually a function of the Medicaid reimbursement structure in the one or more states where the covered entity provides services and the Medicaid payer and service mix of the entity. Some states may require carve-in status. A covered entity may have more than one carve-in/carve-out election; see Chapter 4 for a detailed description. The resulting Medicaid reimbursement and percentages should be included in the forecast as a separate item given the unique nature of this revenue.

Contractual Relationships

To be able to fill and be paid for third-party reimbursed prescriptions, the pharmacy must have a contractual relationship with each payer. That relationship can be in the form of an individual contract or through participation in a network. The latter is most often accessed by contracting with a pharmacy service administrative organization (PSAO). For a fee, the PSAO will provide access to a network made up of dozens of payers. This arrangement provides convenience and efficiency versus self-contracting. The pharmacy gives up the ability to negotiate specific terms but gains advantages from the scale and coverage of the PSAO network. Some payers look to identify

EXHIBIT 8-1. Retail/Specialty Forecast Template Example

	6-Month Count	Annual Count	Rxs per Encounter	Total Rxs	Never Fill Percent	Net New Rxs	Capture Percent	Total Rx Capture
Encounters								
Emergency Dept								
Urgent Care								
Main St Clinic								
Tower Clinic								
Discharges								
Hospital								
Behavioral Health								

	Total Rx Capture	Medicaid Percent	340B Eligible %	Insurance Rev/Rx	Medicaid Rev/Rx	Insurance Revenue	Medicaid Revenue	Total Revenue
Encounters								
Emergency Dept								
Urgent Care								
Main St Clinic								
Tower Clinic								
Discharges								
Hospital								
Behavioral Health								

	Total Rx Capture	Medicaid Percent	340B Eligible %	Insurance COGS/Rx	Medicaid COGS/Rx	Insurance COGS	Medicaid COGS	Total COGS
Encounters								
Emergency Dept								
Urgent Care								
Main St Clinic								
Tower Clinic								
Discharges								
Hospital								
Behavioral Health								

new network members (whether contracting individually or through a network) that are owned by a 340B-covered entity and have access to preferential pricing. These pharmacies may be offered rates of reimbursement that are lower than non-covered entities, so the covered entity will need to evaluate the impact of the proposed rates given the pharmacy's specific circumstances (340B eligibility rate and volume of discounted prescriptions).

A number of payer agreements include direct and indirect remuneration (DIR) fees that involve adjustments to payments substantially after a prescription has been adjudicated (making direct reconciliation difficult). These fees are discussed in the Operating Expenses section of this chapter.

Payers *can* and *do* limit the specific drugs that are covered in an agreement. Traditional drugs are typically included in standard agreements, while drugs classified as "specialty" by the payer may be held out as a separate addendum or managed via a separate, narrow network. The payer may or may not disclose all the criteria used for selecting narrow network providers and is not required to contract with any willing provider.

Staffing Considerations

Health-system owned retail pharmacies may elect to offer patient care services that go well beyond prescription dispensing and basic patient monitoring. The health system is typically motivated to leverage prescription services to improve patient compliance, improve outcomes, and reduce the likelihood of hospital readmission. Convenience services such as bedside delivery and enhanced drug counseling and follow-up communications can also improve patient satisfaction scores. These concierge services require materially higher staffing levels than typical "prescriptions dispensed per labor-hour" formulas predict. It is essential to include these additional staffing costs in the planning process so that they are incorporated into the operations budget should the proposed project be approved.

Health-system retail pharmacy leaders/managers should not assume that the hospital business office will provide effective revenue cycle support at little or no cost. Retail/specialty pharmacy billing, collections, and payment reconciliation are substantially different from traditional hospital and clinic services. High performance revenue cycle management for this service line frequently requires a dedicated team utilizing retail pharmacy-centric software. Such a team can report to finance or pharmacy based on the organization's preference, but the key is that the staffing model utilized in the forecast is adequate in both skill and headcount to meet ongoing service and reporting needs.

KEY POINT

Retail/specialty operations require employees with retail service line expertise to be highly effective.

Staffing for 340B program maintenance and compliance should also be considered in developing a staffing model. Retail and specialty prescriptions should be audited on a regular basis to validate that the qualification process is performing to expectation. Prescription audits should include validation of each prescription in the sample by viewing the same audit trail utilized in a HRSA audit (i.e., the necessary EMR fields and e-prescription or hard copy prescription). Internal and external auditing plans are discussed in a later section of this chapter.

Operating Expenses

Although the two primary expenses in retail and specialty pharmacy are clearly the cost of drugs and labor, other expenses should be monitored and managed. For example, DIR fees are becoming increasing common in payer contracts. The term *DIR* was initially used when describing Medicare Part D plans but has come to describe a variety of fees and reimbursement adjustments between pharmacies and health plans/PBMs. These fees are typically defined in the payer agreement but are often difficult to track given the number of contracts a pharmacy may have at any time. DIR fees are often reconciliations of certain targets (i.e., brand versus generic) or quality measures and are applied after dispensing has occurred and the target measured. A primary concern associated with these fees is that they may be levied at the end of a term (e.g., quarterly or even annually). It can be challenging to tie the fees back to specific prescription transactions as the notification/invoice may not include prescription-specific detail. DIR fees are often categorized as an operating expense, but it may be argued that it is advantageous to treat them as a form of payer-specific contractual allowances to facilitate revenue and profitability analysis of the individual payer agreements. An ongoing assessment of the payer mix and prevailing contract terms is an essential component of the planning process.

Cost of Goods Sold

There is a substantial difference in this expense category when comparing 340B-covered entity-owned pharmacies with pharmacies outside the 340B program. The complexity of PHS and prime vendor discounts, combined with GPO prohibition guidance, make this an area that should be understood and evaluated in detail as part of a retail/specialty forecast as well as ongoing operations. Retail pharmacies subject to the GPO prohibition should give careful consideration to positioning as a *closed* pharmacy (entity patients only) versus *open* pharmacy model. In addition to the cost premium of purchasing medications at the WAC price for patients that are not 340B-eligible, payers may consider the pharmacy's open or closed status as part of the network entry criteria or payment schedule.

The three broad categories of prescriptions processed by retail/specialty pharmacies are generics, brand, and specialty. The first two categories are self-explanatory, while the specialty category requires additional consideration. There is no single definition of what constitutes a specialty drug in the healthcare industry. An early definition[3] of "specialty drug" was based on a set of specific characteristics. A drug with five or more of the attributes listed below was considered a "specialty" product:

- Used to treat complex, chronic conditions.
- Prescribed by a physician specialist.
- Is generally not taken orally (exceptions: hepatitis C, oral chemo, HIV).
- Requires special handling (i.e., cold chain).
- Has unique distribution model (narrow networks, direct ship).
- Has high cost per treatment.
- Requires extensive patient training/follow-up.
- May require patient reimbursement assistance.

Most health plans and PBMs create unique specialty drug lists to define specialty items in an agreement. The drugs included in these lists vary between different plans and PBMs. 340B contract pharmacy agreements also often utilize a list to define what items are to be considered specialty (as dispensing fees often differ between specialty and traditional prescriptions).

KEY POINT

There is no universally accepted definition of a specialty drug. Contracts may define specialty items through the inclusion of a drug list based on user criteria.

Observed average revenue associated with a 30-day supply prescriptions in the three categories differed substantially: *generics* can range from $10 to $30, *branded drugs* are $200 to $300, and *specialty products* can be $600 to $3,500 or substantially higher.[4] These wide ranges require that consideration be given to prescription mix when evaluating prescription volume statistics and gross margin (revenue minus cost of drug) calculations. Cost of goods is also impacted by the class of trade associated with each prescription (**Table 8-2**).

Table 8-2. Prescription Category by Class of Trade

	Generic	Brand	Specialty
CAN, DSH, PED	WAC*	WAC*	WAC*
	PHS*	PSH*	PHS*
CAH, FQHC, RRC	GPO	GPO	GPO
	PHS*	PHS*	PHS*
Non-340B	WAC	WAC	WAC
	GPO	GPO	GPO

*May include prime vendor contracts if covered entity elects to enroll.

CAH: critical access hospital, CAN: freestanding cancer hospital, DSH: disproportionate share hospital, FQHC: federally qualified health clinic, PED: children's hospital, RRC: rural referral center

KEY POINT

The retail market has extremely wide ranges of cost and revenue per prescription, making the monitoring of prescription mix increasingly important.

Retail pharmacies owned by DSHs, PEDs, and CANs are typically limited to the use of WAC and PHS accounts due to the GPO prohibition. The covered entity should enroll with the 340B prime vendor program to access additional sub-PHS and sub-WAC contracts. The covered entity also has the ability to negotiate site-specific purchasing contracts. Covered entities can opt to operate an owned pharmacy outside of the 340B program if the pharmacy meets the following four criteria:

1. It is located at a different physical address than the covered entity.
2. The site is not listed on the Office of Pharmacy Affairs (OPA) web site.
3. It maintains a separate (non-PHS) purchasing account with a wholesaler.
4. The pharmacy does not transfer drugs to covered entity locations listed on the OPA web site.[1]

KEY POINT

A covered entity has the option of operating a retail pharmacy location outside of the 340B program if key conditions are met.

Most entities elect to utilize the PHS and WAC classes of trade combined with 340B prime vendor contracts. PHS pricing can be utilized for all prescription categories that meet the qualification criteria, and WAC pricing is to be used for all prescriptions that do not qualify (or where qualification cannot be clearly determined). Prime vendor pricing is negotiated; PHS pricing is calculated. Consequently, no meaningful *average PHS discount* percentage can be applied to all retail pharmacy situations; every situation is a function of prescription mix. PHS discounts range from 13.5% to 99.99%, but they only apply to drugs that are included in the 340B program. 340B prime vendor contracts extend more broadly and include some non-drug items.

The concept of PHS savings and WAC premium offset is important in retail planning and operations. 340B discounts increase gross margin and ultimately net margins. These gains are offset by any premiums associated with WAC purchases (premium being defined as difference between WAC and GPO prices for same item and quantity). The relative size of the savings/premium is a function of the prescription mix (specific NDCs dispensed) and the ratio of 340B-eligible to 340B-ineligible sales.

Exhibit 8-2 shows two example scenarios to demonstrate the potential impact eligible/ineligible mix and provides two insights:

1. *The importance of proper patient qualification.* There can be a material gross margin loss when a qualified prescription is missed in the screening process (i.e., it is determined to be "non-340B" in error). There is also a material compliance risk if a non-340B prescription is incorrectly qualified as "340B eligible." The impact on gross margin is highly dependent on the drug product. A specialty prescription could have a $2,000 cost of goods swing between a 340B eligible and a 340B non-eligible purchase; a generic prescription may have no price difference at all.

2. *Where WAC expenditures exist, it is advantageous for the entity to utilize the prime vendor program to minimize unnecessary WAC premium exposure.* As the sole group contract portfolio available to covered entities subject to the GPO prohibition, the 340B prime vendor program has no cost and substantial upside potential. Covered entity retail pharmacies can also target key WAC items and negotiate independent agreements where size and scale of a drug product or supply item warrant.

EXHIBIT 8-2. Cost of Goods, Example Scenarios

Scenario A: High % eligible

340B-Eligible Rxs		**340B-Ineligible Rxs**	
GPO reference cost	$200,000	GPO reference cost	$25,000
PHS cost	$100,000	WAC cost	$29,000
340B savings	$100,000	WAC premium	$4,000

Net Cost of Goods vs. GPO = $96,000 gross margin improvement

Scenario B: High % ineligible

340B-Eligible Rxs		**340B-Ineligible Rxs**	
GPO reference cost	$25,000	GPO reference cost	$200,000
PHS cost	$12,000	WAC cost	$225,000
340B savings	$13,000	WAC premium	$25,000

Net Cost of Goods vs. GPO = $12,000 gross margin decline

KEY POINT

Participation in the 340B prime vendor program can significantly reduce the amount of WAC premium experienced in a mixed-use retail environment.

Not all drugs can be purchased by a covered entity at 340B prices or, in some instances, at any price. There are a number of specialty drugs where the manufacturer utilizes *narrow networks* for drug distribution. These networks are allowed as long as no discrimination exists against covered entities.[5] The limited number of specialty drugs that use closed networks may prevent access to 100% of drugs on the market but does not prevent a covered entity from providing specialty services. The business planning process should include identifying the products with closed/limited distribution networks and either excluding those drugs from the forecast or modeling access via a potential contract pharmacy arrangement (where such opportunities exist).

KEY POINT

Some specialty drugs may not be accessible by the health-system retail pharmacy because of manufacturer-defined distribution options.

Forecasting gross margin can be accomplished by estimating approximate volumes by category and class of trade. The cost of goods and subsequent gross margin calculations should mirror the revenue forecast but also include an estimate of the prescriptions that will be 340B eligible or ineligible so that the cost of goods can be adjusted accordingly.

Infrastructure Requirements

Determining capital requirements is particularly important as expenditures typically require a project to be subject to the organization's budgeting process. A pharmacy should have adequate equipment and technology to facilitate efficient, compliant, and safe patient care. Pharmacies that will depend on walk-up prescriptions typically need to be in locations on or near high traffic areas such as a lobby, waiting area, or main hallway. Managing front-end, over-the-counter products may present challenges for a health-system pharmacy. It can be advantageous to locate these pharmacies near other retail locations in the health system. Locations suitable for retail pharmacies are also typically valued by other health-system departments and have the potential to be leased to third-party retail entities (e.g., contract pharmacy). As such, these sites have an inherent opportunity cost that should be considered when evaluating the pharmacy income statement even though a rent charge may not be allocated to the covered entity-owned pharmacy.

Information systems are critical to efficient and effective operations. Pharmacy and 340B software systems should be evaluated to consider an adequate number of work stations, sufficient functionality (i.e., retail revenue cycle management, financial reporting), and any necessary interfaces with health-system technology. When there is the potential for multiple retail locations within the system, the pharmacy technology solution should facilitate standardization, sharing of patient data between locations, and centralized "back office" services such as billing and accounts receivable management. The pharmacy may also require separate 340B software to qualify prescriptions as well as facilitate purchasing and inventory tracking and case management software to monitor specialty pharmacy patients. Integrating retail pharmacy systems and 340B qualification software with health-system e-prescribing systems is highly advantageous where e-prescribing utilization rates are high (>75%) and prescriber location data can be captured in the electronic transaction (to facilitate the 340B qualification process).

LEGAL AND REGULATORY CONSIDERATIONS

340B Program Compliance

All 340B-covered entities are subject to audit by HRSA; as such, they should develop and maintain a comprehensive self-audit plan to manage compliance. A common approach to compliance plan development is to essentially reverse engineer the HRSA audit process by utilizing checklists and reminders that apply to each area of 340B use. **Tables 8-3** and **8-4** illustrate examples of suggested audit areas and tests (facility and pharmacy-specific). The 340B prime vendor also provides sample templates and other useful resources related to audit preparedness.[2] Implementing an audit plan requires adequate staffing resources and effective communications across the internal team responsible for 340B program compliance. The accurate 340B qualification of retail prescriptions has been particularly challenging for many covered entities; this has been especially true for entities with large contract pharmacy networks. Audit activities should be designed to match the scale and complexity of the network and must be continually monitored as electronic data feeds, which are frequently used to assist with the qualification process and may change over time.

Specialty Drug Self-Referral

It is common for specialty prescriptions to be provided from remote, closed pharmacy locations as opposed to a retail storefront. Therefore, the access to a specialty pharmacy frequently originates from a referral by the prescriber or another member of the health-system care team. Many health systems utilize pharmacists to process specialty prior authorization documentation and coordinate specialty pharmacy services given the pharmacist's therapy expertise. Most patients new to specialty drug therapy will not be familiar with the specialty pharmacy market dynamic and will likely ask covered entity personnel for guidance (with the unspoken expectation that the guidance will be unbiased). Specialty drug regimens can ultimately cost $100,000 or more with a substantial patient co-pay responsibility, giving the patient a vested interest in the pharmacy provider decision. If the covered entity owns or has a financial interest in a specialty pharmacy that a patient may be referred to, the health-system's legal counsel and compliance office should make certain that the

Table 8-3. Facility Audit Tests

Test	Description	Data Source
Date of service	Determine if the medications given were administered while the patient was registered as an outpatient.	Patient accounting system Third-party administrator
Hospital-owned pharmacies	Determine if prescriptions filled in a hospital-owned pharmacy were generated in a 340B-eligible location, by an eligible provider, and for an eligible patient.	Hospital information system
Medicaid billing compliance	Ensure appropriate 340B Medicaid billing practices are being utilized.	State Medicaid program
Contract pharmacies	Determine if prescriptions filled in a contract pharmacy were generated in a 340B-eligible location, by an eligible provider, and for an eligible patient.	Third-party administrator or contract pharmacy-specific program

Source: Easterling H, Mills J, Allen N. Developing a 340B self-audit plan. *Pharmacy Purchasing and Products.* 2016;13(7):12-16. Reprinted with permission.

Table 8-4. Pharmacy-Specific Audit Tests

Test	Description	Data Source
Accumulations	Ensure purchasing and dispensing occurred in appropriate quantities	Third-party administrator Hospital information system
Adjustment notes	Ensure adjustments within the accumulator are accurate	Third-party administrator Hospital information system
Distributor	Ensure accuracy of contract pricing	Distributor
OPA database	Ensure accuracy of information in the OPA database	OPA database Hospital Medicare Cost Report
Private label purchases	Ensure all private label purchases followed the GPO provision	Distributor
340B percentage	Compare 340B purchases made versus total purchases	Distributor
Contract pharmacy	Review replenishment discrepancies	Contract pharmacy contacts

Source: Easterling H, Mills J, Allen N. Developing a 340B self-audit plan. *Pharmacy Purchasing and Products.* 2016;13(7):12-16. Reprinted with permission.

specialty pharmacy referral process is consistent with the system's self-referral policy and applicable regulations. Self-referral policies may include language related to:

- Reminding patient that he or she has right to choose a provider (within the constraints of the patient's health plan).
- Providing patients with a list of available specialty pharmacy providers.
- Having covered entity personnel disclose which providers on the list have a relationship with the covered entity.
- Educating covered entity personnel to not provide biased information about competitors (but may share attributes/advantages of the owned or partner specialty pharmacy).
- Not automatically referring patients without a current specialty provider to the covered entity pharmacy.
- Having patients sign a document that verifies choice was offered, options explained, and what provider was selected by the patient or caregiver.

BUSINESS INFRASTRUCTURE

Revenue Cycle

The revenue cycle associated with retail pharmacy is markedly different from that of a hospital or health system. Prescriptions are typically paid for in cash (or cash equivalent) at time of sale, real-time adjudicated with a third-party payer, or a combination of the two (i.e., cash co-pay with the balance paid by the third-party payer). The number of transactions is high, and the value of most transactions is relatively low when compared to hospital inpatient charges. These differences make it very difficult for a health-system business office to absorb the management of retail pharmacy billing and collections while maintaining high collection rates. The narrow margins associated with a retail pharmacy require close financial control and accurate and timely reporting to be successful. This is often best accomplished by managing the retail revenue cycle through software designed for that purpose along with an adequately trained, dedicated staff.

Organizations that have multiple retail and/or specialty locations should utilize standardized reporting methods and look to leverage economies of scale where practical.

KEY POINT

Retail/specialty pharmacy revenue cycle differs substantially from a hospital's revenue cycle and must be treated accordingly.

Financial Reporting: Monthly Income Statement/ Responsibility Report

Health-system-based retail pharmacy can be considered similar to independent retail small chains and should mimic that segment's performance standards where possible. The goal is to have timely and reliable financial reporting with enough granularity that the management team can gain insights into cause and effect of market and program changes. As a covered entity, it is also highly desirable to understand the impact of the 340B program on monthly performance.

Maintaining a granular monthly income statement allows for some level of comparison with independent community pharmacy benchmarks and trends. The National Community Pharmacy Association (NCPA) publishes a financial metrics report based on operating data volunteered by association members. Although these metrics do not correlate perfectly with a covered entity-owned or contracted pharmacy, the market insights can provide valuable comparisons for both pharmacy and hospital administration. Suggested income statement elements are shown in **Table 8-5**. Utilizing detailed financials reduces the likelihood of failure to recognize inefficiency or lagging reimbursement in the face of acceptable net earnings, resulting from 340B cost of goods impact. Reviewing individual performance elements facilitates optimization.

If a health-system-owned pharmacy is serving as a contract pharmacy, it will be necessary to identify and monitor the revenue disbursements and dispensing/administrative fee income associated with those agreements. These elements should be incorporated into the monthly income statements. The cost of goods correlated with contract pharmacy 340B replenishments will appear on the income statement of the covered entity, not the contract pharmacy.

KEY POINT

Granular financial reporting is an important tool in managing retail/specialty operations given the ever changing retail environment.

The retail pharmacy's software should be configured to track the financial performance of individual drug plans so that quarterly or annual financial impact can be reviewed. Many plans utilize a maximum allowable charge (MAC) price list for generic drugs that can lead to some prescriptions having little or even negative margins. This, combined with the previously mentioned DIR fees, has the potential to result in a net loss after considering the cost to dispense.

Health-system-owned retail pharmacies can benefit by regularly evaluating the *cost-to-dispense metric* (i.e., total operating expenses divided by total number of processed prescriptions).

Table 8-5. Retail/Specialty Income Statement

Gross Rx revenues

Contractual allowances

Net Rx revenues

Cost of goods sold

Gross margin

Salaries

Payroll taxes and benefits

Total wage expense

Operating expenses:

- Pharmacy information systems
- Service fees
- Insurance
- Supplies
- Shipping
- Rent
- Utilities
- All other

Total operating expenses

Net before depreciation

The cost to dispense for health-system retail pharmacies can be notably higher than the independent chain counterparts. This difference can be caused by a variety of contributing factors such as:

- The health system's compensation, benefits, and staffing requirements may differ with area retail metrics given the difference in business models. If the health system's compensation and benefits are higher, it can result in paying retail employees more than required; if the compensation is lower, it can result in difficulty in procuring the necessary talent pool.

- The health system may utilize a service model that provides services beyond basic prescriptions' dispensing such as bedside delivery and counseling, free shipping to patient home, follow-up phone calls and consultation, pharmacist clinic support, and education activities. These services often provide value but usually do not result in additional revenue per prescriptions.

- The information systems and automation may not be state-of-the-art or fully optimized. Chains utilize standardized IT solutions and configurations that facilitate communication and ease of use. Purchasing and inventories are carefully monitored, and products are often moved between locations for efficiency.

- Large and small chains centralize many back-office functions, especially related to revenue cycle, to gain economies of scale and optimize oversight and control. The revenue cycle rarely receives the same level of attention within a health system.

- Health-system retail locations are often forced to work with less than optimal square footage given the premium on floor space inside the health system. Cramped workspace can lead to lower productivity and prolonged wait times.

- The health-system customer base will likely have a disproportionately large number of one-time patients (i.e., hospital and emergency discharges) who require a complete information system set-up process for a single dispensing event.

- Uneven demand and unique customer turnaround expectations are common. Hospital discharges occur throughout the day but can have peak times such as mid- to late-morning.

The patient and caregivers often are anxious to depart the hospital once the discharge orders are finalized; if discharge prescriptions have not already been provided, there is probably a finite wait time that will be acceptable (and that wait time can be materially less than what the patient would expect from a traditional chain pharmacy). If discharge prescriptions are a target area, a health system may need to invest in robotics or have variable staffing levels to deal with peak demand. These enhanced service levels often result in a premium cost to dispense.

KEY POINT

Health system-based retail operations frequently face a cost to dispense per prescription that is higher than that of a community retail pharmacy.

Financial Reporting: 340B-Related Retail Metrics

Several 340B-related metrics can be calculated each month to monitor the impact of the program. 340B purchases can be repriced, utilizing the standard retail class of trade drug pricing catalog to estimate 340B savings. WAC purchases can be repriced in the same manner to calculate any premium paid in the month. WAC expenditures are only a concern in the instances where it results in a higher cost of goods, which is not true for all transactions. The net of these two values can be viewed as the *gross program benefit* for those transactions. Understanding the operational costs specifically associated with the 340B program is valuable, such as the transaction fees and infrastructure that are part of qualification, auditing, and reporting. Deducting those costs provide a meaningful estimate of the *net program benefit*, which provides the organization with a sense of what financial impact would be realized if the entity lost program eligibility (see **Exhibit 8-3**).

The net program benefit of a related-party contract pharmacy is the same as a non-related party:

revenue proceeds – replenishment cost of goods – 340B-related fees and expenses

Each covered entity should have policies and procedures that define how and when prescriptions are provided to patients with no ability to pay or a limited ability to pay. It is important to clearly track medication provided free or at a discount and not combine the associated revenue offset with bad debt. *Bad debt* is typically a loss of revenue that should have been realized and, subsequently, should be actively managed in an attempt to minimize or eliminate. Charity care should be a component of the regular financial report. A list of meaningful retail/specialty performance metrics are shown in **Table 8-6.**

An organization may also find it helpful to track specific prescribers' patterns through its information system to enhance capture of specialty and retail pharmacy prescriptions. Communication through direct means or surveys with these providers can uncover barriers for these providers and the associated patients. Data-based communication with organizational leadership may help support additional services to address barriers perceived by providers with low capture rates.

EXHIBIT 8-3. 340B Program Benefit Calculations: Owned Pharmacy

340B transactions priced at retail – 340B transactions = 340B savings

WAC transactions – WAC transactions priced at retail = WAC premium

340B savings – WAC premium = gross program savings

Gross program savings – 340B-related fees/expenses = *net program savings*

Table 8-6. 340B-Related Metrics

340B savings

WAC premium

340B-related expenses

Net program benefit

Free/subsidized care

340B revenue

340B cost of goods

340B gross margin

340B prescription qualification rate

Reversals, credit/rebill

SUMMARY

Retail/specialty pharmacy is often not a core competency of a health system. Meaningful business planning in advance of opening or expanding retail operations can facilitate the identification of potential opportunities/benefits, reduce business risk, and enhance realistic operating expectations. Health-system-owned retail programs can create unique value from the development of patient-centric services and access to treatment and outcomes data.

340B can play a vital role in such a service line. It is essential to have adequate systems, staffing, and policies in place to maintain 340B program compliance and integrity across the enterprise. Retail-centric infrastructure can provide the means to meet the health system's patient prescription service demand. The complexities associated with such operations require adequate financial reporting to manage the business and to address changes in the environment. The ongoing monitoring of prescription mix, revenue, and operating expenses allow a retail/specialty management team to benchmark performance metrics and maintain service line oversight over time.

REFERENCES

1. 340B Drug Pricing Program Notice Release No. 2013-1 Statutory Prohibition on Group Purchasing Organization Participation. http://www.hrsa.gov/opa/programrequirements/policyreleases/prohibition-ongpoparticipation020713.pdf. February 7, 2013; accessed October 14, 2017.

2. 340B Prime Vendor Program web site. https://docs.340bpvp.com/documents/public/resourcecenter/DSH-Self-Audit-Prevention-of-Diversion-and-GPO-Prohibition.docx. June 14, 2016; accessed October 14, 2017.

3. Sauerwald P. Changing the Channel: Developments in US specialty pharmacy distribution. Pharmaceutical Commerce web site. http://pharmaceuticalcommerce.com/business-and-finance/changing-the-channel-developments-in-us-specialty-pharmaceutical-distribution/. October 10, 2009; accessed October 14, 2017.

4. Fein AJ. *The 2016 economic report on retail, mail, and specialty pharmacies.* Pembroke Consulting and Drug Channels Institute; January 2016:4.

5. 340B Drug Pricing Program Notice Release No. 2011-1.1 Clarification of Non-Discrimination Policy. http://www.hrsa.gov/opa/programrequirements/policyreleases/nondiscrimination05232012.pdf. May 23, 2012; accessed October 14, 2017.

CHAPTER 9

Julie Houston, CPhT and
Andrew L. Wilson, PharmD, FASHP

Business and Supply Chain Considerations in 340B Contract Pharmacy

Covered entities have various ways to provide ongoing pharmaceutical care to their patients. In addition to in-house dispensing by pharmacies or by providers, 340B-covered entities can also engage existing pharmacy resources in their community through a contract pharmacy relationship. A 340B contract pharmacy relationship is an arrangement in which the covered entity owns drugs; purchases drugs; pays (or arranges for patients to pay) dispensing fees to one or more contract pharmacies; and contracts with pharmacy to provide pharmacy services.[1]

DEVELOPING A CONTRACT PHARMACY RELATIONSHIP

As in any relationship, understanding the details of the connection and shared responsibilities is the key to success. The 340B program is often misunderstood as a program whose sole purpose is to provide prescription medications at a discount to underinsured or uninsured patients. Thinking of 340B in this singular way can be limiting for contract pharmacies in particular, as they may not assess the full potential impact to their patient relationships, provider and community relationships, and business by "reaching more eligible patients and providing more comprehensive services"[2] through 340B.

The Health Resources and Services Administration (HRSA) has published a detailed outline of 340B compliance-related guidelines for contract pharmacies in the *Federal Register*.[3] A covered entity that uses contract pharmacies has full responsibility and accountability for the compliance of those pharmacies with all requirements of the 340B program, including the prevention of both diversion and duplicate discounts. The HRSA Office of Pharmacy Affairs (OPA) provides regular guidance through the updates to participants and through the 340B prime vendor frequently asked questions (FAQs) posted on the 340B prime vendor web site (https://www.340bpvp.com/controller.html) and Apexus Answers.[4,5] Resources also include a tool to assess compliance considerations in a contract pharmacy arrangement.[6]

KEY POINT

A covered entity that uses contract pharmacies has full responsibility and accountability for the compliance of those pharmacies with all requirements of the 340B program. Use HRSA, 340B prime vendor, and other tools and resources to manage risk.

Participation in a 340B contract pharmacy relationship can be more complex than solely passing on savings to an uninsured qualified patient. Additional patient care support activities including medication compliance and continuity, patient education, and other community-based clinical and patient care programs are a key opportunity in aligning with a safety net provider. Providing discounts on prescriptions is only one of the many ways that safety net providers utilize the 340B program to help provide care to the members of their community. Although outside the scope of this chapter, covered entities and their potential contract pharmacy partners are well-advised to consider innovative services under the auspices of a developing 340B contract pharmacy relationship.

Contract pharmacy relationships are an often misunderstood and criticized component of the 340B program.[7] A 2014 Health and Human Services Office of the Inspector General (HHS OIG) report found that these arrangements created complexities in preventing duplicate discounts and the diversion of 340B drugs to ineligible patients. The report also noted that 340B program participants did not undertake recommended oversight activities.[8] This gap in compliance and oversight activities has also been reflected in HRSA 340B program integrity audit results, where contract pharmacy findings are among the most common citations.[9] All participants in 340B contract pharmacy arrangements would be well-advised to familiarize themselves with current relevant guidance and to engage in quality review and other self-audit activities.

KEY POINT

Familiarity with current HRSA contract pharmacy guidance supported by self-audits, external audits, and HRSA-recommended oversight activities is a best practice.

In the simplest form of 340B contract pharmacy, a 340B-covered entity and a retail pharmacy enter into a relationship where the pharmacy agrees to dispense prescriptions to patients of the covered entity, and the entity supplies 340B-purchased medications and pays the pharmacy a negotiated dispensing fee.

The operational components of the relationship require focus, attention to detail, and some effort including managing inventory swell, assessing and accounting for impact to other fees, discounts and rebates, and payer tracking—especially Medicaid, tracking elements to support 340B program compliance, performing self-audits, and managing a relationship that will evolve as patient behaviors, population health, insurance status, reimbursement rates, and prescribing habits change over time.

HOW 340B WORKS IN A CONTRACT PHARMACY RELATIONSHIP—THE FLOW OF DOLLARS

Entering into a contract pharmacy relationship requires only that a covered entity secures a contracted relationship and enrolls it in the 340B program. HRSA provides detailed instructions regarding registration.[10] Covered entities participating in the 340B program are permitted to use contract pharmacies for the dispensing of 340B drugs, in addition to or in lieu of an in-house pharmacy. Covered entities and their contract pharmacy partners should keep in mind that the intent of the 340B program is to allow safety-net hospitals and clinics to stretch their federal resources as far as possible, reaching more eligible patients and providing more comprehensive services.[2] Numerous models are available for a contract pharmacy relationship, but for the purposes of this chapter we will examine a contract pharmacy relationship between a covered entity and an outside retail pharmacy, where a 340B third-party administrator (TPA) (often called a 340B administrator or 340B TPA) and virtual 340B inventory are being used.

Although separate 340B inventory, manual tracking, and order-splitting methods can be used, the challenges of ongoing relationship management are typically too complex for the latter types to work with all but the smallest and simplest relationships. A 340B TPA-supported model permits auditable tracking—a shared and transparent view of the business and compliance responsibilities of each party—and adds a knowledgeable partner to support changes in 340B rules, guidance, or relationship economics over time. The 340B TPA model is the most commonly used across the industry, from the smallest individual community pharmacy relationship to large-scale networks of disproportionate share hospitals (DSHs) and national pharmacy retailers. In the case example below, we will explore tracking an insured prescription that is deemed 340B eligible.

KEY POINT

Various methods are available to engage in contract pharmacy, including separate inventory and manual methods. This chapter discusses using a 340B administrator—by far the most common; other methods may also be considered.

Covered entities typically find it most beneficial to contract with pharmacies where their patients are already filling prescriptions. In this arrangement, the shared 340B-eligible prescriptions can be converted to 340B, and the entity can realize revenue without requiring any change in patient behavior. A pharmacy in this scenario may fill the prescription under their usual protocol, adjudicating the prescription to the appropriate third-party payer.

EXAMPLE

In this case example, the covered entity has negotiated a contract pharmacy relationship that provides the pharmacy with a $20 dispensing fee and replacement inventory for each 340B-qualified prescription. The pharmacy dispenses a prescription for a branded drug retailing for $100 in total reimbursement, receiving an adjudicated response from the payer telling the pharmacy to collect a $5 co-pay from the patient, while the payer will pay the pharmacy $95, for a total of $100 reimbursement on the claim.

The patient pays the co-pay, collects the prescription, and leaves the pharmacy. At this point, none of the participants is aware of the 340B status of the prescription. The prescription-filling process has taken place in the same way as it usually does. The "back end" work to reveal the results of 340B qualification is about to begin now that the prescription has been filled and adjudicated.

The 340B TPA receives a data feed from the pharmacy's claims switch (e.g., Relay Health) and uses the claim data, along with patient encounter information received from the covered entity to determine if the patient, prescription, and claim qualify for 340B. The qualification process varies by 340B TPA and may involve other data elements. However, it is ultimately under the control of the covered entity. The qualification methods and process will be discussed in more detail later in this chapter.

If the 340B TPA's process determines the claim to represent a 340B-eligible prescription, the 340B TPA initiates an electronic automated clearinghouse (ACH) transfer of funds from the pharmacy to the 340B TPA. The amount of money moved from the pharmacy's account typically follows the following formula:

Total Amount Reimbursed to Pharmacy (Direct from Payer + Co-pay Collected) − Negotiated 340B Dispensing Fee = Amount Collected by 340B TPA

Using our earlier example from above:

$95 + $5 − ($20 dispensing fee negotiated by the pharmacy during the contracting phase with the covered entity) = $80 collected by the 340B TPA.

The 340B TPA generally retains a fee for their services deducted from this $80 (this varies by 340B TPA; we will use $5 in this example), then forwards the remainder amount to the 340B entity ($75 in this example). In this instance, the final transaction is for the covered entity to replace the dispensed inventory for the retail pharmacy; in our example, by purchasing it at $50 (340B price) and shipping the inventory to the contract pharmacy minus providing the covered entity with a $25 retained savings ($75−$50). This is the commonly discussed *bill-to/ship-to* arrangement in 340B contract pharmacy.

From the perspective of the financial transaction, it is important for the pharmacy to understand that they will relinquish the entire third-party payer reimbursement and instead retain the negotiated dispensing fee. A rule of thumb for the retail pharmacy is to understand, in some detail, which prescriptions that they are currently filling will convert to 340B and the net margin on those prescriptions. The dispensing fee that the retail pharmacy negotiates for the 340B contract pharmacy relationship should exceed the average net margin on those claims before the 340B relationship was implemented and include any new costs associated with 340B program management. If it is not, the retail pharmacy will lose money in the 340B partnership.

Although the express purpose of the 340B program is to provide support for the covered entity to extend services, the retail pharmacy partners should carefully consider the costs and nature of care they provide and receive reasonable compensation. An objective, transparent, and thoughtful negotiation between the two parties should arrive at a mutually satisfactory arrangement meeting 340B program objectives. The details of the financial transactions may vary, but the overall method for identifying and sharing proceeds outlined in the case is typical throughout 340B contract pharmacy relationships.

KEY POINT

Although the 340B program's purpose is to provide financial support for the covered entity's services, 340B contract pharmacy partners should understand the costs and rewards of their potential relationship in detail and move forward thoughtfully.

Contract Pharmacy Prescriptions for the Uninsured and Underinsured

Not all 340B prescriptions are covered by commercial insurance plans. Prescriptions for Medicaid are excluded (carved-out) from contract pharmacy under HRSA guidelines, except under specific circumstances.[11] Cash prescriptions may be included at the discretion of the two parties. This is generally done under a larger plan to serve the uninsured as outlined below. Covered entities are encouraged to use the 340B contract pharmacy proceeds outlined above to directly benefit their uninsured and underinsured patients. Many covered entities elect to implement a sliding fee scale, discount card, or other means to assist these patients with prescription costs. Some methods require the pharmacy to recognize certain prescription pads or stamped identification; others may supply the patient with a prescription card that contains a specific bank information number (BIN) and plan code number (PCN) for the pharmacy to adjudicate the cash claim. The details of these programs vary in payment and operational impact to the pharmacy and should be clearly defined in the contract between the two parties.

Within the context of 340B-qualified prescriptions, not all merit the conversion to shared 340B prescriptions described above. The total reimbursement, costs, discounts, fees, and other business considerations may mean that the partners determine not to convert some of the prescriptions to shared 340B status. The covered entity and the retail pharmacy should work with the 340B TPA vendor to understand the risks and benefits of different post-qualification sorting and filtering methods from a financial standpoint (e.g., *all-in*, *brand only*, *winners only*). These options and filtering methods are outlined in more detail below. Depending on the patient and product mix, methods that are beneficial for some relationships may not be for others.

DEVELOPING A CONTRACT PHARMACY AGREEMENT

A 340B contract pharmacy relationship has business elements as in any contract; a detailed description of services provided and responsibilities of each party, a description of the prescriptions to be considered eligible; a schedule of fees and payments; consideration of Medicaid obligations; and a discussion of liability and other terms resolve disputes. An opportunity to renew, to renegotiate fees mid-term, or for one party to opt out of the relationship may also be included. In addition, **Table 9-1** outlines 12 essential elements that HRSA identifies as necessary components of a 340B contract pharmacy agreement.

KEY POINT

The contract pharmacy agreement should address the 12 essential elements outlined by HRSA to support 340B compliance.

340B THIRD-PARTY ADMINISTRATOR ROLES

To better understand the risks and benefits of different qualification methods, it is important to take a closer look at 340B TPAs and the role they play. Although it is not a requirement, most covered entities choose to secure the assistance of a 340B TPA to manage the complexities of 340B, avoid implementing a manual tracking system, and support the daily detail of engaging in a contract pharmacy relationship with a retail pharmacy.

What Does a 340B Third-Party Administrator Do?

For the Covered Entity

- Manages patient encounter and prescription information to determine eligibility.
- Tracks costs and revenues associated with each claim, and manages cash flows between the contract pharmacy and covered entity.
- Tracks and maintains records and dispensed amount accumulations associated with dispensed prescriptions by NDC (National Drug Code) number, places order for replenishment on behalf of the covered entity, and tracks receipt.
- Maintains virtual inventory buckets.
- Produces reports of reimbursement, dispensing fees, 340B savings, and financial settlement.

For the Contract Pharmacy

- Handles post-sale 340B eligibility determination so that the pharmacy does not have to do so at the point of sale.

Table 9-1. Twelve Essential Elements of a Contract Pharmacy Agreement

1.	The agreement states that the covered entity will purchase the drug, maintain title to the drug, and assume responsibility for establishing its price, pursuant to the terms of an HHS grant (if applicable) and any applicable federal, state, and local laws. A *ship-to/bill-to* procedure is used in which the covered entity purchases the drug; the manufacturer/distributor must bill the covered entity for the drug that it purchased, but ships the drug directly to the contract pharmacy.
2.	The agreement will specify the responsibility of the parties to provide comprehensive pharmacy services (e.g., dispensing, recordkeeping, drug utilization review, formulary maintenance, patient profile, patient counseling, medication therapy management services, other clinical pharmacy services).
3.	The agreement states that the covered entity will inform the patient of his or her freedom to choose a pharmacy provider.
4.	The agreement states that the contract pharmacy may provide other services to the covered entity or its patients at the option of the covered entity (e.g., home care, delivery, reimbursement services). Regardless of the services provided by the contract pharmacy, access to 340B pricing will always be restricted to patients of the covered entity.
5.	The agreement states that the contract pharmacy and the covered entity will adhere to all federal, state, and local laws and requirements.
6.	The agreement states that the contract pharmacy will provide the covered entity with reports consistent with customary business practices (e.g., quarterly billing statements, status reports of collections, receiving and dispensing records).
7.	The agreement states that the contract pharmacy, with the assistance of the covered entity, will establish and maintain a tracking system suitable to prevent diversion of section 340B drugs to individuals who are not patients of the covered entity.
8.	The agreement states that the covered entity and the contract pharmacy will develop a system to verify patient eligibility, as defined by HRSA guidelines. Both parties agree that they will not resell or transfer a drug purchased at section 340B prices to an individual who is not a patient of the covered entity.
9.	The agreement states that neither party will use drugs purchased under section 340B to dispense Medicaid prescription, unless the covered entity, the contract pharmacy, and the state Medicaid agency have established an arrangement to prevent duplicate discounts and OPA has been notified and approves of the methodology used.
10.	The agreement states that the covered entity and contract pharmacy will identify the necessary information for the covered entity to meet its ongoing responsibility of ensuring that the elements listed herein are being complied with and establish mechanisms to ensure availability of that information for periodic independent audits performed by the covered entity.
11.	The agreement states both parties understand that they are subject to audits by outside parties (by Husband participating manufacturers) of records that directly pertain to the entity's compliance with the drug resale or transfer prohibition and the prohibition against duplicate discounts.
12.	The agreement states that, upon written request to the covered entity, a copy of the contract pharmacy service agreement will be provided to OPA.

HHS: Health and Human Services, HRSA: Health Resources and Services Administration, OPA: Office of Pharmacy Affairs

Source: Adapted from http://www.hrsa.gov/opa/programrequirements/federalregisternotices/contractpharmacyservices030510.pdf. Accessed September 1, 2016.

- Identifies amounts due to the covered entity, invoices the pharmacy, or performs an ACH transfer of funds.

- Maintains virtual inventory buckets.

- Produces reports of reimbursement, dispensing fees, 340B savings, and financial settlement.

Additionally, a 340B TPA may provide the template contracts for the entity/pharmacy relationship, develop analytics to help assess the contract pharmacy relationship, and provide assistance in registration of the relationship with HRSA. The 340B TPA also provides data and other support if HRSA audits the 340B-covered entity, or when payers, government entities, or others audit the pharmacy. The latter is important since a participating pharmacy will need to account for a separate stream of product (the 340B product) purchased by the hospital and used to fill prescriptions.

Ideally, a covered entity and pharmacy should work together to understand the business details of the relationship before signing a contract and committing to payment terms. 340B contract pharmacy relationships may encounter challenges because one or both parties have differing expectations of how the program should work. In particular, it is important to understand the various ways to impact the prescriptions that are converted to 340B. Even though a claim may qualify as 340B eligible, it may not be selected to be "converted" or filled under the 340B contract pharmacy relationship due to parameters that the 340B TPA and covered entity have elected.

340B SOFTWARE SORTING AND FILTERING MODELS

The 340B statute outlines a straightforward method to determine the eligibility of an outpatient prescription: Did the prescription result from an encounter of care documented in the patient's healthcare record maintained by the entity?[12] The technical challenges of making this match engage numerous rules and evaluations made by the 340B TPA using pharmacy and hospital data. In addition, the qualifying prescriptions may be evaluated for "suitability" for the 340B contract pharmacy relationship.

Examples of Different Approaches

The following are examples of different approaches that a 340B TPA may use, in conjunction with settings made by the 340B-covered entity and their contract pharmacy partner:

- ***Winners Only/Financial Screening of Prescriptions***. Only claims where the covered entity generates net revenue after paying the 340B TPA, the pharmacy dispensing fees, and the cost of replenishment inventory are converted to 340B. This model often results in low cost/low 340B discount generic prescriptions being excluded from the shared 340B prescriptions. This model may have a higher dispensing fee for the pharmacy or may employ a *Gain-Share* model where a percentage of the savings margin made on the claim is shared with the pharmacy. In some models, only prescriptions meeting the *Both Parties Win* are converted, recognizing the interests of the retail pharmacy.

- ***Brand Prescriptions Only***. Single source or multisource branded prescriptions convert to 340B regardless of whether the covered entity loses money. Generic prescriptions are excluded from conversion. This model also may have a higher dispensing fee than an *All Prescriptions* model reflecting the lower prescription qualification rate.

- ***All Prescriptions***. All prescriptions that qualify for 340B are converted to 340B, regardless of profitability. This model generally has a lower dispensing fee than the *Winners/Financial Screening* and *Brand Only* models, as the shared prescriptions are spread across a larger portion of the prescription activity. This may allow a pharmacy to capture a dispensing fee on claims that previously had been losses. The lower dispensing fee, more broadly applied, makes up for collecting the more modest dispensing fee on claims that delivered higher returns to the pharmacy. In this model, the goal is for both parties to understand that they will lose money on some prescriptions and make money on others, but benefit on the large pool of claims. Both the pharmacy and entity should be more profitable on average on the 340B prescriptions than they were before participating in the program.

HOW SHOULD THE CORRECT MODEL BE DETERMINED?

For the parties involved in the contract, it is essential to understand which claims are being filled "today" (in the non-340B environment) that will convert to 340B "tomorrow" (in the 340B environment). This information can be challenging to gather, but pharmacies working with covered entity hospitals and clinics may be able to work with the covered entity to obtain a prescriber list and identify a selection of claims to model and estimate impact. For pharmacies working with covered entity hospitals, some 340B TPAs have the ability to analyze the pharmacy's prescription claims switch data from prior months to determine which claims would have converted to 340B under the proposed model. When all parties are clear on which claims would convert, the partners have several decision points to consider in determining the dispensing fee for those particular claims and how to allocate the proceeds. The pharmacy should consider:

- ■ *Current profitability*. The pharmacy needs to identify profitability on the prescription claims that will convert to 340B.

- ■ *Impact to inventory*. The pharmacy will receive replenishment inventory that is paid for by the covered entity. This inventory will not automatically be incorporated into a pharmacy system's tracking methods or perpetual inventory systems, causing a swell of inventory. (See Inventory Considerations below.)

- ■ *Potential impact to rebates or contracts*. As the covered entity purchases the replenishment product for the pharmacy, the pharmacy may experience a loss in rebates or discounts from their distributor based on their declining direct purchases.

- ■ *Fee impact not related to 340B*. Direct and indirect reimbursement (DIR) fees levied by Medicare Part D and commercial plans are often billed to a pharmacy after the pharmacy has already paid the covered entity. The pharmacy may consider working with the entity to recoup those fees or delay payment to the entity until after DIR fees have been considered in the pharmacy's reimbursement.

- ■ *Administrative efforts*. Even with a 340B TPA managing many aspects of the administration of the program, it is essential that the pharmacy and covered entity regularly audit, check reports, assess inventory levels, manage schedule II controlled substance ordering (if applicable, see Schedule II Orders section below), and assess the success of the 340B program relationship to identify any areas of concern. Both parties should consider the training and labor that will be necessary to optimize the program.

KEY POINT

Covered entities and their partners should explore sorting and filtering methods for qualified prescriptions and make a selection prior to setting fees and determining which prescriptions to include in the 340B relationship.

DISTRIBUTOR CHOICE

Distributor choice is an important consideration for both the covered entity and the pharmacy in the event that the covered entity and pharmacy are not using the same distributor. HRSA guidance and common business practices require that a separate account be set up for each 340B contract pharmacy relationship. The covered entity may wish to open a 340B account with their existing distributor for convenience, billing, reporting, and discounts/rebates. The pharmacy may wish to remain with their distributor for the same reasons and to avoid challenges with inventory swell and non-matched NDCs, particularly on generic items.

If a pharmacy dispenses from an NDC that the distributor of the covered entity does not carry, that prescription will not be recoverable in the 340B program relationship, resulting in a missed opportunity for both parties. Alternatively, the pharmacy may elect to supply a different NDC, but this will result in a need to carry two separate stocks of the same drug, one for 340B patients and one for non-340B—causing further inventory challenges and changes to pharmacy workflow.

INVENTORY CONSIDERATIONS

A retail pharmacy participating in a 340B contract pharmacy relationship will dispense inventory out of their stock, and receive replacement inventory when a full bottle has been dispensed to qualified 340B patients. This process is managed by the 340B TPA. Using the dispensing data from the pharmacy obtained from the prescription claims switch, the 340B TPA vendor is able to track dispensing for the shared 340B account by NDC. Once a full bottle of product has been dispensed to 340B-qualified patients, the NDC for that product may be ordered on a 340B bill-to/ship-to account (bill-to the covered entity, ship-to the pharmacy). The 340B TPA will then decrement the virtual inventory "bucket" or accumulator, the pharmacy will receive replenishment inventory for the inventory previously dispensed to 340B-qualified patients, and the covered entity will receive an invoice from their distributor for the product.

The entity should regularly reconcile invoices with TPA reports, ensuring that the activity on the reports matches with the items and quantities billed. If there is a lapse in billing, contact the 340B TPA immediately to determine the cause. It is also important to identify the cause and determine a resolution. Moreover, the pharmacy should receive timely replenishment to be in the best position to manage the more complex shared inventory in 340B.

The growth of inventory, particularly software-managed perpetual inventory, is a key 340B challenge. Inventory "swell" occurs to some extent in every pharmacy and can be a significant challenge to overcome, particularly if a large percentage of the pharmacy's prescriptions are covered under the 340B relationship. When a pharmacy dispenses out of its own inventory for both 340B and non-340B prescriptions, it will often need to re-order inventory on its own to maintain a sufficient stock of providing prescription services to patients using its non-340B retail account prior to receiving a replacement bottle of replenishment inventory. Later, when a full bottle has been dispensed on the 340B program, the pharmacy will receive the bottle and incorporate it into its inventory—but by this time it will have already purchased a bottle on its own account, resulting in extra inventory on the shelves.

HOW DOES 340B CONTRACT PHARMACY INVENTORY SWELL OCCUR?

For our example, imagine that a contracted 340B pharmacy dispenses prescriptions from a 500-count bottle. At the end of a week, the 500-count bottle is empty; 400 tablets have been dispensed to 340B patients, 100 tablets dispensed to non-340B patients. The pharmacy must reorder a 500-count bottle to continue serving patients, but has insufficient dispenses to receive a bottle from their 340B partner and purchases a new bottle on their own account, retaining the accumulated 400-count 340B tablets. One week later, the pharmacy has dispensed another 100 tablets to 340B patients and has 400 tablets remaining in inventory. Reaching a full bottle accumulation (500 count) dispensed to 340B patients generates a 340B replenishment order to the pharmacy, billed to the covered entity. The pharmacy now has two bottles on the shelf and an inventory of 900 tablets, a swell in inventory of that product. This swell will remain and potentially grow through subsequent episodes of the scenario outlined above.

Additionally, if the pharmacy is using a perpetual inventory system, it may be unable to receive the second replenishment bottle into their electronic inventory and may automatically re-order yet another bottle on their retail account before one is actually needed.

Inventory challenges are a part of the 340B program, and they have a disproportionate impact on contract pharmacy relationships using virtual inventory replenishment. Some pharmacies elect to manage the inventory swell manually, while others work with a 340B TPA that has split-billing capabilities to manage the inventory more seamlessly. At least one 340B TPA has the ability to look at a pharmacy's order and at the available 340B inventory concurrently and then split the order between the two—pulling available stock from the 340B inventory.

As with a hospital split-billing program, when the pharmacy orders five bottles, the 340B TPA may see three bottles available on the 340B account. The TPA would split the order and purchase two bottles on the retail account and three on the 340B account for a total of five (the original order). Without this order split, the pharmacy would order and receive five on its retail account, then later receive three more bottles (billed to the 340B account) for a total of eight.

RETURNS

A pharmacy may consider returning the excess product to their distributor, but this does not represent sound management of the 340B program. Product purchased on the 340B account must also be returned on the 340B account as the legal title to the product remains with the 340B covered entity. The 340B product may not be returned on the retail pharmacy's account.

When product is returned on the 340B account, the credit goes to the covered entity, not the retail pharmacy. This means that the retail pharmacy has relinquished its replacement inventory, which is in effect a substantial portion of its reimbursement for drugs dispensed under the contract. The covered entity and pharmacy may elect to negotiate to pay the pharmacy for the retail cost of the goods that were physically returned and credited to the 340B account; however, this will not be advantageous to the entity as the retail cost of goods will be higher than the 340B cost of goods it originally paid.

CAPTURING PRIOR DISPENSING IN A 340B CONTRACT PHARMACY RELATIONSHIP

Another aspect of 340B inventory management that bears consideration takes place early in the contract pharmacy relationship. Often referred to as *lookbacks* or *clawbacks*, during contract negotiations or upon entering a contract with a pharmacy, either party may seek to include scripts from the previous 90 days—after the contract pharmacy was registered, but before the contract pharmacy was active, to benefit from savings and revenue associated with those claims. Although a clawback is not strictly prohibited by 340B rules (because actual 340B inventory must be purchased to achieve savings and the return credits work as outlined above), trying to capture this activity will severely impact the pharmacy's inventory and margins on previously adjudicated claims. The potential benefit of a clawback is generally outweighed by the complexity of managing purchases, credits, rebates, inventory, and reimbursement. Covered entities and contract pharmacies are encouraged to implement the 340B program rapidly after a 340B contract pharmacy relationship becomes active.

INVENTORY, CLAIM TRUE-UPS, AND REWINDS

On occasion, dispensing activity is such that accumulations do not reach the 340B replenishment level for a specific product over an extended period—typically 90 days. This gap may occur for a variety of reasons, including:

- *The product dispensed was patient-specific*. The 340B patient was the only one using the medication, the use has been discontinued, or the patient is no longer a customer at the pharmacy and a full-bottle size accumulation was never reached.

- *The product is short, out of stock, or discontinued*. The product may have reached a full bottle size but is not available to purchase and ship to the pharmacy.

- *The product is a "slow-mover."* Product is so rarely dispensed to 340B patients that replenishment cannot be achieved during a reasonable amount of time.

Rather than continue the revenue and inventory hold caused by a stalled or broken 340B replenishment process, most partners *true up* their outstanding obligations on a monthly or quarterly basis. Agreements between covered entities and pharmacies vary, but the true-up process usually occurs when no activity has taken place on an NDC for a pre-defined period of time, usually 90–120 days. When this occurs, the parties request that the 340B TPA reverse prescriptions out of the 340B program relationship, reversing the inventory accumulation that may have taken place for that NDC and undoing the payment to the covered entity or repaying the pharmacy. Both the covered entity and pharmacy should understand this process and how it will impact their estimated financials. In some instances the prescription(s) contributing to the incomplete bottle may be subject to a rewind, where the 340B TPA reverses the claim, zeroes out the inventory to be purchased, and returns the fees to the retail pharmacy. In this instance, it is as if the prescription was never qualified and selected for 340B.

KEY POINT

Consider how the parties will resolve excess inventory, rewinds, and true-ups. Include language in the pharmacy agreement and stick to a regular schedule of resolving modest difference vs. fixing larger problems later.

CASH FLOW

Many 340B contract pharmacy arrangements require the pharmacy to pay the entity (via ACH transfer to the 340B TPA) on 30-day terms. For consideration:

- Covered entities may receive invoices from the distributor for replenishment product as often as daily, regardless of whether they have collected funds from the pharmacy.

- Pharmacies may receive bills/ACH transfers from the 340B TPA before the pharmacy has actually received checks from third-party payers.

- Pharmacies are being billed for DIR fees by third-party payers weeks and even months after paying the covered entity. This leaves pharmacies vulnerable to cannibalization of their current business, making less money on 340B prescriptions than they anticipated when the prescriptions were included in the 340B program.

SCHEDULE II ORDERS

The decision to include or exclude Schedule II drugs (CIIs) in the 340B relationship is one that the covered entity and pharmacy should make together, with a clear understanding of the significant administrative burden that inclusion of these products causes. CIIs may represent a financial opportunity—as these prescriptions are converted to 340B, they may drive a revenue stream to the entity and a dispensing fee to the contract pharmacy. For the pharmacy, steps will be added to workflow processes around ordering as well as a need to monitor inventory levels even more closely.

For unscheduled legend drugs, a 340B TPA can place the replenishment orders and have the replenishment sent to the pharmacy. However, for CIIs, the 340B TPA can place the order on the 340B bill-to/ship-to account, but will need to have a method to communicate to the pharmacy that the order has been placed. Once the pharmacy is notified that the order has been placed, they will need to complete a Drug Enforcement Administration (DEA) 222 form for the delivery driver. This extra administrative burden is sometimes not worth the financial benefit of including CIIs in the program. Additionally, if inventory swell occurs, a pharmacy may reach ordering thresholds too quickly on controlled substances, which can cause ordering restrictions on a pharmacy's retail account for CII products.

ONE-TIME ORDERS

Occasionally, the contract pharmacy may need to dispense a particular product that it does not ordinarily carry, or does not plan to carry going forward, to a 340B patient. In this situation, the pharmacy may object to ordering the product on its account, dispensing it, and receiving replenishment product afterward, particularly for one-time dispensing.

In this scenario, a pharmacy, covered entity, and vendor may work together to order the product on the 340B account for shipment to the pharmacy and dispensing to the patient. This will result in a zero accumulation of virtual inventory and no replenishment inventory. All parties should take care to communicate clearly on this process and on how to manage the inventory if the patient does not pick up the prescription and the prescription is returned to stock. The product was purchased on the 340B account up-front and therefore must not be dispensed to a non-340B patient. It is important to set clear processes and procedures in the event that a one-time order must be made.

RETURN TO STOCK AND NEGATIVE ACCUMULATIONS

As a pharmacy goes about its day-to-day business operations, items will occasionally be returned to stock and reversed in the pharmacy system. This process may take place anywhere from 3 to 10 days after a prescription is filled, and usually occurs when a prescription is not picked up by the patient. When a prescription that previously qualified as 340B is reversed, this information is communicated to the 340B TPA through the data they receive from the pharmacy's switch. The 340B TPA then updates their accumulator buckets (e.g., if 30 tablets were filled, the vendor would now return 30 tablets of that NDC to the accumulator). Additionally, the 340B TPA will perform a financial reconciliation, invoicing the covered entity for the dollars associated with that claim and returning those funds or a negotiated payment to the contract pharmacy, less the dispensing fee that was already paid. In this way, the 340B TPA "rewinds" the claim and removes it from 340B eligibility, also ensuring that a manufacturer does not receive a chargeback for a 340B product when there is no corresponding prescription.

But what if a full bottle was filled, replenishment was shipped to the pharmacy, and now the product has been returned to stock? In this instance, once a reversal has taken place, the covered entity and pharmacy see a negative accumulation when they log in to their 340B TPA's system.

EXAMPLE

The pharmacy filled 100 tablets, and the 340B TPA updated the accumulator for that NDC to reflect 100 tablets. After an order was placed and filled, the accumulator reflected 0 tablets for that NDC. Later, when the pharmacy returns the prescription to stock, the 340B TPA updated the accumulator bucket for that NDC to reflect an accumulation of minus 100. In this way, the next 100 tablets will bring the accumulator back to 0, resulting in no charge to the manufacturer and offsetting the original charge for the 100 tablets that were reversed.

Although no hard and fast rule will resolve these challenges, there are two options:

- First, if the NDC is likely to be dispensed in the short term, resolving the negative accumulation, both parties may decide to wait to clear the negative with subsequent dispensing.
- Alternatively, the covered entity should resolve it under its policies by perhaps including offsets from other 340B-related activities or providing a manufacturer refund for the purchase differential.

SUMMARY

340B contract pharmacies remain a work in progress and have many options based on the interests of the partners. There is no one, perfect approach to 340B; no "right" dispensing fee that will work for every pharmacy; no "right" screening method for prescriptions that will ensure that every 340B-converted claim leaves both parties happy; and no perfect inventory management or reporting system that will work without oversight and intervention.

However, with an understanding of the business facets for both the covered entity and the contract pharmacy, both parties can come to the negotiation table better equipped to understand how to work together to avoid common pitfalls from the start, and how to structure a relationship that can flourish going forward. 340B contract pharmacy relationships are an excellent opportunity for many covered entities and pharmacies to work together to better serve their communities while alleviating some of the financial pressures related to decreased payments by third-party payers. Starting off on the right foot is essential, and knowing limitations, setting expectations, structuring a contract appropriately, and performing regular self-audits are key to success.

REFERENCES

1. Health Resources and Services Administration Office of Pharmacy Affairs. Contract Pharmacy Services https://www.hrsa.gov/opa/implementation/contract/index.html. Accessed October 14, 2017.
2. Health Resources and Services Administration Office of Pharmacy Affairs. 340B Drug Pricing Program http://www.hrsa.gov/opa/index.html. Accessed October 14, 2017.
3. Notice Regarding 340B Drug Pricing Program—Contract Pharmacy Services (75 Fed. Reg. 10272 (March 5, 2010). https://www.gpo.gov/fdsys/pkg/FR-2010-03-05/pdf/2010-4755.pdf. Accessed October 14, 2017.
4. Health Resources and Services Administration Office of Pharmacy Affairs; Office of Pharmacy Affairs. Update August 2016: Contract Pharmacy: Important Tips http://www.hrsa.gov/opa/updates/2016/august.html. Accessed October 14, 2017.
5. Apexus 340B Prime Vendor Program. Contract Pharmacy FAQ, 340B Prime Vendor Program https://www.340bpvp.com/resource-center/faqs/contract-pharmacy/. Accessed October 14, 2017.
6. Apexus 340B University. 340B Compliance Self-Assessment: Vendors, https://docs.340bpvp.com/documents/public/resourcecenter/340B_Compliance_SelfAssessment_Vendors.pdf. Accessed October 17, 2017.

7.   Fein A. Drug Channels February 6, 2014: New OIG Report Confirms Our Worst Fears About 340B Contract Pharmacy Abuses http://www.drugchannels.net/2014/02/new-oig-report-confirms-our-worst-fears.html. Accessed October 14, 2017.

8.   Office of Inspector General, Department of Health and Human Services. Contract Pharmacy Arrangements in the 340B Program, OEI-05-13-00431 https://oig.hhs.gov/oei/reports/oei-05-13-00431.pdf. Accessed October 14, 2017.

9.   Health Resources and Services Administration Office of Pharmacy Affairs. Program Integrity. http://www.hrsa.gov/opa/programintegrity/index.html. Accessed October 14, 2017.

10.   Health Resources and Services Administration Office of Pharmacy Affairs. Covered Entities Guide for Public Users Registering a Contract Pharmacy. http://opanet.hrsa.gov/opa/Manuals/OPA%20Database%20Guide%20for%20Public%20Users%20-%20Contract%20Pharmacy.pdf. Accessed October 14, 2017.

11.   Health Resources and Services Administration Office of Pharmacy Affairs. Office of Pharmacy Affairs Update: Contract Pharmacy Oversight. http://www.hrsa.gov/opa/updates/contractpharmacy02052014.html. Accessed October 14, 2017.

12.   Apexus 340B University. 340B Program Self Audit Tool: Diversion and GPO Prohibition. https://docs.340bpvp.com/documents/public/resourcecenter/DSH-Self-Audit-Prevention-of-Diversion-and-GPO-Prohibition.docx. Accessed October 14, 2017.

CHAPTER 10

Chargebacks under 340B Constraints

Katheryne Richardson, PharmD and
Christopher Hatwig, MS, RPh, FASHP

The Health Resources and Services Administration (HRSA), 340B covered entities, distributors, and manufacturers all share a common interest—transparency that the 340B price is provided to the participating covered entities. Considering 340B purchases involve over 30 distributors, hundreds of manufacturers, and approximately 40,000 covered entity sites, the accurate exchange of 340B-related information is critical to sustain 340B program integrity. For the vast majority of 340B transactions, the chargeback is the cornerstone for communicating key information in order to support accurate provision of the 340B price to enrolled covered entities. To describe the pivotal role chargebacks play in supporting the 340B program, this chapter presents an overview of the chargeback process, the stakeholder roles, and special situations associated with chargebacks in the 340B program, as well as challenges and tips for prevention and resolution of chargeback-related problems.

OVERVIEW OF THE CHARGEBACK PROCESS

When a manufacturer sells a drug directly to a purchaser, it is straightforward for the manufacturer to verify eligibility of the sale and ensure the right price is extended to the right customer. However, for the majority of manufacturers, drug sales take place indirectly through national, regional, and specialty pharmacy distributors, where the product is first sold to the distributor at wholesale acquisition cost (WAC) to fill its distribution centers, and later sold to the end customer at a group contract price. To ensure accurate pricing is applied to customers, distributors take membership lists supplied by group purchasing organizations (GPOs), the Federal Government and others, and use that in combination with the manufacturer-supplied *chargeback ID*, a data element that identifies the products, pricing, and eligible customer or group. Manufacturers' use of distributors creates two immediate issues that require a chargeback for resolution:

1. The drug manufacturer must be able to identify the purchasing customer of its product to ensure eligibility and the correct contract price is extended for sales in accordance with federal requirements. Because the distributor sold the drug to the final purchaser, the drug manufacturer requires a mechanism to identify basic information about the purchaser and contract accessed to determine the price that the purchaser should have received.

2. Because the distributor purchased the drug from the manufacturer at WAC, but may have sold the drug to the end customer at discounted contract price (340B, prime vendor program [PVP], GPO, or other), the distributor needs to be made whole for the difference in price between the WAC price and the end customer's contract price.

A *chargeback* is an electronic communication, comprised of many data points, and occurs when the manufacturer sells a product at a higher price to the distributor than the price the distributor has set with the end user. The distributor submits a chargeback to the manufacturer to confirm the end user should receive that price and while enabling the distributor to recover the difference between what the distributor initially paid for the drug and the price that the end user paid.

To ensure that chargebacks occur in a standard manner, the Healthcare Distribution Alliance's (HDA) eCommerce Task Force (eCTF) developed a voluntary implementation guideline to outline electronic standards for price communication between industry stakeholders, "Contract and Chargeback Administration Guidelines for Electronic Data Interchange (EDI), to Support Distributor Service Agreements."[1] Although this document is important for providing guidelines for stakeholders across the pharmaceutical marketplace, manufacturers and distributors in the realm of 340B have also created specific requirements in addition to, or in a departure from the core standards.

GPOs and federal contracts, such as the 340B program, rely on the chargeback process to facilitate accurate pricing. The 340B program presents especially unique challenges that occur with the indirect sales model, including quarterly updates to price files, changing lists of eligible entities, federal reporting requirements for pricing, the impact of contract pharmacies, different standards/ expectations set by the different distributors and manufacturers—and all of this occurs in an environment focused on compliance. Seamless communication among 340B stakeholders is pivotal to ensuring these challenges are handled, and the chargeback process is critical to the entire program's integrity and operational success. A recurring theme in the world of 340B chargebacks is the challenge for manufacturers to validate 340B eligibility—the manufacturer must link standard industry identifiers with the 340B unique ID issued by HRSA, and often incorporates other identifiers such as the Health Industry Number (HIN) or Drug Enforcement Agency (DEA) number as well.

Figure 10-1 illustrates how the chargeback process provides transparency to the manufacturer and distributor, enabling the extension of the correct contract price to the customer, and ensuring the distributor is made whole on the sale.

A summary of some of the identifiers that make the chargeback process work is provided in **Table 10-1**.

Example of How Identifiers Are Used

A single 340B covered entity may have several different distributor accounts, but they may all have the same ship-to address. If the distributor submits chargebacks that only have the ship-to address on it, the manufacturer would have challenges validating the pricing for the appropriate account. The assignment of an additional identifier, such as the HIN to each account, allows for each identification of accurate pricing for each account and simplifies the 340B chargeback processing for all parties.

Additional information about EDI transactions is helpful in understanding terminology used in association with the chargeback process and is summarized in **Table 10-2**.

Each manufacturer establishes criteria for processing its chargebacks, which include a list of data elements required (see examples summarized in **Table 10-3**) as well as rules for the timeframe in which chargebacks may occur (see examples summarized in **Table 10-4**).

HRSA initiated auditing in late 2010 to improve program oversight and integrity. Over time, the number of audits has increased as well as the details examined in the audit. The ordering account and contract load structure must be kept organized for 340B entities, distributors, and manufacturers to support program integrity. HRSA's contracted 340B prime vendor, managed by Apexus, has worked with stakeholders to establish an account structure that supports compliance. Without this fundamental structure for establishing accounts and contract loads, oversight of 340B program integrity would be challenging for HRSA as well as its stakeholder partners. All registered 340B-covered entities purchasing pharmaceuticals directly for eligible patients will have a primary 340B ordering account established with the distributor. Hospitals subject to the GPO prohibition (disproportionate share hospitals [DSH], children's hospitals [PEDS], free-standing cancer hospitals [CAN]) also typically have an outpatient non-GPO/WAC ordering account for 340B ineligible outpatients and neutral inventory, as these hospitals cannot purchase covered outpatient drugs through a traditional GPO. Only certain contract pricing may be loaded to these individual accounts, and this is summarized in prime vendor program tools and in distributor contracts with the 340B PVP.[2,3]

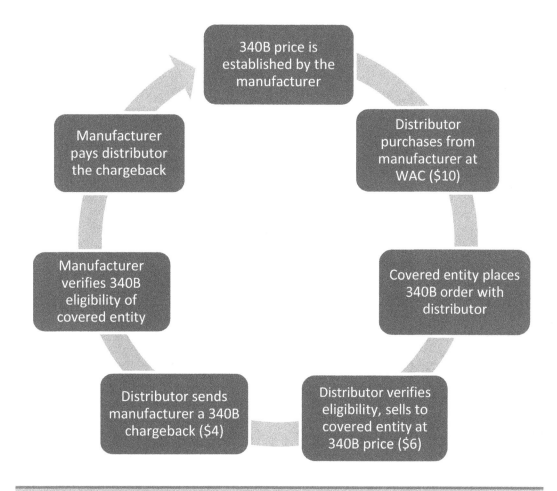

FIGURE 10-1. Chargeback Process

1. 340B price is established by the manufacturer.
2. Distributor purchases from manufacturer at WAC ($10).
3. Covered entity places 340B order with distributor.
4. Distributor reviews HRSA 340B database, verifies 340B eligibility, then sells to covered entity at 340B price ($6).
5. Distributor sends manufacturer a 340B chargeback ($4).
6. Manufacturer verifies 340B eligibility of covered entity (reviews HRSA 340B database).
7. Manufacturer pays distributor the chargeback.

HRSA: Health Resources and Services Administration, WAC: wholesale acquisition cost

Source: Reprinted with permission from 340B University. Apexus 2016.

Table 10-1. Chargeback-Related Identifiers

Identifier	Issued by	Format, Example	Purpose	Comments
340B ID	HRSA/ OPA	Letter prefix (pertaining to 340B entity type), followed by a 5-digit number (unique to parent organizations), followed by an optional child site letter suffix for hospital and CHC child sites only DSH 10000A	A unique 340B identifier for eligible organizations	Some manufacturers' and distributors' systems do not support the 340B ID; because HRSA does not report a unique identifier such as a DEA or HIN for entities and contract pharmacies, manufacturers must connect these identifiers in some way.
Chargeback ID (sometimes referred to as the contract ID)	Manufacturer	Usually alpha numeric	A unique identifier that identifies the products, pricing, and eligible customer or group	This is a standard identifier in the industry and not unique to 340B.
HIN	HIBCC	Unique 9-digit alphanumeric identifier; enumerates the ship-to locations. Requested by, and typically paid for by distributors and manufacturers, and used to identify entities and unique locations	Considered stable, universally recognizable but is designed to identify facility, location, and relationship.	Challenges are created by the 340B contract pharmacy ship-to/bill-to relationship. There are unique 340B HIN Program codes here: http://www.hibcc.org/wp-content/uploads/2016/05/PHS-HIN-Program-Codes.pdf An online module focused on 340B and HIN is here: https://www.brainshark.com/apexus/TopThreeHIN/zHnz15SKwRzHmIOz0?tx=HIBCC Not required by HRSA, but a HIN facilitates business transactions, chargeback processing, among trading partners. Because one 340B entity may have multiple types of accounts and contract pricing, and this same entity may also have the same address, it is the HIN that drives the specificity needed to identify and clarify the chargeback (HIN shows the account, class of trade, contract pharmacy). HIN has the market segment, which identifies the pricing for the account.
DEA #	Drug Enforcement Agency	2 letters, and 7 numbers. EX BM1234567	Identify that a healthcare provider is registered and permitted to write prescriptions for controlled substances.	May be used as a backup identifier for entities that do not have an HIN. The DEA number is mostly used for inpatient chargebacks. It may be used as a backup identifier for manufacturers that cannot accept HINs or 340B IDs on their chargebacks.

CHC: community health centers, DEA: Drug Enforcement Agency, DSH: disproportionate share hospitals, HIBCC: Health Industry Business Communications Council, HIN: Health Industry Number, HRSA: Health Resources and Services Administration, OPA: Office of Pharmacy Affairs

Table 10-2. EDI Transactions Related to the Chargeback Process

EDI Transaction	From, to	Purpose
844	Distributor to manufacturer	Product transfer account adjustment: chargeback request (debit memo)
845	Manufacturer to distributor	Price authorization acknowledgment status: communicates contract price information
849	Manufacturer to distributor	Response to product transfer account adjustment: communicates chargeback discrepancies
997	Manufacturer to distributor	Receipt acknowledgment

EDI: electronic data interchange

Table 10-3. Sample List of 340B Chargeback Data Elements*

- Facility 340B ID, HIN, or DEA number
- Contract number/Chargeback ID
- Product NDC number
- Invoice date
- Invoice number
- Quantity shipped
- Wholesale acquisition cost on date of facility purchase
- Contract price per unit
- Extended chargeback claim

*These vary by manufacturer and distributor.

DEA: Drug Enforcement Agency, HIN: health industry number, ID: identification number, NDC: national drug code

Table 10-4. Sample Manufacturer 340B Chargeback Expectations*

1. Chargebacks, resubmissions, and credit-rebills must be submitted within 60 days of the facility purchase to be eligible for credit. (Ninety days is also common, but some manufacturers will allow up to a year. However, this varies and there is no "standard"; resubmissions may have a longer timeframe than chargebacks.) Chargebacks and/or resubmissions submitted after this period will be automatically denied or rejected as "line item too old" and will not be paid.

2. Chargebacks pursuant to HRSA audits or self-audits may require special actions.

   For example: Advance approval is needed from the manufacturer and agreement to facilitate from the distributor. Timeframes may be established; if the customer goes beyond the timeframe, additional agreement may be required from the parties.

3. Manufacturer may audit the distributors; distributors are expected to maintain accurate records for 2 years.

*May vary by manufacturer.

HRSA: Health Resources and Services Administration

STAKEHOLDER PERSPECTIVES AND ROLES

A basic appreciation for the key stakeholders, their responsibilities, and risks is helpful to understand the chargeback process. This section provides a general overview of that information, with a unique focus on the 340B program.

Distributor

The 340B prime vendor has reported that 340B sales represent a small fraction of U.S. drug sales, but the complexity of the 340B environment and the chargeback process make it the most complicated price file to administer due to pricing being recalculated each quarter. A summary of the distributor's responsibilities include:

- Establish and manage account set-up for each customer.
- Ensure accurate contracts/pricing/accounts receivable/invoicing/chargebacks.
- Handle licensing/identification and verification (DEA, HIN, 340B eligibility).
- Process EDI with 340B systems such as split-billing and contract pharmacy software.
- Manage sales reclassifications between covered entities and manufacturers (if standards from manufacturer and distributor are met).

Risks for the Distributor

1. Ensuring accuracy of data (correct account set-up with correct pricing loaded for each customer) amid quarterly pricing changes and updates to HRSA's covered entity database, manufacturers are not liable to honor chargebacks from ineligible entities or in situations where an entity has incomplete or inaccurate information.

   - There is no "verified" central file of all 340B pricing, as distributors receive more than 40,000 price changes from manufacturers each quarter.
   - 340B contract pharmacy relationships present additional challenges for entity and contract pharmacy identification used in the chargeback submission.
   - Manufacturer requirements are not consistent regarding 340B sales reporting for 340B contract pharmacy.

2. Supporting/managing credit-rebill activity or other adjustments requests from covered entities motivated by maintaining compliance.

3. Being in the middle of covered entities and manufacturers in situations such as chargeback disputes.

Manufacturer

The chargeback process is essential to a manufacturer's operations but especially critical for the 340B program. Chargebacks are the lynchpin for the manufacturer to exchange information with distributors to enable the 340B purchase transaction. The 340B program has special challenges that require additional work for the manufacturer to ensure accuracy. A summary of the manufacturer's responsibilities include:

- Calculate and charge a correct 340B price only to 340B-eligible entities (ceiling price or lower).
- Establish and communicate the chargeback ID for its products, and establish formatting requirements of the chargeback submission for its products with distributors.
- Manage the identifiers necessary to validate chargebacks.
  - Typically use "bill-to" (or sold-to) address on the chargeback, in conjunction with DEA#, 340B ID, and/or HIN to identify the covered entity and the specific account.

Risks for the Manufacturer

Liability for incorrect 340B price extension rests with the manufacturer. An incorrect chargeback may be inappropriately included or excluded from its Medicaid average manufacturer price (AMP) and best price (BP) calculations, which results in inaccurate price reporting. This can have consequences for the manufacturer in overcharging or undercharging the eligible covered entity. The following situations can contribute to inappropriate identification of eligible 340B-covered entities and discrepancies in pricing calculations:

- Lack of common 340B identifiers (HIN, 340B ID, etc.); this may be especially problematic in a contract pharmacy situation.
- HRSA database has new entities added quarterly and often 500 to 1,000 changes per quarter.[4] Information such as address may be edited daily; manufacturers must then constantly download the information in the HRSA database to manufacturer's internal systems to ensure accuracy; monthly or quarterly downloads may miss information.

Covered Entity

The chargeback transaction occurs between the manufacturer and distributor but impacts the covered entity. From the covered entity's perspective, when a chargeback is denied, resolution may be complex. To reduce the likelihood of chargeback denials, responsibility of the entity includes:

- Maintaining accurate HRSA database information.
- Verifying accurate account/contract load from the distributor.

Risks for the Covered Entity

- Relying on manufacturers and distributors to organize purchasing accounts and handle chargebacks accurately.
- Time and effort spent working with stakeholders to resolve potential miscommunications/denials/disputes.

KEY POINT

Be certain that accounts are correctly set for 340B and non-340B purchasing. Correct purchase price relies on chargebacks and also on distributors and manufacturer account set-up.

HRSA Office of Pharmacy Affairs

A summary of HRSA's Office of Pharmacy Affairs (OPA) responsibility includes:

- Determining covered entity eligibility and establishing and maintaining an accurate HRSA 340B database with a unique 340B ID.
- Processing pharmaceutical pricing agreements with each participating manufacturer.
- Creating an administrative dispute resolution process for stakeholders via regulation designed to handle disputes that cannot be resolved through other channels.
- Managing distributor relationships through the PVP.

Risks for HRSA

Inaccuracies in the HRSA 340B database could result in inappropriate chargeback decisions; for example, if the information on the HRSA 340B database is inaccurate or inconsistent with actual address information for a site, this will cause challenges with manufacturers' chargeback decisions.

340B CHARGEBACK SPECIAL SITUATIONS

1. ***340B contract pharmacies present a special circumstance, as most chargeback submissions involve exchange of the ship-to customer****. Because the drug is shipped to the contract pharmacy, it is the sold-to information that becomes critical for a 340B chargeback in a contract pharmacy situation. A unique HIN, with an activity code for contract pharmacy, can be established to identify the relationship between the covered entity and the contract pharmacy. Distributors would use this unique HIN when submitting chargebacks for a contract pharmacy.

2. ***Entities subject to the GPO prohibition establish a unique non-GPO/WAC ordering account with their distributor****. Chargebacks should include unique chargeback IDs, which would identify that the contract pricing loaded and offered was for products purchased in that non-GPO/WAC account. Manufacturers sometimes experience challenges in differentiating between purchasing accounts established at these entities.

3. ***HRSA does not require entity-owned pharmacies co-located within a 340B-registered location to be separately registered****. In fact, entity-owned pharmacies cannot be listed as a child site of the entity on the HRSA database. Because manufacturers use the HRSA database address information in the chargeback validation process, the entity-owned pharmacies become difficult to identify for the manufacturer. A common business practice is to list these pharmacies as a ship-to address associated with the parent entity to provide transparency to the manufacturer. Listing the entity-owned pharmacies in this manner, although not a HRSA requirement, helps the chargeback process operate more smoothly.

4. ***Address changes or moving a location or pharmacy requires advanced planning****. Chargebacks submitted with a new address must match the address on the HRSA web site because that is what the manufacturers use to verify a chargeback. Although the distributor can change an address on an ordering account, if the entity does not change the address on the HRSA database, chargebacks may be denied until the HRSA database is updated to reflect the current address.

5. ***Manufacturers may use chargeback data to support compliance****. For example, Medicaid Exclusion File information may be used in conjunction with chargeback data to identify and investigate potential duplicate discounts. Another example includes a manufacturer reviewing entity purchase records to compare historical purchases (340B versus non GPO/WAC versus GPO) and current purchases. These purchase records, based on the manufacturers' record of the chargebacks, help the manufacturer identify potential irregularities that warrant further investigation.

6. ***Detail the distinction between a chargeback and a credit-rebill****. A credit-rebill is requested by the end user typically because an incorrect price was charged for the item. The credit and rebill transaction occurs after the customer has been invoiced, and in some cases, has paid the invoice. In an effort to refund the customer or to correct the invoicing discrepancy, the distributor will credit the original invoice for the disputed amount, and then re-invoice the customer with the corrected amounts. Distributors will have standards about when credit-rebill is permitted. In cases of 340B noncompliance, distributors typically require that the manufacturer approves credit-rebill activity. The associated transaction will generate a chargeback to the manufacturer once the credit and rebill process has concluded.

KEY POINT

Manufacturers may use chargeback data to support compliance. Plan ahead for changes and be certain that contract pharmacies and owned retail pharmacies are properly registered.

340B CHARGEBACK CHALLENGES AND TIPS FOR PREVENTION/RESOLUTION

When a chargeback has an error, the manufacturer denies the chargeback and communicates an error code to the distributor. This error code communicates the reason for the chargeback denial and allows the distributor to identify why the chargeback was denied, and enables the distributor to submit correct or needed information in order to resolve the chargeback. Error codes are found online.[1] Typically, the manufacturer and distributor work together to resolve chargeback denials, and HRSA does not become involved. For 340B stakeholders, prevention of chargeback issues is the key to smooth operations. To support that goal, the following are a few examples of situations that resulted in chargeback disputes:

1. ***Split-billing software malfunction***. If the split-billing software does not properly function and cannot support order placement, covered entities could order on an inappropriate account. Recently a large-scale malfunction at a major split-billing software vendor resulted in many DSHs ordering inadvertently on the non GPO/WAC account for nearly a week. Because the split-billing software wasn't capturing the 340B eligibility and communicating that to the distributor, the hospital overpaid for drugs during that time interval. While the split-billing vendor did email its clients (entities), the email went to a junk folder for many of the entities, and, therefore, the communication was not received. Although the vendor attempted to reach the covered entities, this lapse in communication compounded the issue, and the lack of received communication extended the time interval for missed chargebacks.

   Once the entities realized this error had occurred, significant time and many orders had been placed, which caused interruptions at the distributors as well, as the distributors were then suddenly overwhelmed with requests to credit-rebill tens of thousands of claims for multiple customers. Because these credit-rebill requests didn't meet the standards in place from the distributors for processing, the covered entities had the majority of these credit-rebill requests denied and were left paying a higher price for drugs than should have been necessary. Although the chargeback system was not the point of failure in this situation, it demonstrates how related technology, such as the split-billing software, can prohibit proper chargebacks from occurring. After a situation like that arises, the domino effect on the stakeholders is very difficult to undo.

   Lessons learned in this scenario include: Assigning a regular review/checkpoint to determine the split-billing software is properly functioning, addressing software malfunctions in the contract with the split-billing vendor, and understanding the credit-rebill expectations from the distributor.

2. ***HRSA instituted a policy for hospital registrations that involved registering individual services in off-site child locations***. For some organizations, this involved removing a 340B-registered main building location and instead registering individual 340B child site locations that represent different departments of that building. This situation caused problems with chargebacks because not all stakeholders use the same identifiers for chargeback processing. In some situations, the main building that was registered had different identifiers than the outpatient pharmacy's information on the pharmacy license (located

in this same building). The disappearance from the HRSA database of the exact name of the original building was problematic for the manufacturer. In many cases, that building information was linked to the DEA and HIN of the pharmacy, and the pharmacy was not registered with HRSA, as pharmacies are not permitted to be registered sites.

Lessons learned in this situation include: Understanding how the distributor and manufacturer identify locations as 340B eligible and how these business practices don't always match with the information and requirements on the HRSA database. Therefore, something as simple as adding the pharmacy information to the HRSA database as a ship-to address can prevent charge-back denials.

3. *When a manufacturer offers pricing for a "sub-set" of the entire 340B participant base, such as sub-WAC pricing for the hospitals subject to the GPO prohibition, but does not give the distributors a list of those eligible entities from which to load, the distributor may use its own process to identify the eligible entities for that particular load.* When a sale is made and the resulting chargeback submission sent, some of the chargebacks may not match the manufacturer's list of eligible entities for that pricing. This would result in a denied chargeback to be resolved between the manufacturer and distributor.

4. *When the distributor sets up an ordering account using the name of the facility the customer provides, but this name does not match the name on the HRSA database, this error is usually caught when the distributor verifies 340B eligibility.* This could also occur when the name of the facility is recorded on the DEA 222 form, which then has to be the exact name on the ordering account, but might be different from the name the entity gave to HRSA when they registered. The distributor is obligated to set up a pharmacy account using the name on DEA registration.

KEY POINT

Split-billing software malfunctions and unique situations can lead to chargeback denials and incorrect prices. Monitor set-ups and pricing regularly, particularly when software changes and updates or HRSA registration changes are made.

SUMMARY

Chargebacks are the method for communication among 340B-covered entities, distributors, and manufacturers that the correct and accurate price is provided to the participating covered entity site. Due to the complexity of the 340B environment, chargebacks encounter various challenges and special situations. Appreciation of common chargeback-related problems can result in prevention or faster resolution for stakeholders. Chargebacks continue to play a critical role in the support of 340B program integrity for stakeholders.

REFERENCES

1. EDI Guidelines for 845-844-849 Contract & Chargeback Administration. Healthcare Distribution web site. https://www.healthcaredistribution.org/resources/edi-guidelines-for-845-844-849-contract-and-chargeback-administration. Accessed October 14, 2017.

2. Account Load Options. Apexus web site. https://docs.340bpvp.com/documents/public/resourcecenter/GPOProhibition_WholesalerWACAccount_LoadOptions.pdf. Accessed October 14, 2017.

3. Distributors page. Apexus web site. https://www.340bpvp.com/resource-center/distributors/. Accessed October 14, 2017.

4. Best Practices for Managing PHS. Model N web site. http://pages.modeln.com/rs/023-STC-548/images/wp_Best_Practices_for_Managing_PHS_340B.pdf. Accessed October 14, 2017.

The authors would like to thank Christopher Clement and BJ Centers of Apexus for their assistance and technical expertise in preparing the chapter.

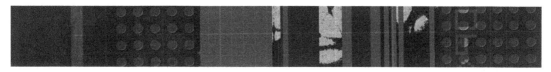

CHAPTER 11

340B Considerations for Rural Hospitals

Charles Cooper, MBA, RPh and
Madeline Carpinelli Wallack, PhD, MS

LEGISLATIVE HISTORY

In 2010, the Patient Protection and Affordable Care Act (PPACA) amended the Public Health Service (PHS) Act to add several new hospital types to the definition of covered entities for 340B. Section 340B(a)(4) now includes certain qualifying children's hospitals, free-standing cancer centers, critical access hospitals (CAHs), rural referral centers (RRCs), and sole community hospitals (SCHs). Under section 340B(a)(4)(N) of the Public Health Service Act, as amended by the ACA, the prohibition against participation in group purchasing organization (GPO) arrangements that applies to 340B-eligible disproportionate share hospitals, children's hospitals, and free-standing cancer hospitals does not apply to critical access hospitals, rural referral centers, or sole community hospitals.[1]

KEY POINT

Because the GPO prohibition does not apply to rural hospitals, they can "shop" across their GPO catalog in addition to 340B pricing. 340B software settings and ordering practices should be tailored accordingly.

UNIQUE CHARACTERISTICS OF RURAL HOSPITALS

The three types of hospitals discussed in this chapter are essential providers in the rural health safety net. Although they are located in smaller markets than their urban counterparts, the demands for providing care are equally or even more complex. Rural hospitals are often the only source of care in small communities where the residents are more likely to be uninsured or underinsured and have below average income and health status.[2] Rural hospitals have fewer physicians, specialists, and advanced clinical capabilities, all while serving more elderly and Medicare patients.[3]

The economic and health service situation in rural areas is generally more critical than in urban areas. There are rural-urban disparities in health conditions associated with several preventable or chronic conditions compounded by the parallel disparity in healthcare infrastructure and professional capacity to attend to these increased needs.[4] Due to the geographic, demographic, and cultural obstacles faced by rural providers, the opportunity to capitalize on pharmaceutical savings through programs like 340B is vital.

The inpatient length of stay in a rural hospital is typically short or even limited by law; as such, there is a greater emphasis on outpatient and primary care services at these hospitals—areas the 340B program is intended to support. Rural hospitals increasingly treat cancer and specialty patients as their communities are experiencing the shift from private practice to hospital-based clinics. Rural hospitals providing access to infusion services for their patients are on the rise; however, because many of these treatments are orphan drugs, the benefit from 340B may be limited. Orphan drugs are described in more detail later in the chapter.

What Characteristics Influence Rural Hospital Participation in 340B?

Rural hospitals have been eligible for 340B since the fall of 2010, yet not all hospitals are enrolled; if they are enrolled, not all of them actively participate in the program.[5] Academic research into potential reasons for the modest level of enrollment suggests that it arises from the fact that the same law expanding 340B to rural hospitals also added new integrity provisions and certain restrictions on the ability to use 340B. The PPACA requires annual recertification of all 340B enrollees, audits of program participants, compliance with the orphan drug exclusion, and potential penalties for covered entity noncompliance.

Rural hospitals participating in 340B have higher overall revenue, a higher volume of outpatient services where drug use is connected (e.g., ambulatory surgery, emergency departments, primary care clinics, home healthcare), the presence of chemotherapy services (where the 340B discount is most valuable), higher pharmacy staffing, and a deeper understanding of the 340B program.[5,6]

KEY POINT

> Rural hospitals face unique challenges in implementing 340B due to personnel limitations, strained finances, and expertise. Thoughtful planning should be undertaken before entering the 340B program.

Additional outreach and education are necessary to increase awareness of rural hospitals' eligibility and to help ensure pharmacy directors and administrators can make informed decisions about participation. Entities must be able to weigh the potential cost-savings benefits alongside costs of compliance since there are both benefits and drawbacks of participating in 340B.

What Makes Running a 340B Program in a Rural Area Unique?

Critical access hospitals, sole community hospitals, and rural referral centers have several common challenges related to resources. This broad characteristic may make the implementation and management of a compliant 340B program more challenging.

First, most rural small hospitals are faced with limited personnel resources. In many cases, the pool of pharmacists and pharmacy technicians can be limited. Even when fully staffed, pharmacist and technicians need to master multiple tasks and do not have the luxury to devote full-time attention to one area. Instead, pharmacy staff needs to multitask between job functions with pharmacists performing some technical duties, and technicians performing other duties such as purchasing. Staffing balance is often delicate in rural hospital environments—any disruption can cause priorities to focus solely on direct patient care and forgo less urgent tasks such as 340B management, auditing, and compliance oversight.

A second characteristic that presents a challenge for these smaller hospitals is the lack of financial resources. Managing a 340B program with today's complexity and regulation requires a third-party software solution. 340B software programs can be prohibitively expensive, not to mention the need for pharmacy and information technology staff to implement software and support ongoing management. Software cost and complexity can limit options and may require a site to implement a less complete or more basic system or a completely manual solution. Although manual solutions can be an effective option for a small 340B operation, the risk of noncompliance may overshadow the financial benefit.

Third, scarce legal, compliance, and administrative resources to support a 340B program can also be a challenge. Legal and compliance functions are often contracted, and the contractors may not possess a detailed understanding of 340B program requirements. Since so many aspects of 340B program compliance require legal review and assessment, a lack of understanding can create unwanted risk. In the same way, administrative support (e.g., 340B coordinator, individual, or team that can be in charge of risk), audit, and compliance management can be in short supply. Historically, in-depth knowledge of the 340B program resided solely in the pharmacy, and in many cases, it still does. With increased program scrutiny and complexity, the pharmacist in charge ideally would rely on a cross-functional support team. This may not be available, and reliance on contracted consultants often is the best option.

Orphan Drug Exclusion

The week following the passage of the PPACA, section 2302 of the Health Care and Education Reconciliation Act included an amendment that excludes drugs that have received the U.S. Food and Drug Administration's (FDA) designation of "orphan" from 340B eligibility for the hospitals identified in this chapter. By excluding these drugs as "non-covered" under 340B, rural hospitals' potential 340B savings were materially impacted while their compliance requirements have increased.

Orphan drugs are often the highest cost products in the marketplace, meaning that rural hospitals do not have the full access to the discount program for key high expense items as do their urban counterparts. In 2012, this chapter's authors collaborated on a project to review the prevalence of orphan drug purchases and to calculate the price differentials between the 340B price and the hospitals' current cost at 18 critical access hospitals.[7] The study found that the 18 CAHs' purchases of orphan drugs comprise an average of 44% of the total annual drug budgets, but only 5% of units purchased, representing a high proportion of their expenditures. In the aggregate, the 18 hospitals studied would have saved $3.1 million ($171,000 average per hospital) had purchases of drugs with orphan designations been made at the 340B price. The study concluded that the high prevalence of orphan drug use and considerable potential for cost reduction through the 340B program demonstrate the loss of benefit to the hospitals, federal government, and the states.

Since 2010, the orphan drug exclusion has been marred by struggles with interpretation, including failed regulation and then guidance from the Health Resources and Services Administration (HRSA) following a lengthy lawsuit by the Pharmaceutical Manufacturers and Researchers of America (PhRMA). Some manufacturers are offering voluntary discounts to rural hospitals with "like-340B" pricing, but the practice is new and inconsistent, leaving many of these entities confused as to how and when they can use 340B and remain compliant.

What Makes a Drug "Orphan"?

In general, the Orphan Drug Act of 1983 provides financial incentives and market exclusivity to manufacturers to develop drugs for rare diseases that affect a small portion of the population, generally fewer than 200,000 people.[8] The motivation behind the Orphan Drug Act is to support the development of therapies for diseases where the potential market for such a drug and subsequent ability to recover investment costs might be limited. Arguably, these orphan drugs would not be as likely to make it to market without the incentives.

The FDA has two orphan drug classifications: an *orphan designation* and *approval for an orphan indication*. For products with an orphan designation, the manufacturer must demonstrate that the product is of potential use for a rare condition. As of the date of publication, the FDA has granted 4,499 orphan designations.[9] For products with an approval for the orphan indication, the manufacturers met the requirements of a new drug approval (NDA), which is a more rigorous process that leads to marketing approval and includes establishing the safety and efficacy of the drug via clinical trials. Products may obtain approval for more than one orphan indication. The FDA has granted 671 NDA approvals for orphan indication. Requests and approvals for both types of indication have had significant growth in the last 3 years with the designations up 61% (2,795 in 2013 compared to 4,499) and a 55% increase in NDA approvals (432 in 2013 compared to 671) by April of 2013. With more drugs gaining orphan indications, the financial impact on rural hospitals participating in the 340B program is expected to increase.

2011–2015: Challenges to Interpreting the Orphan Exclusion

On May 20, 2011, HRSA published their proposed regulations in the *Federal Register* outlining how they intend to implement the exclusion under the 340B program.[10] Included in the language of the proposed regulations is the statement that, "it is critical that HHS recognizes these covered entities' ability to benefit from the 340B program savings so there is sufficient value for them to participate in the 340B program." As such, under the proposed regulations, HRSA clarified that orphan drugs—when used for the rare condition or disease for which that orphan drug was designated under the Federal Food, Drug and Cosmetic Act and has received marketing approval by the FDA—are excluded as covered outpatient drugs for the newly-eligible 340B covered entities. Covered entities are to institute "tracking and record-keeping requirements to demonstrate compliance with the limits on the use of orphan drugs…it will be necessary for the covered entities to create separate purchasing accounts and improve inventory and auditing capacity." The U.S. Department of Health and Human Services (HHS) received 50 comments and published the final rule on July 23, 2013, with an effective date of October 1, 2013. Few changes were made between the proposed and final rules, but many manufacturers remained opposed to HHS's interpretation of the orphan drug exclusion. As such, PhRMA, on behalf of its members, filed suit in federal district court on September 27, 2013 to stop the implementation of the orphan drug rule.

After much debate, On October 14, 2015, the U.S. District Court for the District of Columbia vacated HRSA's Orphan Drug Interpretive Rule.[11] This means that for the affected rural hospitals, the term "covered outpatient drug" does not include a drug designated by the FDA for a rare disease or condition irrespective of its use. Manufacturers are not required to provide these covered entities orphan drugs under the 340B program; however, they may voluntarily offer discounts on orphan drugs to these hospitals.

KEY POINT

The Orphan Drug exclusion complicates management of 340B program compliance and diminishes savings opportunity. Rural hospitals should seek individual contracts for orphan drugs and track financial results accordingly.

340B for Rural Hospitals: Before You Begin

To participate in the 340B program, an eligible facility must apply first apply to HRSA and the Office of Pharmacy Affairs (OPA). However, prior to making the decision to enroll in the 340B program, a smaller facility must first assess if the scope of services offered would support participation for the facility and their patients. As discussed previously, participating facilities need a significant ambulatory presence to support 340B participation. Facilities that are acute care focused may not have sufficient ambulatory encounters and activity to justify the cost of establishing a program, but it is important to thoroughly assess the opportunity. To make this assessment, many facilities either conduct an internal analysis or contract with consultants to estimate the costs and benefits of participation. Participation in the 340B program entails the costs to implement the program, ongoing maintenance, software fees, and personnel costs. The personnel costs to maintain a compliant program and support software systems are easily overlooked or underestimated.

Aside from the potential gains to the institution, rural hospitals must also consider the needs of their patients. In many cases, the rural hospital is the only access point for healthcare and may be the sole access point for prescription medications. By definition, these facilities are miles away from another healthcare access point. Rural hospitals carry a higher burden of charity and uncompensated care. Patients in need of medications that have a high deductible plan or are uninsured often rely on the facility to provide the medication at low cost or no cost. This support is clearly one of the intents of the 340B program—to ensure needy patients have access to medications and that the facility can provide them at a reduced cost. With small patient volumes in rural communities with poorer populations, this critical need is often challenging to meet.

Rural hospitals are often aligned with other healthcare providers in their communities. The hospital is usually affiliated with or under common ownership with the local nursing home. Many rural hospitals have swing beds or skilled nursing facilities within their building. It is essential to understand how these patient care areas are related to the hospital and understand HRSA's guidance on where the patient–provider relationship occurred to qualify a medication order for 340B.

Most rural facilities have a combination of contracted providers and employed providers. 340B qualification software systems link dispensed or administered medications to the facility (in part) by a provider match; facilities need to differentiate providers who are based at the hospital versus those primarily based at a private office. Specialists from larger medical centers may come to the facility on a routine basis and may rent space and/or bill from their home institution or through the 340B facility. Understanding these unique relationships and fitting them into the 340B program implementation is critical for compliance, since the organization and location in which they practice and how the practice is organized must be reimbursable to qualify for 340B.

A key consideration for rural hospitals prior to entering 340B is referral relationships. Many rural facilities offer ambulatory infusion services for their patients, supported by orders from local providers (who may have a variety of relationships to the 340B facility) and providers through referrals. A common scenario has a patient where the hospital is responsible for primary care related to the facility and has issued referral orders to a specialist in another community. Care delivered at the 340B hospital offers the patient the convenience of treatment without the need to travel; however, sorting through the relationship can have compliance implications for the 340B program. Assessment of the referral process for a patient to a specialist should be reviewed with legal counsel and risk management with a focus on the use of 340B drugs. Many infusion drugs are very expensive, and the cost of keeping them in inventory can be prohibitive. Having the ability to access these drugs at lower cost through the 340B program is beneficial for the hospital to provide valuable infusion services to its patients.

As previously discussed, rural hospitals face a significant hurdle by having FDA-designated orphan drugs excluded from their 340B program. Many orphan drugs are drugs used in the ambulatory infusion area. Accommodating to the exclusion of orphan drugs requires the facility to have detailed knowledge of the drugs with an orphan indication and to consider the higher costs associated with patient care. Understanding orphan drugs can be difficult because the FDA and HRSA-compiled lists do not extend to the product and NDC level and the policy complexities mean that the lists themselves may not be reflective of current manufacturer and NDA status. Practically speaking, there is no readily available and useable list of orphan drugs. Some manufacturers have voluntarily offered discounted prices on orphan drugs for rural facilities, but these prices need to be properly treated as an individual discount as well by distributors and 340B software systems. Upon audit request, these purchases should be properly reported in data requests from HRSA.

Many rural hospitals may not have the resources to operate a full-service retail pharmacy and access 340B medications to dispense prescriptions. Rural hospitals should consider the ability to access 340B for ambulatory prescriptions through one or more contract pharmacy arrangements with pharmacies in their service area. Contract pharmacy arrangements require contracting between multiple partners and generally use a 340B third-party administrator (TPA) software solution to consistently qualify 340B claims and to manage the *bill-to/ship-to* relationship between partners. Smaller local relationships can be managed more simply using separate inventory or manual tracking, although this is not common. It is imperative that the hospital's 340B program leadership understand the compliance requirements, business complexity, and details involved with setting configurations for a contract pharmacy relationship. HRSA is clear that the covered entity is responsible for all compliance aspects of a contract pharmacy arrangement. Third-party software vendors and retail pharmacies with their own software solutions can make these arrangements easy to set up, but it is imperative that the covered entity is aware of all of the details and contractual obligations. In the process of setting up the necessary data feeds and qualification filters, the entity must have a thorough understanding of outcomes expected and risks involved. Post-implementation, it is imperative to continually monitor the qualification processes in addition to financial metrics to ensure the systems are working as intended. Refer to Chapter 9, Business and Supply Chain Considerations in 340B Contract Pharmacy, for a more detailed discussion.

Many rural hospitals are a part of a larger healthcare system. These arrangements are beneficial for many reasons and can lend central support for small hospitals participating in the 340B program. When a small facility is a part of a larger system, it is important to define the governance and business accountability for the entity's 340B program. Central corporate pharmacy, compliance, supply chain, and information technology resources of a health system can offer support not typically available to the covered entity such as legal or IT expertise and may have resources dedicated to supporting system-wide 340B initiatives. Defining the role of central support versus local support is important. 340B program dynamics are embedded in details and daily activities at the local level. The covered entity site will be in the best position to support compliant practices and monitor activities on a daily basis, such as changes in purchase orders or review and address self-audit findings. On the other hand, a central support team can monitor regulatory changes, assist with contracts, benchmarking, and policy development. Developing a working balance and understanding of each role is important to maximizing the 340B system performance. Regardless of the health system's view, 340B status is local and the covered entity holds full accountability for compliance. The local authorizing official, pharmacy director, and operations leadership should be well versed, well informed, and engaged in 340B, even when program support benefits from corporate resources and oversight.

Rural hospitals need to properly vet all third-party vendors recognizing their unique needs. This includes in-house support and services and contract pharmacy relationships. Bedsides selecting the "right fit," smaller hospitals have to verify that the vendor will provide tailored resources and sufficient attention, since those same vendors are working with larger clients with differing needs. It is important to stay engaged and to be certain vendors perform and assist with the unique needs of the smaller facility. Networking with "like" facilities through interest groups and associations is also important.

RECOMMENDED BEST PRACTICES

Do the Math

The convergence of new 340B program requirements, draft program guidance, HRSA audit focus, heightened program scrutiny, and an already steep learning curve for a federal program have created a challenging and interesting decision-making paradigm for rural hospital executives. The growing and complex program requirements necessitate an increased investment in compliance; these increased compliance costs must be weighed against the anticipated and realized value of the program. Through the 340B program, covered entities can improve medication access and simultaneously improve the finances of the hospital to sustain and increase care to patients in need. However, pharmacists at these hospitals are particularly overextended and rural hospitals experience higher pharmacist vacancy rates, have fewer resources overall, and have a high percentage of Medicare patients who require more professional time. Thus, the value equation of 340B participation (cost of implementation and ongoing operation vs. realized savings) for these hospitals may be positive, neutral, or even negative depending upon the characteristics of the hospital.

Develop a Team

Support and resources are an important aspect of making any 340B program function optimally. All facilities need to have trained and experienced personnel to support the 340B program at the pharmacy and IT level, and monitor daily activity. With large numbers of transactions occurring within system, routine changes and updates in clinical, financial, supply chain, and 340B software, gaps, downtime, interface errors, and functional failures can occur and may be undetected for long periods of time. All 340B programs should have the goal to detect errors or omissions as soon as possible.

The pharmacy buyer or pharmacist/technician who is placing a drug order must have enough knowledge of the revenue cycle and supply chain set-up to detect variances that might indicate a system problem or missed opportunity. If a facility is part of a larger system, the central office must rely on the local team to monitor daily activity. Information technology personnel (or personnel knowledgeable about the IT set-up) must monitor daily file transfers and data exchanges to ensure there is no disruption or changes in service.

Monitoring 340B activity is critical. The feedback from self-audits and external audits is essential to understanding weak points, incorrect data feeds, and other potential problems. Ideally, self-audits include daily, weekly, monthly, quarterly, and yearly activities with personnel assigned to complete the audits and to provide oversight and assurance of policy change.

It is a best practice to establish a formal meeting schedule of key leaders within the organization—a 340B Program Oversight Committee, create an agenda to review key metrics and compliance against expected standards, and review any emerging issues. Because most personnel in smaller facilities are multitasking, one should identify key internal resources, educate them to the details of the program, and recruit them to help assess and continuously monitor the program. A thorough understanding and buy-in from senior management is critical, and having a team to help the entity navigate through changes, decisions, quality management, and compliance issues is a key element of success.

KEY POINT

It is a best practice to establish a 340B Program Oversight Committee, create an agenda and regular meetings to review key metrics and compliance against expected standards, and assess emerging issues.

Right Size 340B Program Resources

Rural hospitals considering participation in the 340B program or those enrolled but not yet participating should compute their potential savings and weigh them against the time and costs that will be required to ensure appropriate billing, adequate record keeping, and effective inventory management. Included in this value equation are variables such as total outpatient drug costs, payer percentages, percent of outpatient drugs purchased with orphan indications, estimated software fee, additional staffing, and external audit support. Rural hospitals should also consider the value of a retail pharmacy—either in-house or through contract pharmacy relationships.

If the decision is made to enter the 340B program, it is imperative to have enough personnel time dedicated to maintain and monitor the program. It is not possible to dedicate personnel to a single function, but personnel must be identified and assigned to key aspects of 340B program management and oversight. When a rural facility is part of a larger system, it is important to identify roles and responsibilities at the site and central level. Central oversight may not provide timely and detailed insight, detect subtle changes in purchasing patterns that might indicate over or under qualification of 340B transactions. Site personnel may be focused away from 340B program management or monitoring activities with changes in staffing patterns or workload; if the entity is part of a larger system, a central role can provide supplemental support and oversight to fill the gaps. The most important function of a well-run 340B program is to have a clear understanding of regulations, program expectations and strategy to meet them, and assigned roles to personnel. Oversight of daily activity is critical as well as governance at the senior leadership and board level.

When starting a new 340B program, it is essential to budget personnel time to implement and maintain the program. As the program progresses, it is imperative to continually monitor personnel needs. When decisions are made to expand the 340B program (e.g., adding contract pharmacies), additional personnel time must be considered. A well run, compliant 340B program will help an institution care for their underserved patients, but will require resources to meet this goal.

It is nearly impossible to run a fully implemented 340B program without software support. Some 340B TPA software systems provide a full complement of services for all settings, including hospital split billing, ambulatory clinics and retail pharmacies, and contract pharmacy networks. Other TPAs specialize in only one aspect of the program. Some vendors offer a full suite of services to support their clients, while others focus solely on technology. As discussed previously, some vendors have services tailored to the small and rural 340B participant community, while others are more "one size fits all." 340B TPA software selection will depend on several variables but ease of managing one system across all areas is likely most valuable for the smaller 340B facility.

If a 340B TPA claims to offer a "fully managed" system, providing additional support and services, the entity still has the responsibility to understand how the program works and to monitor the same activities and outcomes. It is a critical misstep for a facility to turn over all aspects of program management to a third-party administrator. This is especially true for managing a contract pharmacy arrangement. Understanding the details of data inputs into a software system, filters and settings to guide qualification criteria, supply chain connectivity, and general software functions (e.g., security, HIPAA compliance, reliability) are extremely important. If the 340B program team doesn't understand the data coming into the system and the methodologies employed to make qualification decisions, they won't be able to monitor the system outcomes effectively.

KEY POINT

Rural hospitals' 340B programs are most successful when leadership understands regulatory and IT requirements, limited resources are allocated appropriately, and all affected departments are engaged with current operations and future strategy.

Rural hospitals should develop a robust self-audit and compliance monitoring program with support beyond the pharmacy. A well-informed, multidisciplinary 340B oversight committee is the safest way to promote a culture of compliance and system knowledge. Monitoring programs should be able to detect errors that could result in over qualification as soon as possible for immediate correction. The program should also monitor for prescriptions or drugs administered that the software did not qualify, but should have. A 340B program should be as compliant on both ends of the spectrum as possible—missed qualification and identification of 340B-eligible patients can be as harmful as qualifying a 340B-ineligible patient, although the latter is non-compliant. Again, personnel time must be devoted to this function as well as establishing an expectation of program compliance.

SUMMARY

The 340B program advantages offered to participating rural hospitals are substantial and well-aligned with program objectives. Rural hospitals are encumbered with the unique operating and financial challenge of managing the exclusion of orphan drugs and the difficulties of effectively including 340B in a small scale operation. However, the benefits and costs associated with 340B participation, in light of compliance considerations, can allow the 340B program to support the mission and care obligations of rural hospitals.

REFERENCES

1. The Patient Protection and Affordable Care Act, Pub.L. No 111-148. § 7101, 124 Stat. 119; 2010.

2. National Rural Health Association. What's different about rural healthcare? https://www.rural-healthweb.org/about-nrha/about-rural-health-care. Accessed October 14, 2017.

3. Henriksen M, Walzer N. Illinois critical access hospitals: Enhancing quality of care in rural Illinois. [White Paper]. Center for Governmental Studies: Northern Illinois University; 2012. http://cgs.niu.edu/services/CWED/Health_Care_Policy/ICAHN/4.10.2012_interactive.pdf. Accessed October 14, 2017.

4. Gamm L, Hutchinson L, Dabney B, et al. Rural healthy people 2010: A companion document to healthy people 2010. Volume 3—rural health research gateway. (No. 2013). College Station, TX: The Texas A&M University System Health Science Center, School of Rural Public Health; 2003.

5. Wallack MC. "The 340B Drug Discount Program: Enrollment and Participation among Critical Access Hospitals." University of Minnesota; 2013:168 pp. 3589211.

6. Schur C, Cheung K, Radford A, et al. 340B drug pricing program: results of a survey of participating hospitals. (Working Paper #90). Chapel Hill, NC: Report to the Office of Rural Health Policy; 2007.

7. Wallack M, Sorensen T. "Excluding Orphan Drugs from the 340B Drug Discount Program: The Impact on 18 Critical Access Hospitals." Innovations in Pharmacy. 2012;(3):1.

8. The Orphan Drug Act. Pub. L. No. 97-414 96 Stat. 2049; 1983.

9. U.S. Food and Drug Administration. "Search Orphan Drug Designations and Approvals." Available at: https://www.accessdata.fda.gov/scripts/opdlisting/oopd/listResult.cfm. Accessed March 15, 2018.

10. "Notice of Proposed Rulemaking, Exclusion of Orphan Drugs for Certain Covered Entities under 340B Program." *Federal Register*. 2011;(76)8:29183. https://www.gpo.gov/fdsys/granule/FR-2011-05-20/2011-12423. Accessed October 14, 2017.

11. United States District Court for the District of Columbia. *"Pharmaceutical Manufacturers and Researchers of America v United States Department of Health and Human Services."* Civil Action No 14-1685 (RC); 2015. https://ecf.dcd.uscourts.gov/cgi-bin/show_public_doc?2014cv1685-29. Accessed October 14, 2017.

APPENDIX A: KEY RESOURCES FOR RURAL 340B HOSPITALS

The following are among the organizations that provide support for rural hospitals participating in the 340B program:

- National Rural Health Association: http://www.ruralhealthweb.org/
- National Rural Health Resources Center:

  https://www.ruralcenter.org/category/categories/340b-information
- American Hospital Association: http://www.aha.org/advocacy-issues/340b/index.shtml
- Apexus: https://www.340bpvp.com/resourceCenter/faqSearch.html?category=content&Ntt=rural https://www.apexus.com/solutions/education/pvp-education/340b-tools

  https://www.340bpvp.com/content/contentSearch.html?category=content&Ntt=critical+access&main-submit=

CHAPTER 12

340B Implementation and Operations Considerations for Free-standing Cancer Centers

Krist Azizian, PharmD;
John P. Gray, PharmD, MS, BCPS; and
Kim Le, PharmD

Free-standing cancer centers (FSCCs) were recently made potentially 340B eligible entities. The majority of the statutes, rules, and guidance related to the FSCC's participation in the 340B program are identical to the provisions of disproportionate share hospitals (DSHs). The orphan drug exclusion, which excludes drugs with an orphan indication from the definition of a covered outpatient drug for free-standing cancer centers, is the notable exception and drives numerous strategic and operational decisions related to participation in the 340B program.

FREE-STANDING CANCER CENTERS DEFINED

FSCCs, as defined by Section 1886(d)(1)(B)(v) of the Social Security Act, are independent non-profit entities distinct from other organizations, such as universities and medical centers, with which they may maintain affiliation agreements.[1,2] In 2010, with the passage of the Patient Protection and Affordable Care Act (ACA), institutions eligible to participate in the 340B program as covered entities was broadened to include free-standing cancer hospitals, critical access hospitals, sole community hospitals, rural referral centers, and pediatric hospitals.[3] Unlike the facilities identified as covered entities in the original 1992 legislation, the majority of the newly added covered entities, including FSCCs, are subject to additional statutory requirements as defined in the Health Care and Education Reconciliation Act (HCERA)—the most significant of which is the orphan drug exclusion.[4] The complex legal and regulatory history of the orphan drug exclusion is covered elsewhere in the book (see Chapters 3 and 11). The focus of this chapter will be the practical, operational implications of implementing and managing a 340B program that confront a FSCC considering 340B program entry.

KEY POINT

A FSCC is an independent, non-profit entity that treats patients with cancer. FSCCs were made eligible to participate in the 340B program with the passage of the Patient Protection and Affordable Care Act.

UNIQUE CONSIDERATIONS FOR FSCCs

The Orphan Drug Exclusion

Congress passed and signed the Orphan Drug Act into law in 1983 with the stated purpose of incentivizing the development of drugs to treat rare diseases and conditions for which adequate treatments have not been developed.[5] With the passage of the ACA and the HCERA, FSCCs became eligible to participate as covered entities in the 340B program with the added restriction that orphan drugs are not considered covered outpatient drugs. Following passage of the ACA, the Health Resources and Services Administration (HRSA) engaged in rulemaking and the development of interpretive guidance that was intended to direct covered entities, manufacturers, and others in complying with the orphan drug exclusion. Ultimately, the regulations and guidance promulgated by HRSA were invalidated through legal action[6]; therefore, the original broad exclusion of orphan drugs as covered outpatient drugs stands with limited guidance and support provided to the FSCCs from HRSA.

The first of several layers of complexity associated with the orphan drug exclusion is the fact that a drug may carry FDA approval for multiple indications, some of which may be orphan indications and some of which may not. Because of the broad exclusion of any drug with any orphan indication from the definition of a covered outpatient drug, manufacturers of numerous drugs may not offer FSCCs the opportunity to make a purchase at a statutorily-calculated 340B price. For example, because midazolam carries an orphan indication for the treatment of status epilepticus, the manufacturer that holds the orphan designation is not required to offer a FSCC the discounted 340B price for that drug even when it is utilized for a non-orphan indication. The financial impact of this exclusion can be significant.

KEY POINT

Drugs with an orphan indication, as defined by the Orphan Drug Act, are not considered covered outpatient drugs for FSCCs.

Group Purchasing Organization Prohibition

The prohibition on group purchasing organization (GPO) participation applies to covered entities that are registered as DSHs, pediatric hospitals, and FSCCs.[7] 42 U.S.C. Section 256b(a)(4)(L)(iii) states that the covered entity may not "obtain covered outpatient drugs through a group purchasing organization or other group purchasing arrangement." The provisions of the orphan drug exclusion notwithstanding, a *covered outpatient drug* is defined in Section 1927(k) of the Social Security Act to include "prescription medications, over-the-counter medications that are ordered on as a prescription, biological products that are dispensed pursuant to a prescription (excluding vaccines), and FDA-approved insulin."[8] Because orphan drugs do not meet the definition of a covered outpatient drug, the GPO prohibition does not apply to drugs with an orphan indication for FSCCs. Therefore, FSCCs may purchase drugs with an orphan indication via traditional GPO arrangements and may also have the opportunity to engage in special purchasing agreements to access sub-wholesale acquisition cost (WAC) pricing for drugs with an orphan designation.

Specialty Pharmacy Considerations

Since the early 2000s, significant growth has occurred in the development and marketing of oral anti-cancer agents.[9,10] As of May 2018, at least 70 oral medications currently on the market are indicated for the treatment of malignancies with 25% of new oncologic agents in the development pipeline represented by oral agents.[11] Further, more than 30% of cancer drug costs in 2015 in the United States were for medications dispensed by retail pharmacies, which is an increase from 25% 10 years ago.[12] The high cost, complexity, and risk associated with the self-administration of oral anti-cancer agents drives payers to encourage, and in some instances, mandate that patients obtain these medications from designated specialty pharmacies. Specifically, payers may require the use of accredited specialty pharmacies (e.g., specialty pharmacy accreditation through URAC) and/ or select medications that may be subject to limited distribution via a small cohort of pharmacies. As such, FSCCs that are 340B covered entities should develop a long-term specialty pharmacy strategy, which (broadly) could include an in-house specialty pharmacy and/or strategic contract pharmacy arrangements with specialty pharmacies.

The Cancer Hospital–Patient Relationship

Unlike the traditional hospital–patient relationship, which may be transactional in nature and focused on an acute inpatient treatment episode, patients of cancer hospitals receive a broader scope of services (e.g., guided meditation, cancer survivorship, care planning) on a continuing basis, including continuity care services. Patients of cancer hospitals tend to approach the management of their conditions as engaged consumers rather than passive recipients of health information.[13] The unique relationship between the cancer hospital and the patient results in more patient touch-points, improved continuity of care, and potentially improved treatment outcomes. This holistic approach to the care of patients with cancer extends to medication management such that, unlike traditional hospitals, the cancer hospital is well-positioned to capture a greater proportion of ambulatory and discharge prescription volume. Capture of these prescriptions may be achieved via the development of an in-house specialty pharmacy, the execution of thoughtful contract pharmacy arrangements, or a combination of these two strategies.

KEY POINT

The relationship between a FSCC and the patients it serves is often more longitudinal than the traditional hospital–patient relationship, which may present the FSCC with greater opportunities to secure prescription volume through in-house or contract pharmacies.

340B PROGRAM IMPLEMENTATION CONSIDERATIONS

Assessment of Eligibility

When preparing to apply to participate in the 340B drug pricing program, a set of discrete eligibility criteria must be met by the FSCC. Much like DSH registration, the hospital (1) must certify that it is either a private non-profit hospital under contract with state or local government to provide healthcare services to low-income individuals who are not eligible for Medicare or Medicaid, (2) is owned or operated by a unit of state or local government, or (3) is a public or private nonprofit corporation that is formally granted governmental powers by a unit of state or local government.[14] Also similar to DSH registration, the hospital must certify that for the most recent cost-reporting period, the hospital had a disproportionate share adjustment percentage of greater than 11.75%. Because FSCCs do not receive disproportionate share adjustment payments, they must perform a calculation to estimate the disproportionate share percentage based on payer mix.[15] This calculation and the DSH enrollment process are described in detail in an earlier chapter (see Chapter 4, The Basics of 340B Program Implementation).

During the application process, the FSCC may elect to identify outpatient locations that have a different physical address from the facility as child sites that are eligible to purchase, dispense, and/or administer 340B drugs.[16,17] As with child site eligibility for DSHs, the outpatient facility must be listed on a reimbursable line of the covered entity's most recently filed Medicare cost report.[18] Lines 50 through 118 of Worksheet A of the Medicare cost report are potentially reimbursable.[19]

Assessment of 340B Program Viability

As is true with implementing any 340B program, a FSCC should perform a detailed analysis of the potential costs, benefits, and risks of implementing a 340B program. The preceding and following sections of this chapter highlight the many potential consequences of implementing a 340B program at a FSCC, which should be considered. Because medications with an orphan indication are not covered outpatient drugs, it is likely that a material portion of the FSCC-dispensed drugs will be excluded from 340B. Therefore, the orphan drug exclusion may significantly limit the FSCC's potential savings. At the same time, the FSCC will incur many, if not all, of the same program implementation and maintenance costs (e.g., third-party administrator [TPA] costs, personnel expenses for program management). Ultimately, the FSCC should develop an estimate of the likely savings realized on covered outpatient drugs (and additional contract pharmacy revenue, if applicable) and the projected costs of managing the program to determine whether enrolling in the 340B program will improve the FSCC's overall financial position. This assessment should also weigh the potential regulatory risks associated with participation in the 340B program. FSCC may determine that the increased regulatory risk associated with participation outweighs the estimated financial benefits.

Contract Pharmacy Arrangements

Although the mechanics of contract pharmacy arrangements for a FSCC are essentially identical to DSHs, the specialized nature of the medications prescribed at a cancer center warrants careful development and selection of contract pharmacy arrangements. Standard contract pharmacy offerings from national retail and specialty pharmacies and the business arrangements offered through 340B administrators are likely to be unsuitable without modifications. It is incumbent on the cancer center to assess the medications prescribed and the associated prescription volume. A useful exercise would be to cohort prescriptions as "specialty" or "conventional" prescriptions. The volume of prescriptions for conventional medications may be greater than the volume of prescriptions for specialty medications; however, the potential costs and revenue associated with the specialty prescriptions may be significantly greater than for the conventional prescriptions.

Understanding the organization's payer mix is essential to developing a thoughtful contract pharmacy strategy. Specifically, a thorough understanding the organization's commercial and government payers is required to select the most appropriate pharmacies with which to contract, especially given that a cohort of commercial payers are strategically driving specialty pharmacy prescription volume to payer-owned or contracted pharmacies while Medicaid must be carved out. The organization should attempt to ascertain the pharmacies that currently capture the largest proportion of specialty prescriptions generated within the facility. With knowledge of payer mix and prescription volume, the organization should narrow the list of specialty pharmacies with which to contract to ensure that all patients have access to medications in their complex chemotherapy regimens.

In addition to the strategic considerations described above, assessment of the quality and scope of services as well as the coordination of care provided by potential contract pharmacy partners are of great importance. The organization should expect seamless communication among the patient, the institution, and the contract pharmacy regarding authorization status, medication adherence, and tolerability concerns. Some institutions have developed relationships with their contract pharmacies that permit the organization to view their patient's records in the pharmacy electronic record system. The organization should engage in routine meetings with a representative from each contract pharmacy to ensure accountability with regulatory requirements, predetermined performance standards, and quality standards.

Third-Party Administrators

The purchasing and inventory-management functions of a 340B TPA will be discussed in detail later in this chapter; therefore, the following discussion explains the ways in which the 340B TPA can support contract pharmacy operations. The performance requirements for a 340B TPA for a FSCC are nearly identical to those of a 340B TPA for any covered entity with the notable exception of managing the orphan drug exclusion. When selecting, implementing, and monitoring the performance of a TPA, the FSCC should understand the methods, process, and the scope of the 340B TPA's orphan drug list. A comparison to the HRSA and U.S. Food and Drug Administration (FDA) sources (discussed later in this chapter) and the methods used by the FSCC's distributor to manage contracts and other designations is necessary to support proper orphan drug management under the 340B program. The FSCC should also understand how drugs with orphan indications that do not qualify as 340B eligible are tracked and managed during validation testing and in ongoing operations.

OPERATIONAL CONSIDERATIONS

Purchasing and Inventory Management

A FSCC will almost certainly provide services to patients who are eligible to receive 340B drugs and also other services that do not meet 340B eligibility requirements. As a result, the organization will need to establish and maintain a number of purchasing accounts with its pharmacy distributor and potentially individual pharmaceutical manufacturers with separate purchasing contracts. To ensure compliance with the GPO prohibition and the orphan drug exclusion, the organization must, at a minimum, maintain three separate purchasing accounts—a 340B account, a GPO account, and a non-contract or WAC account.[20] The 340B account is used to purchase non-orphan medications and manufacturer-discounted orphan drugs (in cases in which manufacturers offer special discounts to 340B-eligible institutions). The GPO purchasing account is utilized to purchase drugs that are not considered covered outpatient drugs (e.g., orphan drugs, vaccines) and drugs used in inpatient care settings. The WAC purchasing account is used to purchase any covered outpatient drug that, for any reason, does not qualify as 340B eligible. The 340B TPA typically manages the assignment of purchasing across these accounts under a virtual inventory through connections to the FSCC's electronic medical record or patient financial system and the FSCC's pharmaceutical distributor. Individual manually managed accounts may also support purchasing and inventory management.

Fundamentally, the organization has three inventory management options to prevent diversion of 340B drugs to ineligible patients.

The First Option

The first option is to purchase and maintain two separate physical inventories—one inventory of drugs purchased at the 340B price, and a second separate inventory of drugs purchased at the appropriate non-340B price (i.e., managing, dispensing, and administering the medications accordingly).[21]

The Second Option

The second option is to operate a virtual inventory replenishment model in which all initial purchases are made at non-340B/non-GPO pricing, and subsequent purchases are based on the accumulated capacity to purchase drugs at the 340B price (or WAC or GPO) based on past utilization. The replenishment model is typically operationalized by using 340B TPA split-billing software, which tracks information about all drugs ordered, dispensed, and administered, and applies defined tests and rules to assess eligibility for replenishment of inventory with 340B or non-340B drugs.

The physical inventory model of inventory management may represent a rational strategy for areas within the cancer center for which all medications are dispensed and administered in a 340B-eligible outpatient area; for example, an infusion center in which only employed (or contracted) physicians order medications for patients of the 340B covered entity. In this situation, where diversion of 340B drugs to ineligible patients is not a concern, utilizing a physical inventory model removes the complexity of developing and monitoring the qualification tests within a split-billing system. This mitigates the risk of missing opportunities to purchase eligible medications at the 340B discounted price.

To properly implement a physical inventory management strategy beyond the simple "clean 340B" example above, the individual performing the purchasing as well as the pharmacy team dispensing and administering drugs must have an in-depth knowledge of the orphan drug exclusion and, based on that, whether a drug may be dispensed, administered, and purchased through the 340B, GPO, or WAC purchasing account and then act accordingly. Several sources of information can guide purchasing activities, including the orphan drug list on the HRSA web site, the FDA orphan drug designations and approvals web site, and past purchase history.[4,22] Other disadvantages of the physical inventory management strategy are the financial and space implications of maintaining duplicate inventories of 340B and non-340B drug.

KEY POINT

In outpatient areas in the FSCC that only serve 340B-eligible patients, it may be beneficial to implement a separate physical inventory model of 340B program management.

The virtual inventory replenishment model of inventory management represents the most rational strategy for mixed-use areas (e.g., procedural areas) in which a cohort of patients are 340B eligible and others are not. To make real-time determinations about whether a 340B drug or non-340B drug should be dispensed to a patient in a mixed-use area, in a complex organization like a FSCC, would be impossible to support. Various tools exist to assist organizations in reviewing the performance and selection of a 340B TPA split-billing software vendor to support a replenishment model of inventory management.[21] The FSCC should perform an in-depth assessment of the 340B TPA split-billing software capabilities' logic and support to accurately apply the orphan drug exclusion in addition to other 340B rules outlined elsewhere.

The Third Option

The third option is to implement a blended approach in which the cancer hospital and associated outpatient departments utilize a replenishment model, and the organization's outpatient infusion centers maintain separate 340B and non-340B physical inventories. This approach mitigates (1) the potential to miss 340B savings in the infusion areas due to the complexity of the implementation and oversight of split-billing software and (2) the risk of diversion of 340B drugs in the mixed-use areas of the cancer hospital. The disadvantage of this blended approach is that the organization will need to implement and maintain a split-billing software system and manage three separate physical inventories (340B, non-340B, and mixed-use). However, as outlined, the advantages in each care area are clear and make option three attractive when considering the potential compliance, savings, resource requirements, and risk.

Billing Considerations

Preparing and submitting outpatient and retail pharmacy claims for 340B medications is covered elsewhere in this book and is beyond the scope of this chapter. However, a brief review and discussion is warranted. As with DSH hospitals, the FSCC must be certain to follow all applicable state Medicaid billing rules to prevent duplicate discounts for physician-administered drugs in 340B child sites. Although the requirements vary by state, examples of these rules include indicating the use of the 340B drug by use of a modifier code in a payer-specified field of the UB04 or CMS-1500 claim form and billing at the actual acquisition cost (AAC) of the drug administered.[23-25] The covered entity is solely responsible for understanding and applying these rules for all state Medicaid agencies to which it submits claims.

The organization should obtain the state's Medicaid provider manuals and, when necessary, establish contact with a representative from the state's Medicaid agencies to ensure proper billing practices. As regional referral centers, FSCC's service areas encompass a broad swath of states. 340B program leadership should examine the requirements for each state billed and be certain that provider numbers, coding, and the cost basis for billing are correct. Chapter 4 provides a more complete treatment of Medicaid options.

340B PROGRAM SUSTAINABILITY

Two critical aspects of maintaining a sustainable 340B program at a FSCC are, *first*, obtaining the best possible pricing for drugs, especially those with an orphan indication, and therefore not eligible for 340B pricing; and, *second*, ensuring program compliance.

Direct Contracting

In recent years, pharmaceutical manufacturers have demonstrated an increased willingness to negotiate direct purchase contracts. The ability to negotiate direct contracts for drugs not eligible for 340B, such as drugs with orphan indications, is a potentially significant boon to the FSCC. However, one potential barrier for FSCCs to negotiate and execute direct manufacturer contracts is the GPO prohibition. Specifically, in some cases, FSCCs are affiliated with other hospitals as part of a larger health system and, traditionally, direct contracts have been negotiated at the health-system level. In the event of multiple 340B covered entities within the health system, negotiation of direct contracts with manufacturers at the health-system level would be in violation of the GPO prohibition. To prevent potential violations of the GPO prohibition, each 340B covered entity within the health system must separately negotiate and execute direct purchase contracts.[7, 26]

The direct contracting approach may be advantageous to the FSCC because the organization may be able to negotiate deeper discounts for high-cost, anti-cancer agents based on the ability to drive volume to one manufacturer's product. Additionally, the organization's GPO might not have aggressively negotiated for the best possible price for niche, infrequently utilized anti-cancer agents. The direct contracting approach can be time consuming and may not result in a favorable contract if the organization cannot arrive at mutually agreeable terms with the manufacturer. Additionally, the pharmacy will need to monitor its purchasing accounts to ensure that the appropriate pricing for direct contracts has been loaded.

Orphan Drug Expanded Pricing

Historically, two factors may have created a barrier to pharmaceutical manufacturers offering discounted prices to FSCC hospitals. The *first* was the fact that FSCCs are subject to the GPO prohibition that prohibits the FSCC from accepting discounted prices on covered outpatient drugs.[27] With the recent District Court ruling on the orphan drug provision of the HCERA, it is clear that all drugs with an orphan indication are not covered outpatient drugs for FSCCs.[6] Therefore, a FSCC may accept discounted pricing on drugs with an orphan indication, many of which are novel, high-cost anti-cancer agents, without fear of violating the orphan drug exclusion.

The *second* barrier to pharmaceutical manufacturers offering discounted prices on non-covered outpatient drugs to 340B-covered entities has been the result of concerns related to the calculation of best price. The *best price* is "the lowest price available [price] from the manufacturer during the rebate period to any distributor, retailer, provider, health maintenance organization, nonprofit entity, or governmental entity in the United States in any pricing structure (including capitated payments), in the same quarter for which the average manufacturer price is computed."[28] When manufacturers provide rebates to state Medicaid agencies, the rebate amount is based on the best price; therefore, manufacturers are reluctant to offer pricing schemes that could lower best price. A recent Centers for Medicare & Medicaid Services (CMS) final rule on covered outpatient drugs and the Medicaid program has clarified that the price charged to 340B covered entities, whether it is a 340B price or not, should be excluded from the calculation of the best price.[27] This clarification in the calculation of best price should alleviate the concern among pharmaceutical manufacturers that discounted pricing offered to FSCCs could adversely impact the best price.

A small number of pharmaceutical manufacturers have collaborated with the FSCCs that participate in the 340B program to offer discounted prices on drugs with orphan indications. Certainly, the ability to purchase these (often high-cost) medications at a discounted price without expending the effort to negotiate direct contracts is a potential benefit to FSCCs. However, unlike a direct contract with defined terms, these discounts are fully at the discretion of the manufacturers and may be revoked at any time. Frequently, these manufacturer discounts are loaded in the 340B purchasing account with the organization's distributor; this is to ensure that only 340B covered entities access these discounts. However, these discounts are not considered a 340B price and may differ from the 340B price. Because—in accessing these discounts—the covered entity may make non-340B purchases within their 340B distributor accounts, the organization should maintain documentation of the reason that these non-340B prices are loaded in the 340B account. If possible, the distributor should flag these manufacturer discounts as such in the 340B account.

KEY POINT

> Opportunities exist for the FSCC to engage in direct contracting with pharmaceutical manufacturers and/or accept special discounts on drugs with orphan indications.

Program Self-Auditing and Compliance

As is the case with all aspects of 340B program implementation and monitoring, compliance with 340B statutes, rules, and guidance is the responsibility of the covered entity.[29] It is incumbent on the covered entity to implement multiple compliance activities (e.g., self-audit, independent audit) across all elements of the program. The HRSA-required annual program recertification is an opportunity to review and validate all elements or program eligibility and registration status.[30] In particular, a FSCC-covered entity should utilize annual recertification to validate that the organization continues to meet the 340B program eligibility requirements, specifically the estimated disproportionate share percentage.[31,32] Additionally, the organization should download all information currently displayed in the 340B database on the HRSA web site and validate the accuracy of the information in each field.[33] In large, complex organizations, special attention should be paid to addresses, including suite numbers, of child sites to ensure an exact match between the database and the license. In reviewing child site locations, the organization should prepare a crosswalk of registered child sites to the associated reimbursable line on the most recent Medicare cost report or cost report trial balance. This exercise is an opportunity to detect both improperly listed child sites and to identify reimbursable locations that could be considered for future 340B child site designation.

Finally, the organization should access the most recent Medicaid Exclusion File from the HRSA web site to validate that the "carve-in/carve-out" decisions for each child site are properly noted.[34,35] Although not compulsory, a less comprehensive quarterly review of the accuracy of the organization's information in the HRSA 340B database and Medicaid Exclusion File is prudent, especially in a complex organization in which clinic locations and licensure status may change.

If a 340B TPA is utilized to qualify contract pharmacy prescriptions and/or manage a virtual inventory system, the accuracy of the data feeds provided to the TPA is critically important to optimize 340B savings and/or contract pharmacy prescription volume and to support program compliance. Because the business and compliance risks associated with inaccurate data feeds to the 340B TPA are significant, a best practice is to perform a daily check of the data feeds. This review should include an assessment of the size (e.g., number of lines of data) and nature of data being transmitted. This frequent review will facilitate rapid identification and correction of technical errors that, if unchecked, could result in significant compliance risks (e.g., potential diversion of 340B drugs due to improper accumulation in a split-billing system) or adversely impact 340B program savings.

To ensure program compliance, the covered entity should perform routine audits of appropriate dispensing of 340B drugs in all 340B service areas including covered outpatient areas, in-house retail pharmacies, and contract pharmacies.[36] The mechanics and audit parameters are similar for all 340B areas with some variation in the data source and assessment of those data. Recommended audit parameters of a FSCC participating in the 340B program include:

- Ensuring that it maintains records of the patient's health care; this assessment will likely be straightforward in the era of electronic medical records.
- Validating that the patient received healthcare services from a provider who is employed by the organization or provides services under a contractual arrangement.
- Reconciling and matching the national provider identifier (NPI) number of all ordering providers in the FSCC's 340B-eligible provider list.
- Assessing that each patient had outpatient status at the time of drug administration and that the patient received services at an eligible outpatient location (in a reimbursable line of the most recent Medicare cost report).
- Validating that the medication's administration resulted in appropriate accumulation (appropriate NDC, quantity, and purchase) if a virtual inventory management system is utilized.

KEY POINT

Activities to ensure 340B program compliance within the FSCC should mirror those undertaken at a DSH with added policy oversight and practices supporting appropriate handling of drugs with an orphan indication.

If the organization engages in contract pharmacy arrangements, then HRSA mandates additional monitoring requirements to ensure that the covered entity is taking appropriate actions to prevent diversion of 340B drugs and duplicate discounts under Medicaid.[37,38] The *Federal Register* notice on contract pharmacy services mandates that the covered entity establishes practices to "compare its prescribing records with the contract pharmacy's dispensing records to detect potential irregularities." If the organization utilizes a 340B TPA to support contract pharmacy operations, the data feeds into the system may be useful in performing such a comparison. The notice on contract pharmacy services also notes that HRSA expects "annual audits performed by an independent, outside auditor with experience auditing pharmacies."

SUMMARY

FSCC participation in the 340B program has unique elements among the covered entity types in the 340B program. A detailed and deliberate approach to understanding the challenges and opportunities and developing policies, practices, and operational support can lead to a compliant, high-performing 340B program for a FSCC.

REFERENCES

1. Freestanding cancer hospitals. Health Resources and Services Administration web site. http://www.hrsa.gov/opa/eligibilityandregistration/hospitals/freestandingcancercenters/index.html. Accessed October 11, 2017.

2. Simone JV. Understanding cancer centers. *J Clin Oncol.* 2002;20(23):4503-4507.

3. Patient Protection and Affordable Care Act, HR 3590, 111th Cong (2010). https://www.gpo.gov/fdsys/pkg/PLAW-111publ148/pdf/PLAW-111publ148.pdf. Accessed August 26, 2016.

4. Orphan drug exclusion. Health Resources and Services Administration web site. https://www.hrsa.gov/opa/program-requirements/orphan-drug-exclusion/index.html. Accessed October 11, 2017.

5. The Orphan Drug Act. US Food and Drug Administration web site. http://www.fda.gov/regulatoryinformation/legislation/significantamendmentstothefdcact/orphandrugact/default.htm. Accessed October 11, 2017.

6. Pharmaceutical Research and Manufacturers of America v United States Department of Health and Human Services, case no. 14-1685 (D.D.C. Oct. 14, 2015). https://ecf.dcd.uscourts.gov/cgi-bin/show_public_doc?2014cv1685-29. Accessed October 11, 2017.

7. Statutory prohibition on group purchasing organization participation. Health Resources and Services Administration web site. http://www.hrsa.gov/opa/programrequirements/policyreleases/prohibitionongpoparticipation020713.pdf. Published February 7, 2013; accessed October 11, 2017.

8. Glossary of 340B terms. Apexus 340B Tools web site. https://docs.340bpvp.com/documents/public/resourcecenter/glossary.pdf. Updated May 26, 2016; accessed October 11, 2017.

9. Weingart SN, Brown E, Bach PB, et al. NCCN task force report: oral chemotherapy. *J Natl Compr Canc Netw.* 2008;6(suppl 3):S1-S14.

10. Mancini R, Wilson D. A pharmacist-managed oral chemotherapy program. *Oncology Issues.* January/February 2012:28-31. https://accc-cancer.org/oncology_issues/articles/JF12/JF12-A-Pharmacist-Managed-Oral-Chemotherapy-Program.pdf. Accessed October 11, 2017.

11. Oral chemotherapy monitoring and counseling chart. Avella Specialty Pharmacy web site. https://info.avella.com/oral-chemo-chart. Published June 1, 2016; accessed October 11, 2017.

12. Global oncology trend report. IMS Health web site. http://www.imshealth.com/en/thought-leadership/ims-institute/reports/global-oncology-trend-report-a-review-of-2015-and-outlook-to-2020. Accessed October 11, 2017.

13. Diefenbach M, Turner G, Carpenter KM, et al. Cancer and patient-physician communication. *J Health Commun.* 2009;14(suppl 1):57-65.

14. 340B hospital eligibility criteria. Apexus 340B Tools web site. https://docs.340bpvp.com/documents/public/resourcecenter/Hospital_Eligibility_Criteria.pdf. Updated May 6, 2015; accessed October 11, 2017.

15. Criteria for hospital participation in the 340B drug discount program. 340B Health 340B Resources web site. http://www.340bhealth.org/340b-resources/340b-program/criteria-for-hospital-participation. Accessed October 11, 2017.

16. 340B program DSH self-audit tool: eligibility. Apexus 340B Tools web site. https://docs.340bpvp.com/documents/public/resourcecenter/DSH-Self-Audit-Eligibility.docx. Updated June 14, 2016; accessed October 11, 2017.

17. Eligibility requirements FAQs. Apexus 340B FAQ web site. https://www.340bpvp.com/resource-center/faqs/eligibility-requirements/. Accessed October 11, 2017.

18. Notice regarding section 602 of the veterans' health care act of 1992 outpatient hospital facilities. *Fed Regist*. 1994;59(180):47884-47886.

19. 340B university sample worksheet. Apexus 340B Tools web site. https://docs.340bpvp.com/documents/public/resourcecenter/new_worksheet_a.pdf. Accessed October 11, 2017.

20. Strategies to minimize unnecessary WAC exposure. Apexus 340B Tools web site. https://docs.340bpvp.com/documents/public/resourcecenter/340b_minimize_wac_exposure.pdf. Updated May 6, 2015; accessed October 11, 2017.

21. Split-billing software considerations checklist. Apexus 340B Tools web site. https://docs.340bpvp.com/documents/public/resourcecenter/Split-Billing_Decision_Checklist.pdf. Updated February 12, 2016; accessed October 11, 2017.

22. Search orphan drug designations and approvals. Food and FDA Orphan Drug Designation and Approvals. US Food and Drug Administration web site. https://www.accessdata.fda.gov/scripts/opdlisting/oopd/. Accessed October 11, 2017.

23. 340B and Medicaid. Apexus web site. https://www.340bpvp.com/resource-center/faqs/medicaid--duplicate-discounts/. Accessed October 11, 2017.

24. Overview of the 340B drug pricing program. 340B Health 340B Resources web site. http://www.340bhealth.org/340b-resources/340b-program/overview/. Accessed October 11, 2017.

25. Contract pharmacy FAQs. Apexus 340B FAQ web site. https://www.340bpvp.com/resource-center/faqs/contract-pharmacy/. Accessed October 11, 2017.

26. Policy/implementation GPO prohibition FAQs. Apexus 340B FAQ web site. https://www.340bpvp.com/resourceCenter/faqSearch.html?FAQs=GPO%20Prohibition&category=content&method=gn. Accessed October 11, 2017.

27. 340B health analysis of orphan drug exclusion. 340B Health 340B Resources web site. http://www.340bhealth.org/news/340bhealth-update/340b-health-analysis-of-orphan-drug-exclusion . Published June 24, 2016; accessed October 11, 2017.

28. Determination of best price, 42 USC §447.505 (2015).

29. Program integrity. Health Resources and Services Administration web site. http://www.hrsa.gov/opa/programintegrity/index.html. Accessed October 11, 2017.

30. Annual recertification. Health Resources and Services Administration web site. http://www.hrsa.gov/opa/programrequirements/recertification/index.html. Accessed October 11, 2017.

31. HRSA recertification attestation language. Apexus 340B Tools web site. https://docs.340bpvp.com/documents/public/resourcecenter/HRSA_Recertification_Attestation_Language.pdf . Updated March 29, 2016; accessed October 11, 2017.

32. Annual Recertification. Health Resources and Services Administration web site. https://www.hrsa.gov/opa/recertification/recertification.html. Accessed October 11, 2017.

33. 340B Office of Pharmacy Affairs Information System. Health Resources and Services Administration web site. https://www.hrsa.gov/opa/340b-opais/index.html. Accessed October 11, 2017.

34. 340B database Medicaid exclusion file. Health Resources and Services Administration Website. https://340bopais.hrsa.gov/medicaidexclusionfiles. Accessed October 11, 2016.

35. The Medicaid exclusion file: important clarifications. Health Resources and Services Administration web site. http://www.hrsa.gov/opa/updates/151009monthlyupdate.pdf. Published October 2015; accessed October 11, 2016.

36. 340B compliance self-assessment: self-audit process. Apexus 340B Tools web site. https://docs.340bpvp.com/documents/public/resourcecenter/DSH_340B_Compliance_SelfAssessment_Data-Transactions.pdf. Updated May 6, 2015; accessed October 11, 2016.

37. Contract pharmacy services. Health Resources and Services Administration web site. http://www.hrsa.gov/opa/implementation/contract/. Accessed October 11, 2016.

38. Notice regarding 340B drug pricing program – contract pharmacy services. *Fed Regist*. 2010; 75(43):10272-10279.

CHAPTER 13

Developing a High-Performing 340B Program

Gregg Niemiec, BS, RPh and
Andrew L. Wilson, PharmD, FASHP

Beyond compliance with 340B rules and Apexus best practices, what constitutes a high-performing 340B program? How can a 340B covered entity (CE) combine measurement of financial value with effective compliance, while managing the non-340B objectives required of a high-performing pharmacy service? Compliance is a must, but efficiency and resource optimization are paramount in the delivery of pharmacy services. Adding another process domain to the pharmacy department creates additional management challenges and further complicates an already complex supply chain. In the 340B program, results that appear as "savings" are not solely a financial activity but come with some portion of compliance risk and may also represent an opportunity to improve pharmacy purchasing, the drug supply chain, and revenue cycle performance. Participation in the 340B program with the attendant activities and tasks to manage 340B business performance can bring unexpected benefits in pharmacy business performance to the organization. A 340B CE carries financial benefit that is designed to help a healthcare organization support care for uninsured and underinsured patients in their service area. A hospital that meets the current 340B eligibility criteria is hard pressed to argue against participation, with the material savings on the cost of drugs delivered to outpatients.

Business and 340B program decisions in a CE often revolve around the cost and performance of a patient care program or service. A hospital has numerous options to prepare reports that measure and visualize 340B program value, but what should be measured and how? Although pharmacy services and pharmacists can measure value to the healthcare system using performance metrics, 340B provides an additional value catalyst. The use of performance metrics supports process improvements and determines strategic priorities using key performance indicators (KPI). Targets and goals for KPI metrics can be built into team objectives and drive individual performance:

- How should the KPIs of 340B program performance be measured?
- How can you create the internal KPI benchmarks that identify trends and manage the controllable elements of 340B with focused attention on the ones that matter most?
- Can 340B program performance be benchmarked externally, and if so, how? It is important to match organizational factors of your health system with peers in addition to internal benchmarking.
- Which therapeutic areas, drugs, and processes should be tracked and trended?
- How can reports be used to drill into therapeutic class and individual drugs to see the impact of formulary and practice changes on 340B savings?
- Conversely, how might 340B alter or enable a new formulary strategy?

■ What are the drivers of 340B savings, and where does savings opportunity leak through system gaps? Note that the operations and business performance factors to be assembled and examined may be affected by high-priced items with large 340B savings rates; a modest number of high-cost, high-discount drugs may drive overall savings.

Leadership knowledge of the focus and impact of 340B can be key to managing risk and utility, where savings and costs are concentrated, and understanding how this might change over time. Purchase at wholesale acquisition cost (WAC) is generally viewed as a failure or gap in the 340B systems that the hospital employs. *WAC savings leak* is likely modest if 340B software is set up properly and the hospital's revenue cycle and supply chain processes are well-managed, but will bear continued oversight and evaluation.

This chapter describes methods to calculate and assess 340B savings and the factors that drive 340B program performance along with health-system leadership communication strategy.

INFLUENCES ON 340B FINANCIAL PERFORMANCE

Variables that influence 340B financial performance are outlined in Table 13-1 (see discussion and table later in the chapter). Key influences include CE type, Medicaid carve-in/carve-out status, charge volumes, purchase price and activity by account type, group purchasing organization (GPO) price, patient diagnosis/therapy/acuity, service line and location, medical staff relationship to the organization, and payer status. Each variable has a differing impact on 340B savings and fosters change at different rates, affecting savings over time. To understand and quantify its impact on KPI benchmarks, each variable should be monitored regularly in a structured manner. As an example, the addition of new services or medical staff prescribing new therapies will influence the number and type of drugs purchased. Service locations added or removed from the "above the line" costs on the Medicare cost report and, therefore, provider-based status will also have material impact. A service that was provided by medical staff, which was not part of the organization's reimbursement structure, may become an eligible part of the health system such that billing and costs become 340B eligible. On a day-to-day basis, drug shortages affecting availability, resulting in switches between the drug products with different national drug codes (NDCs) can impact cost. Depending on the alternate NDC, variation in the GPO and purchase price can change significantly. The variables described have short-, mid-, and longer-term implications for 340B program performance and should be evaluated at different frequencies.

KEY POINT

340B program performance and savings is complex and depends on organizational factors beyond the 340B qualifications. Managing the 340B program to the highest benefit requires a sustained, systematic, data-based approach.

THE 340B PRICE

The calculation of 340B price for a drug is based on language from the Medicaid Drug Rebate Program (MDRP) and definition of a *covered outpatient drug*.[1] A drug's 340B price depends on how it is classified; as single source, innovator multiple source, non-innovator multi-source, a clotting factor, or a drug used exclusively in the pediatric population. A specific 340B price is calculated by subtracting the unit rebate amount (URA) based on its rebate percentage from its average manufacturer price (AMP). The AMP and 340B price calculation is described in more detail in Chapter 3.

A drug's 340B package price is:

[AMP – URA] X [package quantity]

Statutory language allows for adjustments to the price calculation over time; for instance, a drug's calculation changes are limited based on the consumer price index urban (CPI-U). Because the impact of 340B discounts and price changes is supported by the mix and volume of products used, a best practice is to use local purchase data to create trends in pricing for specific products or therapeutic classes of interest over time and by account type.

Apexus, the 340B program prime vendor (340B PVP), has established a portfolio of sub-340B and sub-WAC prices on generic and some branded drugs for 340B CEs. Although not strictly 340B prices, the impact of these contracted prices should also be tracked and assessed as they impact savings and contribute to avoidance of additional WAC expense. Distributor catalogs and contract files provide details regarding the actual nature of the price (e.g., 340B, Apexus, WAC, GPO) in each account and offer a basis for calculating 340B savings as outlined below.

As a sidebar to tracking and management activities, the absence of a 340B price or a swing in 340B price not compatible with 340B rules may also be apparent. These gaps and potential errors should be investigated and resolved through contacting the distributor, manufacturer, or in the final instance, the Health Resources and Service Administration (HRSA) Office of Pharmacy Affairs (OPA).

UNDERSTANDING THE 340B SAVINGS CALCULATION

With an understanding of 340B price, the calculation of 340B savings can be undertaken. Although there may be reasons to benchmark 340B savings against the average wholesale price (AWP), WAC, or other benchmark prices, it is generally accepted that the comparison is made to the prevailing price at which the hospital would purchase the drug if the hospital were not a 340B participant. This is typically the current GPO price for the specific class of trade (acute care, ambulatory care, retail pharmacy).

Thus, the two price variables are: (1) the actual 340B or 340B PVP contract purchase price, and (2) the corresponding or proximate GPO catalog price.

GPO price at time of (or proximate to) purchase is the price the hospital would have paid if it was not in the 340B program. GPO catalog prices change periodically based on market forces that result in contract negotiations and subsequent price movement. On occasion, a health system will change GPOs resulting in a complete reset of pricing and a new catalog. Best practice for calculating accurate 340B savings is to collect a full catalog at GPO price at the time of each 340B and WAC purchase and store it for use at the time of calculation. *340B program savings is the sum of the difference between the baseline GPO price and the 340B price.*

A more complete view of 340B savings recognizes that hospitals subject to the GPO prohibition incur additional expense for purchasing items at WAC price under virtual inventory rules.[2] A WAC purchase typically occurs when purchasing inventory of an NDC not previously purchased, for additions to (growth of) shelf inventory, or in hospitals that carve out Medicaid prescriptions. To complete the savings picture, the difference between the baseline GPO price and the WAC on the date of purchase, is multiplied by the purchase quantity; this *WAC premium* is subtracted from the calculated savings to fully outline the net 340B program savings.

KEY POINT

Split-billing software (SBS) programs can provide a basis for evaluating 340B program savings and effectiveness. Familiarize the 340B leadership team with the data sources, calculations, and reporting methods before making use of the SBS to report 340B results.

SBS programs for 340B program management can facilitate savings calculations. Prior to considering the use of SBS-reported savings, as a first step, review the price calculation method(s) and determine the formula(s) and data sources used in the calculations. SBS vendors typically receive electronic data interchange (EDI) feeds from distributors and many suppliers. These EDI feeds provide baseline price catalogs and the purchase invoices as the source for 340B or WAC price paid and the proximate GPO price. However, not all suppliers' catalog and invoice information are available via EDI; in some instances, reference prices may be absent, dated, or incorrect, necessitating manual production and maintenance of (1) catalog prices and (2) manual entry or import of purchase data into the SBS. Although these gaps may account for a small number of items and purchases, they can represent high-cost or specialty items that contribute significantly to savings, necessitating verification and data entry to ensure a correct result. The authors have seen challenges for hospitals that rely solely on SBS and don't identify gaps in capture of GPO prices and manually correct dated or incorrect prices from EDI feeds, resulting in inaccurate reporting of savings. The staff time needed to maintain catalogs and back-fill missing or incorrect price data can be significant and may be a contributing factor to a gap in savings recognition.

If capture methods for proximate catalog prices result in missing GPO prices, an option for obtaining the GPO price is to extract them from purchase data in other accounts (e.g., a GPO purchase) that allows for correct entry of the price by item and quarter. This method relies on the purchase of each item on the GPO account, which may not be the case for all drugs. The scope and nature of this activity will vary based on the SBS used, the details of EDI transmission, and direct purchase volume. However, the idea is the same; if there are prices missing for a specific purchase, no savings can be calculated. The authors find that prices are most often missing from direct (non-distributor) purchases, whether drop-ship or direct. Because these items are often high-cost drugs, savings calculations that exclude them result in under-reporting of 340B savings or WAC premium. To ensure accurate savings reports from SBS:

- Communicate with the SBS vendor, distributor, and direct vendors to ensure that correct pricing and sales data are communicated to the SBS system. This should include a regular review of missing and incorrect data as vendor relationships change and technical updates occur.

- Pharmacy operations staff should maintain proximate prices in the SBS system in non-EDI catalogs at least quarterly, or more frequently if savings are reported monthly, or when savings are used in purchase determinations (e.g., if an item purchase at WAC is dependent on price differential).

- Monitor EDI catalogs to discover missing or errant GPO prices of unusual values, and scrub the data to ensure accurate and complete calculations.

Apart from the SBS 340B savings calculation, areas where dispensing and purchases are not run through the SBS (i.e., "clean" inventory areas where 100% 340B drugs are used) should be calculated separately. In any instance, a full vetting and maintenance schedule should be completed if the SBS is used as a source for any or all of the 340B savings information.

KEY POINT

Validate reference pricing and be certain that all purchases are fully captured and included in SBS 340B performance reports. Supplement SBS reports with manual data entry if information is not captured electronically.

PERFORMING THE 340B SAVINGS CALCULATION

After pricing is secured for each purchase event, the savings calculation consists of the sum of two price differences.

Savings for 340B buys is:

$\sum$ ([GPO price – 340B price] X [purchase quantity])

Savings for WAC buys is:

$\sum$ ([GPO price – WAC price] X [purchased quantity])

WAC premium is the "negative" savings (additional cost) resulting when the GPO price is lower than the WAC price for a specific purchase event. Purchases in the WAC account contribute the greater proportion of premium. However, if the 340B prime vendor's negotiated WAC price is less than hospital's GPO price, the delta is positive and can contribute to net savings. The latter might occur with a 340B PVP sub-WAC price. Although the 340B price is commonly understood to be the lowest available price and the price in the WAC account to be the highest, with the GPO price falling between them, a number of situations exist where the price hierarchy differs. CEs are well-advised to do the math at the level of detail described. When the spend, savings, and premium values are calculated for each purchase, their aggregations can be made for each facility over time and in various views to outline savings performance.

MOVING FROM 340B SAVINGS TO 340B PROGRAM PERFORMANCE MONITORING

The goals of 340B program performance monitoring can be broadly outlined as using data to:

- Optimize 340B savings by maximizing outpatient drug charge capture, leading to compliant purchases under 340B and GPO price schedules.
- Minimize purchase premium associated with WAC purchases.
- Manage the hospital's formulary, supply chain, and other clinical and business processes to optimize drug and product management, including 340B elements.
- Provide accurate and timely assessment, action, and communication of results to internal stakeholders.

Performing the 340B savings assessment over time can provide a detailed and nuanced understanding of savings contributions by drug and location as well as support changes in operational processes and product selection, resolve pricing issues, and optimize 340B savings. Data elements and KPIs for 340B program performance include tracking of charge frequency and quantity by service location, package accumulation, and changes in drug spend over time. If a 340B SBS is in place, a specific form of a full perpetual inventory is in place. In addition to investigating 340B opportunities, the pursuit of variances may increase revenue through improved charge capture and offer opportunities to improve overall efficiency through decreased loss, waste, and spoilage of inventory.

EXAMPLE

Example Health System (EHS) consists of two 340B facilities, Hospital A and Hospital B located in the suburbs of a large city. Hospital A is 400-bed community hospital with adult, pediatric, and rehabilitation services; Hospital B is a smaller 200-bed community hospital with adult inpatient, outpatient infusion, and emergency department services. In referencing the Office of Pharmacy Affairs (OPA) web site, both facilities are disproportionate share hospitals (DSHs) listed as carving out Medicaid and have the Medicare cost report profile for locations and operational variables found in **Table 13-1** below. **Table 13-2** provides an outline of corresponding key elements of EHS facility Medicare cost report data.

The person charged with tracking EHS's 340B program performance must have or develop a variety of tools to aggregate data into actionable information that provide operational insight for pharmacy leadership reporting. Although SBS programs generally provide access to numerous reports, additional assessment and understanding of pharmacy and hospital operations are key to developing insights into 340B program performance. Pharmacy leaders should ensure that the pharmacy business manager, 340B program manager, or individuals learn the reporting suite of the SBS and develop strong spreadsheet and analytic skills to create insights beyond the basics. Pharmacy leaders should be familiar with the metrics available for measuring 340B program performance, including drug spend profile, 340B savings, WAC spend, WAC premium, and metrics of activity related to patient care volumes and dispensing. These metrics for our two EHS facilities are listed in **Table 13-3.**

REVENUE CYCLE AND CHARGE CAPTURE INTEGRITY AS KEY ELEMENTS OF 340B SUCCESS

When the EHS 340B program is in place and the facility has installed and stabilized SBS, attention should be focused on trends in drug spend and savings. It is valuable to periodically review charge capture by eligible location in each facility and to evaluate the extent to which charge capture is functioning correctly. Information technology updates and changes, movement and changes in service locations, and the addition of new services and locations create the potential for missed data or mischaracterized data that may impact business or compliance, or both. The 340B manager should use the SBS to review current patient volumes and charges by location to see where care is delivered (see **Table 13-4**). Regular comparisons to the Medicare cost report and trial balance should be made to confirm 340B eligibility. Compare hospital information system charge data, charge frequency, and charge quantity to SBS charge capture by location (**Table 13-5**) quarterly, or at a minimum, every six months to ensure that all charges are captured and that SBS recognizes all services and locations appropriately. A review of charges by site, by service location, and by class can be prepared from SBS reports providing a validation step to outline where charges and drug spend by outpatient (OP) status reside (**Table 13-6**). A review of SBS accumulations should be performed regularly. Outliers, where overly large accumulations or negative status is noted, may denote mismatches in product information or data settings. In all instances, outliers should be resolved to mitigate savings loss and identify and resolve the potential compliance issue.

Table 13-1. 340B Program Performance Variables

CE Type	Health System	Hospital Volumes	Service Lines	Contracts	Drugs Stocked	SBS
DSH	# of Hospital (s)	Bed count	Oncology	GPO Pricing	# of NDC – GCN	Prices
SCH	# of Clinics	Discharges	Hematology	DSH IP Pricing	# of NDC SKU	Catalogs
CAH	# or MOB	Locations of Service	Endocrinology	340B Pricing	# Items in Catalog	Charge feed
RRC	Rehab	Patient Days	Surgery	340B Prime Vendor Pricing	# of Direct Purchases	Packages
Pediatric	LTC	Charges IP/OP		Primary Distributor	# of Primary Purchases	
Cancer	Cancer Center	Drug Orders		Secondary Distributor	# of Secondary Purchases	
Medicaid status		Doses Dispensed				
		Discharge Prescriptions				
		Medicaid patients				

CAH: critical access hospital, CE: covered entity, DSH: disproportionate share hospital, IP/OP: inpatient/outpatient, LTC: long-term care, NDC = national drug code, MOB: medical office building, rehab: rehabilitation, RRC: rural referral center, SCH: sole community hospital

Table 13-2. Example Health System Medicare Cost Report Items

Hospital	Hospital A	Hospital B	Total
Beds	400	200	600
Discharges	18,000	13,000	31,000
Gross Revenue	$400,000,000	$1,400,000,000	$1,800,000,000
Medicaid Discharges	4,400	2,700	7,100
Medicaid Discharge %	24%	21%	23%
Patient Days	80,000	70,000	150,000
OP Charges	25,000,000	32,000,000	57,000,000
Total Charges	51,000,000	43,000,000	94,000,000
OP %	49%	74%	61%
Gross Revenue/Bed	$1,000,000	$7,000,000	$3,000,000
Discharges/Bed	45	65	52
OP Charges/Bed	62,500	160,000	95,000
OP Charges/Patient Day	313	457	380
Total Charges/Bed	127,500	215,000	156,667

OP: outpatient

Table 13-3. Example Health System Spend/Savings Performance

Description	Hospital A	Hospital B	Total
Spend @ GPO	$8,256,288	$5,529,094	$13,785,382
Savings Gross	$951,681	$1,844,656	$2,796,337
Premium	($153,286)	($29,491)	($182,776)
Savings Net	$798,396	$1,815,165	$2,613,561
Savings Rate	9.7%	32.8%	19%
Premium Rate	−2.1%	−0.8%	−1.7%
Spend Current	$7,304,607	$3,684,438	$10,989,045
WAC Spend %	40%	29%	36%

WAC: wholesale acquisition cost

REVIEW SPEND AND SAVINGS TRENDS BY ACCOUNT

340B SBS reports should be used to outline and support a review of spend and savings trends in each account on a scheduled basis, typically monthly at a minimum. Review of these data is useful in tracking and spotting changes each month. Use SBS reports to answer questions about 340B program performance such as:

- How much was saved at each service location this month?
- What would drug spend be at non-340B price?
- Where are savings rates highest and why?
- Has savings changed from prior months; if yes, is the variance explained by changes in activity or inputs?

An examination of **Figures 13-1 through 13-3** (on pages 188 through 190) for the EHS example demonstrates that the cost of current drug purchases, if fully purchased at GPO contract prices, would be $13.9 million—23% more than the current cost of $10.9 million. In other words, for 2016, EHS achieved a 19% discount from GPO-priced spend in combined savings from the two hospitals. Looking at the performance of the sites, the savings contributions may, at first, seem counterintuitive. Patient volume at Hospital A is 58% of the discharge volume (Table 13-2) and accounts for $7.3 million (67%) of current spend (see Table 13-3) for EHS, while Hospital B has 42% of discharges—a drug cost for the period of $3.7 million (33%). Inpatient GPO spend at Hospital A is almost 50% of total spend (Figure 13-2). The inpatient spend at Hospital B comprises only 27.5% of spend (Figure 13-3) with PHS and WAC accounts at 43% and 29.5% of drug spend respectively, reflecting differences in the service mix and populations served at the two locations. EHS's net 340B savings totals $2.6 million, but it is split as 30% at Hospital A and 70% at Hospital B, even though the larger Hospital A facility has the greater overall drug spend (Figure 13-1). The difference in 340B program impact turns on the mix of services between facilities; in the smaller Hospital B, 6.4% of visits, 1.5% of charges, and 44.4% of drug cost are attributed to ambulatory outpatient infusion services seen in **Tables** 13-4, 13-5, 13-6, and **13-7**.

In contrast, Hospital A's infusion service represents 0.8% of visits, 0.13% of charges, and 8% of drug expense. The same inversion is seen when we look at rates of savings and premium seen in **Figures 13-5 through 13-7** (on pages 192 through 194). The system averages a 19.5% savings rate and (–)3.5% WAC premium rate while the smaller hospital has the higher savings rate of 33% and a lower premium of (–)2.6% compared to the larger site 10% savings rate and (–)3.9% premium rate, which is counter-intuitive unless additional review is completed.

Table 13-4. Example Health System Patient Visits by Site

Hospital A	Ambulatory OP	Inpatient	Outpatient	Visits
Blank	-	5.0%	0.2%	5.2%
Cardiac	-	0.0%	0.6%	0.6%
Diagnostic	-	0.0%	11.5%	11.5%
Emergency	0.00	14.4%	48.5%	62.9%
Infusion	0.8%	0.0%	0.0%	0.8%
Lab	-	-	0.0%	0.0%
Observation	-	0.43%	0.1%	0.5%
Pain	-	-	0.0%	0.0%
Pediatric	-	0.00%	0.3%	0.3%
Radiology	0.00	0.05%	10.3%	10.4%
Surgery	-	0.3%	6.3%	6.6%
Treatment	0.1%	0.0%	0.1%	0.3%
Women's Health	0.0%	0.6%	0.4%	1.0%
GRAND TOTAL	**0.9%**	**20.8%**	**78.3%**	**100.0%**

Blank: no activity/no result

Hospital B	Ambulatory OP	Inpatient	Outpatient	Visits
Blank	-	4.4%	1.2%	5.5%
Cardiac	0.0%	0.0%	1.6%	1.6%
Diagnostic	-	-	0.0%	0.0%
Emergency	-	0.13	49.7%	62.7%
Infusion	6.4%	-	0.2%	6.6%
Lab	-	-	0.5%	0.5%
Observation	-	-	0.0%	0.0%
Pain	-	-	6.1%	6.1%
Radiology	-	-	8.0%	8.0%
Surgery	-	0.2%	8.5%	8.7%
Treatment	0.0%	0.0%	0.2%	0.2%
Women's Health	-	-	0.00	0.00
GRAND TOTAL	**6.4%**	**17.6%**	**76.0%**	**100.0%**

Table 13-5. Example Health System Charge Frequency

Hospital A	Ambulatory OP	Inpatient	Outpatient	Charge Frequency
Blank	-	12.3%	0.2%	12.5%
Cardiac	-	0.0%	0.1%	0.1%
Diagnostic	-	0.0%	2.0%	2.0%
Emergency	0.00%	64.3%	12.0%	76.3%
Infusion	0.13%	0.0%	0.0%	0.1%
Lab	-	-	0.0%	0.0%
Observation	-	0.67%	0.0%	0.7%
Pain	-	-	0.0%	0.0%
Pediatric	-	0.0%	0.1%	0.1%
Radiology	0.00	0.2%	0.9%	1.1%
Surgery	-	1.0%	5.2%	6.1%
Treatment	0.01%	0.0%	0.0%	0.0%
Women's Health	0.00%	0.9%	0.1%	0.9%
GRAND TOTAL	**0.1%**	**79.3%**	**20.6%**	**100.0%**

Blank: no activity/no result

Hospital B	Ambulatory OP	Inpatient	Outpatient	Charge Frequency
Blank	-	19.1%	0.3%	19.5%
Cardiac	0.0%	0.0%	0.2%	0.2%
Diagnostic	-	-	0.0%	0.0%
Emergency	-	59%	12.0%	71.1%
Infusion	1.5%	-	0.0%	1.5%
Lab	-	-	0.0%	0.0%
Observation	-	-	0.0%	0.0%
Pain	-	-	1.5%	1.5%
Radiology	-	-	0.6%	0.6%
Surgery	-	0.7%	4.9%	5.6%
Treatment	0.0%	0.0%	0.0%	0.1%
Women's Health	-	-	0.00	0.00
GRAND TOTAL	**1.5%**	**79.0%**	**19.5%**	**100.0%**

Table 13-6. Example Health System Drug Cost Distribution

Hospital A	Ambulatory OP	Inpatient	Outpatient	Drug Cost
Blank		11.2%	0.1%	11.3%
Cardiac			0.3%	0.3%
Diagnostic		0.0%	3.4%	3.4%
Emergency		57.5%	8.4%	65.9%
Infusion	8.4%		0.1%	8.5%
Lab				
Observation		0.5%	0.0%	0.5%
Pain				
Pediatric		0.0%	1.2%	1.3%
Radiology		0.2%	0.6%	0.8%
Surgery		0.9%	6.0%	6.9%
Treatment			0.6%	0.6%
Women's Health		0.5%	0.0%	0.6%
GRAND TOTAL	**8.4%**	**70.9%**	**20.8%**	**100.0%**

Blank: no activity/no result

Hospital B	Ambulatory OP	Inpatient	Outpatient	Drug Cost
Blank	-	6.1%	0.8%	6.8%
Cardiac	0.0%	0.0%	0.7%	0.7%
Diagnostic	-	-	0.0%	0.0%
Emergency	-	38%	4.5%	42.3%
Infusion	44.7%	-	0.6%	45.3%
Lab	-	-	0.0%	0.0%
Observation	-	-	0.0%	0.0%
Pain	-	-	0.4%	0.4%
Radiology	-	-	0.2%	0.2%
Surgery	-	0.4%	3.8%	4.2%
Treatment	0.0%	0.0%	0.0%	0.0%
Women's Health	-	-	-	-
GRAND TOTAL	**44.7%**	**44.2%**	**11.1%**	**100.0%**

Table 13-7. Contribution to Savings by Account

Account Type	340B		WAC			
Site	Premium	Savings Net	Premium	Savings Net	Total Premium	Total Savings Net
Site A	($49,066)	$951,680	($239,290)	($153,287)	($288,363)	$798,393
Site B	($22,572)	$1,844,657	($73,164)	($29,487)	($94,737)	$1,815,170
GRAND TOTAL	**($70,642)**	**$2,796,337**	**($312,458)**	**($182,774)**	**($383,100)**	**$2,613,563**

WAC: wholesale acquisition cost

KEY POINT

> Simple comparisons and benchmarking of 340B program performance should be used cautiously, as facility characteristics can drive apparent variance in performance that is not a real actionable difference.

These observations suggest that a simple comparison of two or more CE facilities can be deceiving and that business performance is strongly influenced by outpatient mix and the nature of the therapies provided. Hospital B provides an infusion service inside the hospital's four walls and so, while smaller and having a more modest drug spend, provides 340B-eligible outpatient doses out of the main pharmacy that drive 340B eligibility of drug spend and the corresponding savings values. External benchmarking—comparisons of a single 340B hospital facility or health system to another—may not be as valuable as benchmarking hospital-specific spend and savings rates over time. Detailed internal benchmarking is generally better for monitoring 340B program performance than comparisons based on global non-340B statistics or more casual comparisons. Elements of a strong approach to capturing and understanding 340B savings include:

- Understanding in detail how the hospital's SBS system calculates savings, and using reports accordingly.
- Using SBS reports to take a closer look at spend/savings trends and build internal reports and processes to benchmark savings in addition to reviewing simple report results.
- Monitoring report results monthly or more frequently and acting to resolve issues and take advantage of opportunities.
- Considering internal benchmarking as key to process improvement. Be cautious and focused on details in making comparisons to other 340B hospitals.

EVALUATE 340B SAVINGS BY THERAPEUTIC CLASS

What drugs make the greatest contribution to 340B savings? Reviewing spend and net savings by drug class can provide a deeper understanding of 340B program performance and provide insight into where, and to what extent, 340B discount supports business results. A structured approach to modeling how savings accrues and is distributed across the health system is outlined in **Table 13-8.** Hospitals that review costs by product line, therapeutic area, or business unit may see a dramatic difference in 340B program impact when the results are viewed at a granular level. Even within a therapeutic area (e.g., oncology infusion), drug discount rates vary widely and 340B benefit and cost or offset may be focused in a specific treatment or diagnoses where high cost and/or high discount drugs are used.

Table 13-8. EHS Hospital A Savings Top 5 Drug Classes

GPI Class	Savings Net	% of Savings	Savings Rate	Spend Current	% of Spend
Inflammatory Bowel Agents	$316,849	40.0%	53.8%	$272,867	2.5%
Immune Serums	$125,871	16.0%	96.5%	$4,612	0.1%
Thrombolytic Enzymes	$48,331	5.0%	26.2%	$122,784	1.1%
Selective Costimulation Modulators	$43,298	6.0%	61.0%	$30,433	0.3%
Sympathomimetics	$40,124	5.0%	23.3%	$132,186	1.2%
Sub-Total	$584,895	72%	51%	$562,882	5.1%
GRAND TOTAL	$798,396	100%	10%	$7,304,607	66.5%

For EHS, the top five drug classes (17.4% of drug spend) contribute $2 million (77%) of 340B savings for the system. At Hospital A, the top five classes contribute $573,816, 72% of the total $798,396 340B savings. At Hospital B, savings is even more concentrated: $1,524,791 of $1,815,165; 84% of total savings are contributed by the top five classes as described in **Table 13-9**. Although there is some consistency between the two facilities, the specific therapeutic classes and drugs generating savings are not identical. Differences in patient care and clinical offerings may figure as importantly as formulary decisions and 340B savings optimization strategies in determining results. Understanding the contribution of savings to classes of drugs can confirm spend and savings trends and can assist in predicting how and when savings might change as innovator drugs become available in generic form or a biosimilar enters the market. Because a significant portion of 340B discount for a "tenured" innovator drug can be accrued through the inflation limit factor of the discount formula, older drugs generally have higher discount rates than newly introduced competitors that enter the market at the statutory 340B discount rate. The natural course of disease in patients and in the population may also influence savings trends. As an example, savings arising from hepatitis C therapies, Sovaldi® or Harvoni®, may decline as patients are cured and fewer new patients require therapy.

KEY POINT

340B savings rates vary widely by product, formulary class, and therapeutic category. Granular assessments of 340B savings trends can reveal additional opportunity and potential savings risk.

WAC PREMIUM IMPACT ON 340B SAVINGS

As mentioned above, net savings can be eroded by the additional cost of purchasing items at WAC under 340B GPO prohibition rules. The "premium" associated with these purchases is generally described as the difference between the GPO price that would have been paid and the actual price paid. As discussed, some WAC purchases generate no premium because a lower GPO price is not available; in some instances, the WAC price may be lower than the GPO price where the 340B prime vendor has a contract price available. Table 13-8 shows EHS net savings for the 340B and

Table 13-9. EHS Hospital B Savings Top 5 Drug Classes

GPI Class	Savings Net	% of Savings	Savings Rate	Spend Current	% of Spend
Inflammatory Bowel Agents	$766,862	42%	54%	$667,215	6.1%
Multiple Sclerosis Agents	$368,564	20%	82%	$81,436	0.7%
Immune Serums	$238,551	13%	34%	$487,628	4.3%
Hematopoietic Growth Factors	$87,739	5%	57%	$148,226	0.6%
Somatostatic Agents	$63,074	3%	79%	$16,990	0.2%
Sub-Total	$1,524,790	84%	54%	$1,401,495	11.9%
GRAND TOTAL	$1,815,165	100%	33%	$3,684,438	33.5%

WAC accounts for each hospital, with the negative and positive contributions of each. It includes the number of drug classes and the number of purchase events for each account.

340B purchases yield net positive savings, but note that there are deductions from savings (premium) at both Hospital A (–)$49,064, and Hospital B (–)$21,572. These results may be due to erroneous pricing in the savings calculation, a lagging 340B price for items rapidly decreasing in price, or for items that do not have a 340B price. The WAC impact, a premium of $239,290 at Hospital A and $73,164 at Hospital B (Table 13-7) may contain opportunities for improvement. If all premium spend were eliminated, then EHS 340B savings approach $3 million.

Two-thirds of the WAC premium value for EHS hospitals resides in the top five therapeutic classes (**Figures 13-8** and **13-9**, pages 195 and 196) and a short list of NDCs. A focus on the short list means that a focus on the trend over time as changes are made to decrease premium can outline success and additional opportunities. As an example, from Hospital A (Figure 13-8), operational changes might include adding Ofirmev to a 340B exclusion table in the SBS, changing vancomycin order management to capture the various NDCs used to compound more completely and accurately, and reviewing ketorolac utilization and charge capture. Hospital B (Figure 13-8) shows similar challenges and includes Imatinib, which appears to be a new formulary addition or may not be properly added to the SBS crosswalk catalog. Naloxone charge capture also appears as a possible revenue cycle leak. Detailed review and recognition of gaps and leaks allow for actions to optimize 340B program results.

There are many reasons for WAC account spend occurring as part of a 340B hospital's dispensing, purchasing, and supply chain processes. WAC purchases arise from dispenses not captured in charge data, drug products used to compound multiple doses, and unrecognized waste not captured as part of a patient charge, among others. In this instance, since both EHS hospitals carve out Medicaid, drugs purchased to replenish dispenses to Medicaid patients will be made at a non-340B/non-GPO WAC price. Apexus lists nine strategies for minimizing WAC exposure that can be used as a checklist for hospitals subject to the GPO prohibition requirement.[3] First on the list is a WAC purchase report analysis to identify why items are purchased on the WAC account and to determine solutions to change purchasing patterns. A simple evaluation of WAC account spend alone can be deceiving because not all NDCs entail a purchase at a premium, and as described above, not all WAC spending is directly actionable (e.g., EHS carves out Medicaid). A number of NDCs purchased on the WAC account have contract pricing through the 340B PVP and may contribute to net program savings rather than deduct from it.

The most effective method to quantify a WAC premium is to aggregate premium spend by account, by class, and by drug. Table 13-8 and Table 13-9 show WAC premium data for EHS Hospitals A and B, respectively, using the top five classes and items contributing the most WAC premium exposure by hospital. Hospital A accrues a total WAC premium of (–)$288,354 compared to Hospital B where WAC premium totals (–)$94,736. The top five classes contain 13 items and 29 different NDCs that contribute (–)$100,258 in premium at Hospital A and 10 items comprised of 14 different NDCs totaling (–)$20,605 at Hospital B. This kind of drill-down by hierarchy can help guide assessment of potential optimization opportunities. Reasons for the WAC spend can arise from those described above. Surgical and anesthesia charges are common in creating missed charges and WAC spend and premium, where a procedure or case tray is used to provide drugs that are replaced and charged manually. Formulary changes, product changes, and charge master changes may also lead to gaps that cause WAC spend growth. These can be readily remedied if regularly tracked and managed.

SUMMARY

A high-performing 340B program exists inside a hospital pharmacy that is not exclusively 340B. Managing revenue cycle, formulary decisions, and the pharmacy supply chain well supports 340B program performance. Conversely, 340B requirements support a higher bar for pharmacy leaders to manage their business and supply chain processes. A structured review of SBS reports along with regular assessment of program performance and variance, can support high performance in a compliant 340B program.

REFERENCES

1. Social Security. Compilation of the Social Security Laws. Payment for Covered Outpatient Drugs. https://www.ssa.gov/OP_Home/ssact/title19/1927.htm. Accessed October 17, 2017.

2. Office of Pharmacy Affairs, Healthcare Systems Bureau, Health Resources and Services Administration, Department of Health and Human Services. *Statutory Prohibition on Group Purchasing Organization Participation.* Release 2013-1. https://www.hrsa.gov/sites/default/files/opa/programrequirements/policyreleases/prohibitionongpoparticipation020713.pdf. Accessed October 17, 2017.

3. Strategies to Minimize Unnecessary WAC Exposure a Checklist for Hospitals Subject to the GPO Prohibition https://docs.340bpvp.com/documents/public/resourcecenter/340b_minimize_wac_exposure.pdf. Accessed October 17, 2017.

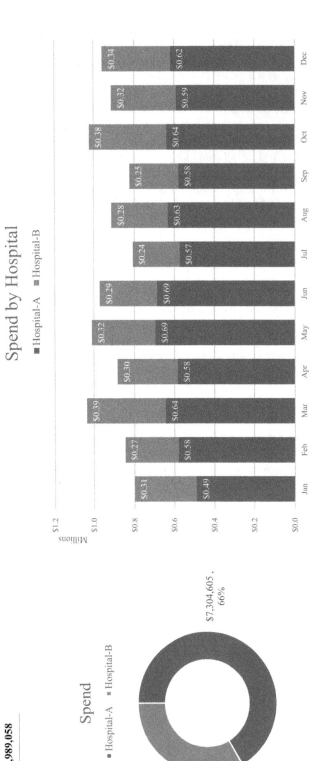

FIGURE 13-1. Example Health System Drug Spend

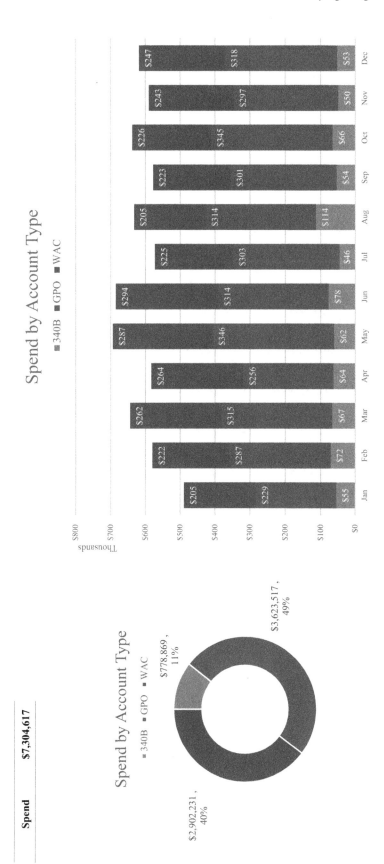

FIGURE 13-2. EHS Drug Spend Hospital A

Acc: account, GPO: group purchasing organization, WAC: wholesale acquisition cost

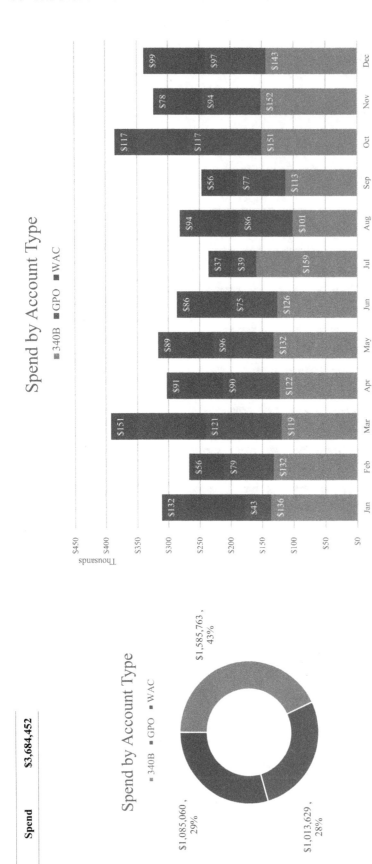

FIGURE 13-3. EHS Drug Spend Hospital B

Acc: account, GPO: group purchasing organization, WAC: wholesale acquisition cost

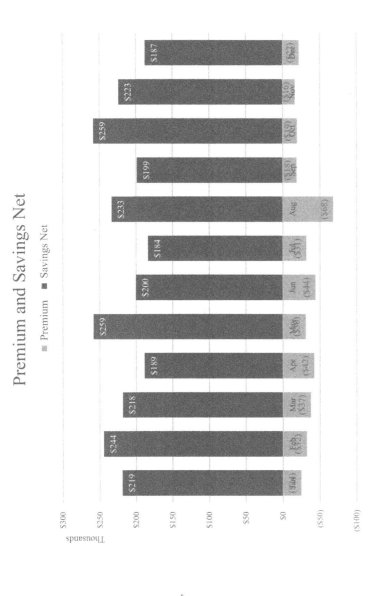

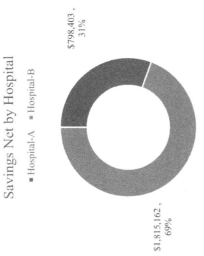

FIGURE 13-4. Example Health System 340B Savings

Savings	$2,613,551
Premium	($182,775)
Savings Rate	20 %
Premium Rate	-1.7 %
Savings Opportunity	$2,796,326

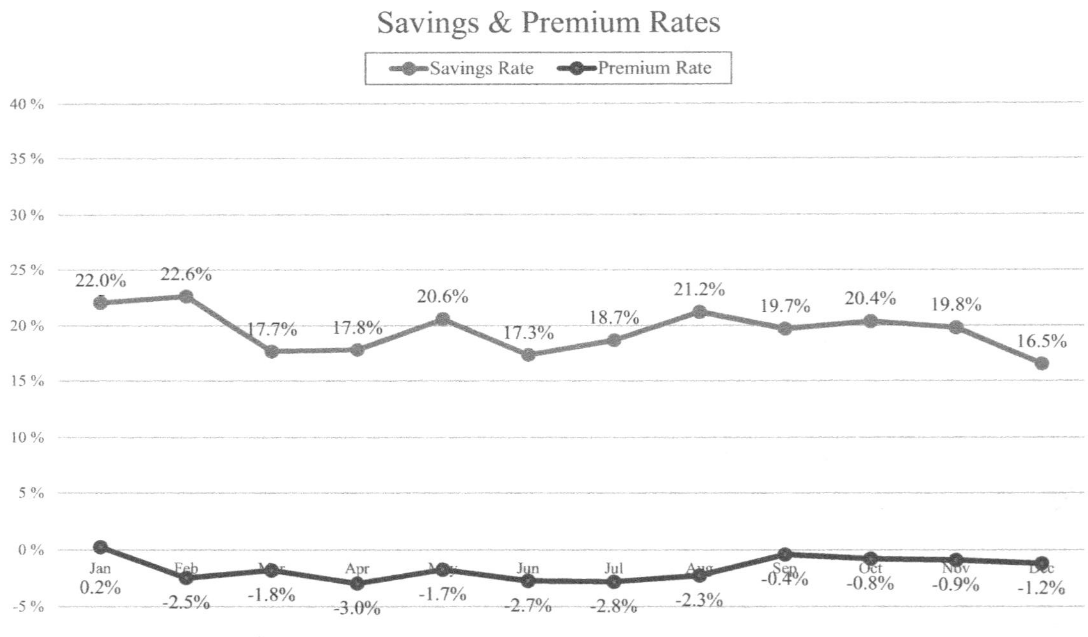

Savings & Premium Rates

—●— Savings Rate —●— Premium Rate

	Jan	Feb	Mar	Apr	May	Jun	Jul	Aug	Sep	Oct	Nov	Dec
Savings	22.0%	22.6%	17.7%	17.8%	20.6%	17.3%	18.7%	21.2%	19.7%	20.4%	19.8%	16.5%
Premium	0.2%	-2.5%	-1.8%	-3.0%	-1.7%	-2.7%	-2.8%	-2.3%	-0.4%	-0.8%	-0.9%	-1.2%

FIGURE 13-5. Example Health System 340B Savings Rates

Savings	$798,395
Premium	($153,286)
Savings Rate	10 %
Premium Rate	-2.1 %
Savings Opportunity	$951,681

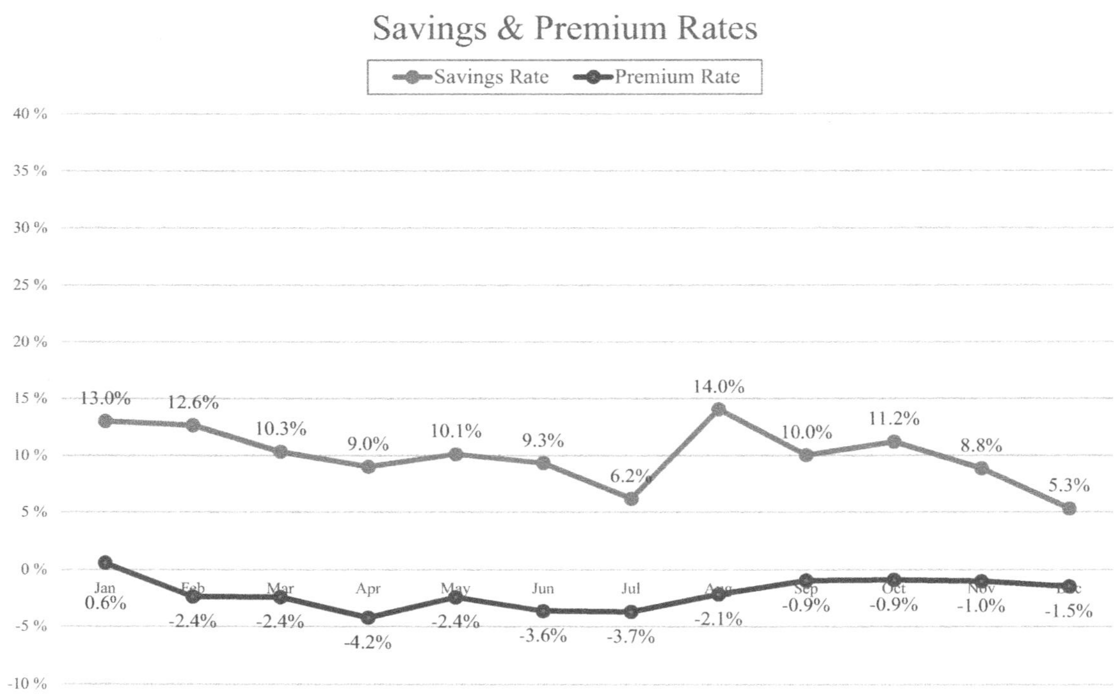

FIGURE 13-6. EHS Hospital A 340B Savings Rate

Savings & Premium Rates

Savings	$1,815,156
Premium	($29,489)
Savings Rate	33 %
Premium Rate	-0.8 %
Savings Opportunity	$1,844,645

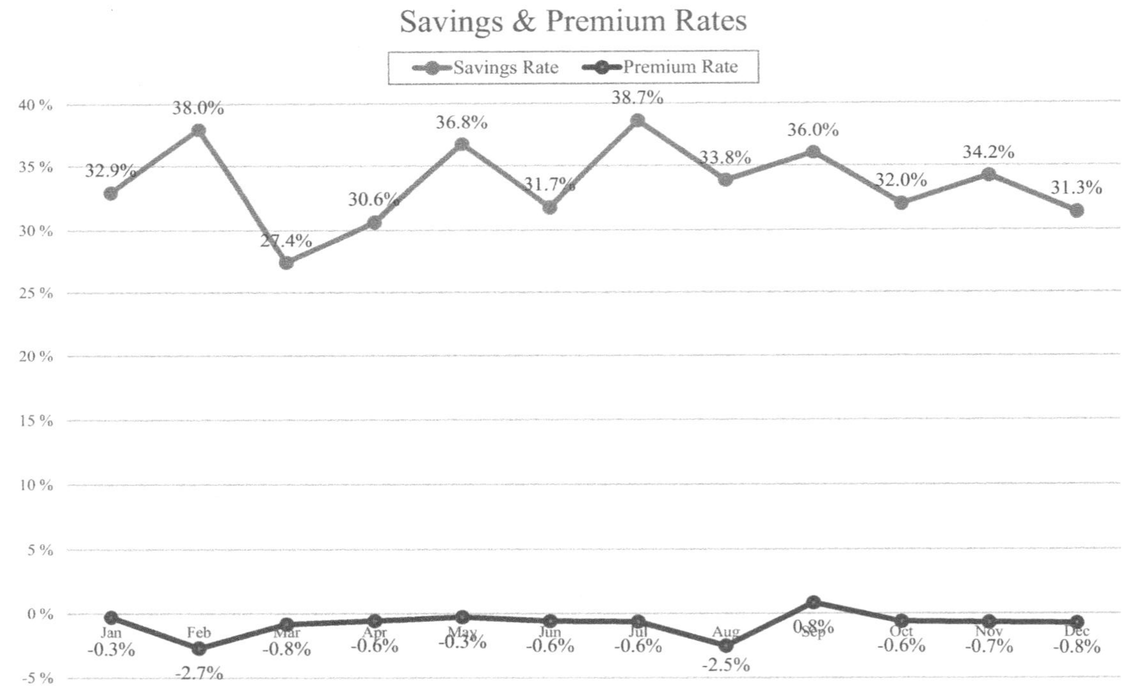

FIGURE 13-7. EHS Hospital B 340B Savings Rate

Five Classes with Most Premium in WAC Account

Premium Total	($153,286)
Premium Rate	-2.1 %

GPI Class / Drug Product	Premium
Analgesics Other	**($38,367)**
Ofirmev 1,000 mg/100 mL Vial (100 mL) 24 Vial	($35,956)
Tylenol 325 mg Tablet (100 Ea) 10 Blist Pack	($2,411)
Anti-infective Agents - Misc.	**($28,590)**
Bacitracin 50,000 Units Vial (1 Ea) 10 Vial	($13,155)
Metronidazole 500 mg Tablet (100 Ea) 1 Blist Pack	($51)
Vancomycin 1 g Vial (1 Ea) 10 Vial	($9,003)
Vancomycin 500 mg Vial (1 Ea) 10 Vial	($88)
Vancomycin HCl 5 g Vial (1 Ea) 1 Vial	($6,293)
Penicillin Combinations	**($9,075)**
Amox-Clav 400–57 mg/5 mLSusp (75 mL) 1 Bottle	($442)
Amox-Clav 875–125 mg Tablet (100 Ea) 1 Bottle	($198)
Ampicillin-Sulbactam 3 g Vial (1 Ea) 10 Vial	($30)
Bicillin C-R 1.2 Million Unit (2 mL) 10 Syringe	($79)
Piperacil-Tazobact 2.25 g Vial (1 Ea) 10 Vial	($935)
Piperacil-Tazobact 3.375 g Vial (1 Ea) 10 Vial	($4,762)
Piperacil-Tazobact 40.5 g (1 Ea) 1 Bottle	($67)
Piperacil-Tazobact 40.5 g (1 Ea) 1 Vial	($574)
Unasyn 3 g Vial (1 Ea) 10 Vial	($1,988)
Vasodilators	**($10,732)**
Hydralazine 20 mg/mL Vial (1 mL) 25 Vial	($871)
Hydralazine 25 mg Tablet (100 Ea) 1 Blist Pack	($36)
Nitropress 50 mg/2 mL Vial (2 mL) 1 Vial	($9,825)
Nonsteroidal Anti-inflammatory Agents (NSAIDs)	**($13,395)**
Children Ibuprofen 100 mg/5 mL (5 mL) 100 Cup	($699)
Indomethacin 1 mg Vial (1 Ea) 1 Vial	($150)
Ketorolac 10 mg Tablet (100 Ea) 1 Bottle	($133)
Ketorolac 15 mg/mL Vial (1 mL) 25 Vial	($487)
Ketorolac 30 mg/mL Vial (1 mL) 25 Vial	($11,453)
Ketorolac 60 Mg/2 Ml Vial (2 mL) 25 Vial	($473)
Grand Total	**($100,159)**

Five Classes Most Premium Spend in WAC

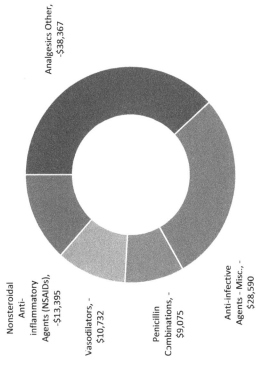

Analgesics Other, -$38,367

Nonsteroidal Anti-inflammatory Agents (NSAIDs), -$13,395

Vasodilators, -$10,732

Penicillin Combinations, -$9,075

Anti-infective Agents - Misc., -$28,590

FIGURE 13-8. WAC Premium Study Hospital A (Bottom Five by Drug Class)

GPO: group purchasing organization, WAC: wholesale acquisition cost

Five Classes with Most Premium in WAC Account

Premium Total	($29,489)
Premium Rate	-0.8%

GPI Class / Drug Product	Premium
Anti-infective Agents - Misc.	**($5,642)**
Aztreonam 2 g Vial (1 Ea) 10 Vial	($1,473)
Bacitracin 50,000 Units Vial (1 Ea) 10 Vial	($2,488)
Pentam 300 Vial (1 Ea) 10 Vial	($292)
Vancomycin 1 g Vial (1 Ea) 10 Vial	($805)
Vancomycin 500 mg Vial (1 Ea) 10 Vial	($584)
Opioid Antagonists	**($3,869)**
Naloxone 2 mg/2 mL Syringe (2 mL) 10 Syringe	($3,869)
Penicillin Combinations	**($5,470)**
Amox-Clav 875–125 Mg Tablet (100 Ea) 1 Bottle	($52)
Piperacil-Tazobact 2.25 g Vial (1 Ea) 10 Vial	($748)
Piperacil-Tazobact 3.375 g Vial (1 Ea) 10 Vial	($547)
Piperacil-Tazobact 4.5 g Vial (1 Ea) 10 Vial	($64)
Zosyn 2.25 Gm/50 Ml Galaxy Bag (50 mL) 24 Bag	($1,536)
Zosyn 3.375 Gm/50 Ml Galaxy (50 mL) 24 Bag	($2,523)
Antineoplastic Enzyme Inhibitors	**($3,252)**
Imatinib Mesylate 100 mg Tab (90 Ea) 1 Bottle	($3,252)
Toxoid Combinations	**($2,373)**
Boostrix Tdap Vaccine Vial (0.5 mL) 10 Vial	($2,373)
Grand Total	**($20,606)**

Five Classes Most Premium Spend in WAC

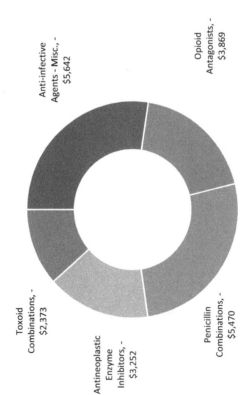

Anti-infective Agents - Misc., - $5,642

Opioid Antagonists, - $3,869

Penicillin Combinations, - $5,470

Antineoplastic Enzyme Inhibitors, - $3,252

Toxoid Combinations, - $2,373

FIGURE 13-9. WAC Premium Study Hospital B (Bottom Five by Drug Class)

GPO: group purchasing organization, WAC: wholesale acquisition cost

CHAPTER 14

Financial Management in the 340B Program

Andrew L. Wilson, PharmD, FASHP

The financial management of pharmaceutical supply and costs has long been an element of managing a health-system pharmacy. Inventory, procurement, and supply chain cost management have been key pharmacy leadership responsibilities for the institution and patients that they serve. As the U.S. healthcare system has evolved and health systems have become increasingly complex, drug costs, inflation, utilization changes, shortages, and reimbursement have also come into play. Several chapters in this *340B Program Handbook* address the details of managing a hospital supply chain that contains 340B; this chapter discusses how pharmacy leaders should consider the financial consequences and impact of 340B on hospital financial indicators and decisions. In addition to the base discounts offered under 340B, key performance indicators for department financial performance will read differently for a 340B hospital than for its non-340B counterpart.

This chapter is not designed to provide a full basis for financial management of a health-system pharmacy; readers are referred to the core text for that purpose.[1] The pervasive nature of 340B creates some obvious considerations in any financial model, business result, or performance indicator. A case can be made that the 340B program's impact should be an element of any financial performance overview. 340B impact should also be a consideration in any granular look at services or processes that are drug cost driven. However, some key areas such as 340B contribution require thoughtful and detailed consideration. This chapter covers elements of four chapters from the core text through a 340B lens:

- Forecasting pharmaceutical expenditures
- Understanding drug expense using administrative data
- Managing cost basics
- Analyzing budget variance and controlling operating results

At the very least, purchase price differentials across 340B-elgible outpatient areas and areas of the hospital where 340B does not apply are substantial. 340B discounts on branded drugs are, at a minimum, 23.1%; for multisource generic drugs, it is 15%. Discounts run higher for tenured branded drugs where the 340B discount is influenced by the cumulative price increases over the life of the product. Considering that the cost used in product selection, formulary management, profitability, and pricing is the 340B price where it prevails, hospital leadership's focus on the actual acquisition cost of a drug or biologic has a critical 340B dimension. Surfacing this element of the cost equation is a vital element of financial management of a 340B hospital pharmacy. Although benefits are substantial, it is rare for 340B price differential alone to drive policy and formulary choices. More often, 340B differentials are misunderstood and less than fully teased out in benchmarks and other performance metrics. As a result, pharmacy leaders, their departments, and health systems may make decisions with an incomplete understanding of the 340B underpinnings.

FORECASTING PHARMACEUTICAL EXPENDITURES

Forecasting future drug expenditures is a challenging annual exercise that includes both external influences (e.g., new drug introductions, practice standard changes) and assessment of the internal environment (e.g., patient and payer mix, program and service planning) to arrive at a forward-looking estimate. Vermeulen et al. recommend a nine-step process to build a reliable forecast.[2] The process is outlined in **Table 14-1** along with 340B specific elements. Beyond the structured steps outlined in the table, a key element of forecasting for 340B hospitals is to build separate budgets for the following:

- Outpatient drug expense (340B and non-340B)
- Inpatient (GPO/non-340B) expenditures

Although most steps throughout the forecasting process remain the same, several elements can lead to substantive differences in performance and should guide a thoughtful forecast development. New drugs enter the market at a 340B cost; 23.1% lower for branded drugs and 15% lower for multisource generics when compared to the corresponding market price for inpatient and non-340B outpatient use.

Because 304B price growth is capped at inflation based on the consumer price index for urban consumers (CPI-U), price increases forecast for other markets should be tempered for 340B purchases accordingly. 340B prices and purchases are insulated from inflation above a trailing CPI-U base after release at the initial market price. Because ASHP, IQVIA, and others do not track 340B sales separately in creating public forecasts, 340B facilities should consider alternatives to the price elements of common public forecasts in local estimates. 340B purchase discounts will be greater than statutory requirements in an environment where manufacturer price increases exceed CPI-U in each year, or over a sustained period. Provider-based hospital clinics for 340B hospitals should, therefore, consider inflation and price increase penalties to be nominal. Clinic growth and development (e.g., acquisition and transfer of non-340B-eligible clinic locations to 340B-eligible, provider-based sites) may lead to a deflationary effect as discounts accrued on the "340B side" of the business exceed typical market-based "non-340B-side" group purchasing organization (GPO) discounts.

KEY POINT

The basics of health-system pharmacy financial management remain in place in a 340B hospital, but the different cost-basis and pricing behavior of 340B drugs necessitates separate analysis and consideration of drug costs in 340B hospitals.

Assessments of the market size of the 340B program at near 44% of aggregate purchases are probably accurate.[3] 340B purchases have grown from one-third to one-half of all hospital drug purchases in the market, with impact differentially weighted toward high-cost drugs, including infusion and specialty drugs. The impact is differentially weighted by location/hospital; in many hospitals and integrated delivery networks, 340B purchases are equal or exceed standard GPO or hospital class of trade purchases. A clear and complete understanding of 340B price and associated changes will provide the basis for more accurate and useful forecasts.

It is reasonable to consider that 340B purchases mirror the market changes in general, but at a lower cost. The 340B-influenced business decisions in participating hospitals are probably not formulary decisions; they are likely decisions to open, close, or expand pharmacy services and clinics, including retail and specialty pharmacy and prescription services to the uninsured, underinsured, and others.

Table 14-1. Steps to Forecast Drug Expenditures

Step	Action	340B Considerations
1	Obtain and analyze data	Separately collect and analyze inpatient and outpatient (340B) purchase and utilization data.
2	Review past performance	Consider activity review and trends in subsets as above. Also consider the transition of care between areas of care over the prior period.
3	Build high-priority medication budget	Consider new drug introductions and usage trends by location and focus on price inflation in 340B independent of standard forecasts.
4	Build new product budget	Forecast utilization by location (IP/OP) and consider structural discounts available at launch (e.g., 23.1% statutory discount) for 340B purchases.
5	Build the non-formulary budget	Forecast utilization by location (IP/OP) and consider 340B purchase discounts and price growth.
6	Build low-priority budget	Forecast utilization by location (IP/OP) and consider 340B purchase discounts and price growth.
7	Establish a cost containment plan	Include plans proper, compliant 340B program management and minimization of WAC spend for DSH hospitals.
8	Finalize medication budget	Consider providing budget detail in two parts (340B/non-340B).
9	Vigilance	Include 340B performance elements in spend and budget vigilance.

DSH: disproportionate share hospitals, IP/OP: inpatient/outpatient, WAC: wholesale acquisition cost

Source: Adapted with permission from Vermeulen LC, Hoffman, JM, Shah ND. Forecasting pharmaceutical expenditures. In Wilson AL, ed. *Financial Management for Health-System Pharmacists.* Bethesda, MD: ASHP; 2009.

Arguably, 340B hospitals are more likely to find the retail, specialty, and in-clinic administered drug market more financially hospitable based on the discount availability. However, the base of operational efficiency and payer mix remain a key to considering the degree of positive impact. 340B cannot rescue a poor plan or a "bad idea," but it can assist a program that financial results would otherwise constrain. In the end, the well-managed hospital pharmacy with access to 340B that has a clear view of the actual cost of doing business, and a full understanding of the unique contribution of 340B to the result is well armed to proceed.

UNDERSTANDING 340B DRUG EXPENSE USING ADMINISTRATIVE DATA

Oinonen[4] outlines five steps in evaluating drug expense considering administrative data, with a focus on collecting, organizing, and understanding the data. Although drug cost is often a driver for a health system's interest in each process procedure or prescribing pattern, the discount behavior outlined above may alter or mute the cost signal for 340B hospitals. A review of the contribution of 340B pricing to the cost and business performance elements is critical to retaining perspective while using administrative data to set formulary policy and practice guidelines. Although the widely cited trope is that 340B hospitals choose expensive therapy, this behavior might be best described as a thoughtful response to cost, albeit one that may be markedly different from the non-340B market.

MANAGING COST BASICS

This last observation applies as well to cost accounting and cost management of drug expense[5] in 340B hospitals, which experience wide differential between the cost and contribution of the same drug used in the inpatient and outpatient environments. The casual practice of using blended cost for all purchases of a given item will lead to an incorrect calculation of cost in both inpatient and outpatient settings. As with the areas outlined above, a two-part process to manage cost in the inpatient (GPO) and outpatient (340B) environments is warranted. 340B hospitals incur measurably higher cost to manage 340B supply chains, including software, manpower, and internal and external audits. These costs can be allocated to the 340B side specifically or across the entire supply chain based on local preferences and practices. Hospitals subject to the GPO prohibition also incur a premium for purchasing 340B-inelgible outpatient drugs and new inventory items at full wholesale acquisition cost (WAC) if a virtual inventory system is used. These costs should also be captured and allocated.

> ### KEY POINT
>
> 340B hospitals incur substantial administrative expense to support proper 304B program management. These costs should be catalogued and allocated in cost management systems.

ANALYZING BUDGET VARIANCE AND CONTROLLING OPERATING RESULTS

Budget variance analysis also demands a two-part approach. In assessing the drivers of variance—volume change, price increases, one-time occurrences, inventory fluctuation, and monitoring of expensive highly variable mediation[6]—all areas perform the same as the non-340B environment except for the muted price variance for 340B versus open market, non-340B purchases. As Stevenson advises,[6] a focus on the details of drugs contributing to the variance is the first step; 340B hospitals have the additional advantage of detailed and focused revenue cycle and 340B software to permit tighter management and more granular attribution of utilization and other practice changes.

Virtual inventory management under 340B rules provides detailed and focused information to permit some of the tightest inventory management practice in health-system pharmacy. Pharmacy leaders are encouraged to implement and manage them according to business objectives and compliance requests.

SUMMARY

The 304B program offers substantive cost relief to participating hospitals. However, because of the nature of the program, drug costs behave differently than in the non-340B environment. In addition to statutory discounts, 340B hospitals enjoy insulation from price increases above the general inflation rate. Drug cost forecasts, budgets, and cost benchmarking should identify, categorize, and consider 340B cost differently than the inpatient portion of the budget which is the typical focus of health-system pharmacy and finance.

REFERENCES

1. Wilson AL, ed. *Financial Management for Health-System Pharmacists*. Bethesda, MD: ASHP; 2009.

2. Vermeulen LC, Hoffman, JM, Shah ND. Forecasting pharmaceutical expenditures. In Wilson AL, ed., *Financial Management for Health-System Pharmacists*. Bethesda, MD: ASHP; 2009.

3. Fein A. Drug Channels: 340B Purchases Hit $12 Billion in 2015—and Almost Half of the Hospital Market. http://www.drugchannels.net/2016/02/340b-purchases-hit-12-billion-in.html. Posted February 23, 2016; accessed November 5, 2017.

4. Oinonen M. Understanding drug expense using administrative data. In Wilson AL, ed., *Financial Management for Health-System Pharmacists*. Bethesda, MD: ASHP; 2009.

5. Armitstead JA, Hamlin AR, Centers T. Cost management basics. In Wilson AL, ed., *Financial Management for Health-System Pharmacists*. Bethesda, MD: ASHP; 2009.

6. Stevenson JG, Schuman A. Budget variance analysis and controlling operating results. In Wilson AL, ed., *Financial Management for Health-System Pharmacists*. Bethesda, MD: ASHP; 2009.

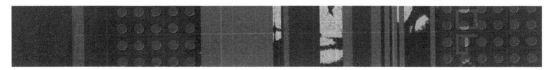

CHAPTER 15

Preparing for and Surviving a HRSA Audit

Kavish Choudhary, PharmD, MS;
Lauren Meekins, PharmD, MS, BCPS; and
William Black, MBA, PharmD, MS, BCPS

BACKGROUND

340B of the Veteran's Healthcare Act of 1992 requires that pharmaceutical manufacturers provide discounts on covered outpatient medications to participating covered entities. The Health Resources and Services Administration (HRSA) Office of Pharmacy Affairs (OPA) is responsible for the oversight and integrity of the 340B program. HRSA ensures the integrity of the program— by both the eligible entities and manufacturers—through promulgation of guidance and other support, including audits. Specifically, Section 42 of the United States Code (USC) 256b(a)(5)(C) states that HRSA has the authority to audit both the covered entity and manufacturer.[1]

HRSA has been empowered to audit participating covered entities and manufacturers from the inception of the 340B program and historically has conducted audits and other investigations for cause. With the increased scrutiny and public discussion of the 340B program, HRSA has increased the oversight of program implementation through random audits and targeted audits based on criteria that HRSA believes represent higher compliance risk scenarios (e.g., multiple child sites, large contract pharmacy networks, dramatic shifts in purchasing patterns). In addition to audits, HRSA has demonstrated a commitment to regular review of program participation through annual recertification and attestation. Covered entities share in the responsibility of upholding program integrity with required self-disclosures of material breaches. The intent of this chapter is providing guidance to covered entities to facilitate adherence to 340B program integrity and to meet the challenges of internal program oversight and external audits. Annual recertification and self-disclosures are highlighted, but the primary focus of this chapter is covered entity audits. A general overview and outline is provided, along with applicable strategies and infrastructure development, that covered entities can utilize in preparation for an audit.

HRSA posts audit results from previous fiscal years on their web site as they are finalized, permitting covered entities an opportunity to identify trends, areas of program integrity, and interest to HRSA as well as common challenges, failures, and the ensuing corrective actions and penalties.[1] All covered entities are well-advised to undertake preparation for a HRSA audit, as OPA audits approximately 200 covered entities annually, with a focus on hospitals. Over the first 5 years of HRSA audits, nearly three-quarters of audited hospitals report an audit finding and more than half have a manufacturer repayment associated with the finding. Review of the web site shows an outline of the audit process and may identify the auditors' focal points that may need to be addressed as well as provide a description of the audit process. Diversion of 340B drugs to ineligible patients is the most common finding followed by an inaccurate listing on the HRSA database and duplicate discount violations.

> ## KEY POINT
>
> HRSA's audit focus changes over time. Reviewing posted audit results and networking with recently audited peers is a "best practice" to stay aligned with HRSA's current audit focus and methods.

Covered entities should anticipate a HRSA audit to focus on Medicaid duplicate discounts, elements of program implementation and operations related to the group purchasing organization (GPO) prohibition, determination of provider eligibility, a full review of parent/child locations on the Medicare cost report, and a review of policies and procedures.[1] Based on the visibility of the 340B program and close Congressional oversight, hospital covered entities should anticipate a HRSA audit every 3–5 years with a focus on:

- Medicaid duplicate discounts
- Key elements of 340B program implementation and operations, including virtual inventory management and contract pharmacy
- A review of data and practices related to the GPO prohibition
- An assessment of methods used to determine and manage provider eligibility
- A review of parent/child locations on the Medicare cost report
- A review of policies and procedures

During the audit, the covered entity should not expect to review charity care programs, use or application of 340B savings, nor any specifics regarding justification of any vendor or technology that supports 340B compliance.

Contract pharmacies will not be reviewed in detail in this chapter. Covered entities that utilize contract pharmacies introduce additional complexity to their 340B program. Guidance for navigating the business and compliance considerations of contract pharmacy are found in Chapter 9. Audits of covered entities that do not utilize contract pharmacies should expect to skip that portion of the audit. Note, however, that contract pharmacy oversight remains among the most cited audit findings.[2,3]

Best practices, ideas, and recommendations in this chapter cannot guarantee a successful audit result. However, the effectiveness of the policies, practices, and advice in this chapter has been demonstrated by covered entities in successful audits. Preparation, sound covered entity infrastructure, and undertaking a constant state of readiness for an audit with an eye to upholding the integrity of the 340B program are all keys to a successful audit.

HRSA INTEGRITY MEASURES

Annual Recertification

The annual recertification process requires the covered entity to attest to meeting qualification to participate in the 340B program and to the covered entity's compliance with 340B program requirements.[1] HRSA, the 340B prime vendor, and others offer detailed guidance for recertification through webinars and materials published on their respective web sites.[1,4,5] Covered entities need to be aware of the recertification timelines, as failure to follow them will present eligibility challenges and may cause a covered entity to be removed from the program if fully missed. All covered entities must recertify, including federally qualified health centers, Ryan White HIV/AIDS program grantees, specific hospitals (e.g., disproportionate share, critical access, children's), and specialized clinics.

HRSA sets recertification periods annually, and email notifications with information about the recertification process are sent to the listed primary contact and authorizing official outlining the process. During the recertification period, the covered entity updates the 340B database and certifies, or attests, that all the information listed on the HRSA web site is accurate and that the covered entity is compliant with the program.[4,5] Key elements of the attestation statement that should be reviewed by covered entity leadership include:

- Accurate listing of the details of the covered entity
- A review of covered entity eligibility requirements to ensure that the organization remains eligible
- A review of policies and activities to preclude diversion and Medicaid duplicate discount in accordance with the attestation language
- Recordkeeping policies
- If the covered entity uses contract pharmacies, a review of OPA requirements
- A review of self-reporting requirements[5]
- An acknowledgment that a breach of 340B program requirements may lead to repayment obligations and disqualification from the 304B program.

HRSA audit results highlight the fact that proper and complete listings of the various data elements and covered locations remain an area in need of improvement.[2,3] Specifically, is the published information on the HRSA web site regarding the covered entity complete and accurate?

KEY POINT

In addition to reviewing the HRSA web listing and completing the attestations to remain in the 340B program, annual HRSA recertification is an optimal time to perform a full structural review of a covered entity's 340B program.

HRSA's web site can and should be updated on an ongoing basis as changes occur. Covered entities should undertake a regular schedule of reviewing program locations and HRSA-listed information between recertification. Although the HRSA web site listing can be updated during the recertification process, ideally, change requests are made in real time as the covered entity opens and closes facilities, acquires or moves sites of care, or changes their relationship with contract pharmacies prior to the recertification period. This permits the covered entity's authorizing official to attest that the correct information is posted. Covered entities are also well advised to maintain a current and accurate listing of the authorizing official and primary contact to ensure that notices regarding recertification are received. Failure to recertify will cause a covered entity to be removed from the program, requiring them to apply for readmission in the next quarterly enrollment period—losing 340B benefits for the intervening period.

Annual recertification is a major underpinning for the covered entity audit, as the covered entity attests that the information on the HRSA web site is accurate.[1] Once the authorizing official attests to the accuracy of the information, HRSA holds the covered entity accountable. Ensuring the accuracy of the web site is a cornerstone of a successful covered entity audit. Although all information of the annual recertification is important, areas of focus when preparing for a covered entity audit should include the following:

- Parent (primary) site location and address
- Child site location and address

- Correct corresponding identification of all locations on the most recently submitted Medicare cost report, including a match of names and relevant descriptions.[1] Include an assessment of the Trial Balance sheet to ensure that costs and revenues are posted to each child site location.

In addition to verification of the correct addresses and tracing the location to the Medicare cost report, covered entities must ensure all eligible locations that may utilize or dispense 340B drugs are listed on the web site. This includes ship-to locations.

During the recertification process, the authorizing official and the listed primary contact of the covered entity are notified. If a covered entity has multiple child sites with different listed primary contacts, each contact will receive a message regarding recertification. However, only the authorizing official receives login information to add or change the listing and to provide the attestation of compliance. The authorizing official is the only individual at the covered entity who can update the web site and attest to the accuracy of the information.

Self-Disclosures[6-8]

HRSA guidance offers covered entities enrolled in the 340B program a method to address compliance issues and manage a corrective action plan (CAP) through self-disclosure. During the annual recertification, the authorizing official attests that any material breach will be self-disclosed to HRSA and the affected manufacturers. Specifically, "the covered entity acknowledges its responsibility to contact HRSA as soon as reasonably possible if there is any… material breach by the covered entity of any of the foregoing [points of 340B compliance]."[9] Although numerous heuristics are offered by consultants, Apexus, and others, any noncompliance within the 340B program can be considered a material breach.[7] Specifically, any event that leads to the covered entity to have a diversion and/or application of duplicate discounts or to violate the GPO prohibition can be considered a material breach. The most common material breaches include:

- Covered entity providing 340B drug to ineligible patients
- Covered entity unable to track 340B drug inventory
- Covered entity purchases medication at 340B cost, bills Medicaid, and Medicaid subsequently submits and receives rebate (duplicate discount violation)
- Covered entity purchasing GPO-contracted covered outpatient drugs

Although the duplicate discount violation generally occurs in concert with Medicaid, from HRSA's perspective, the covered entity assumes responsibility, as it is their responsibility to track government notices regarding proper treatment of Medicaid claims from the various state Medicaid programs that they bill, to properly manage or exclude claims for Medicaid patients, and to provide notice to Medicaid through the maintenance of provider number listings and Medicaid indicators in the HRSA database.

When a covered entity undergoes a HRSA audit, any information regarding prior and ongoing self-disclosures are subject to review. Apexus 340B University offers a toolset describing the key elements of self-disclosure and the development of a CAP.[10] An outline of the elements of an appropriate response to a material breach are also discussed in Chapter 3.

HRSA's focus during the audit is not to review the initial breach, but rather to assess the status of the CAP. Actions taken should be consistent with the CAP proposed to and accepted by HRSA. The covered entity should be prepared to produce relevant documentation regarding the self-disclosure, including correspondence with the manufacturers, and to outline ongoing actions completing the CAP. Although HRSA has not stated so publicly, it is reasonable to presume that HRSA's risk-based approach to developing an annual audit plan considers the types of material breaches reported by covered entities through self-disclosure, and further that covered entity history of breach(es) and CAPs is a consideration in development of the audit plan.

During a HRSA audit, covered entity's policies and procedures are reviewed. Policies and procedures regarding material breaches need to outline the following within a covered entity:

- Process for identifying material breaches
- Process for notifying and continued correspondence with HRSA
- Process for notifying and continued correspondence with manufacturers
- Process for creating CAP[7,10]

Covered entities that have submitted self-disclosures should expect a comprehensive review of prior and ongoing self-disclosures during a HRSA audit, including the implementation of policies, practices, and operational changes to prevent future breaches. In addition, the covered entity may be subject to further review of policies and procedures regarding self-disclosures. The covered entity needs to be prepared to address any changes that have been made since the breach that led to the self-disclosures.

Covered Entity Audits

HRSA is granted the authority to audit both the covered entity and manufacturers through Section 42 of USC 256b(a)(5)(C). Although manufacturers can be audited, the focus of this chapter is on covered entity audits. Per HRSA, the intent of the onsite audit is to review the covered entity's use of the 340B program. *Specifically, a covered entity should expect HRSA to review the following: policies and procedures, drug distribution system, GPO exclusion, patient definition, and duplicate discounts.*[1]

A covered entity should be prepared for a HRSA audit at any time. HRSA has publicly committed to audit covered entities regularly to ensure program integrity and compliance. HRSA will send written notification to the authorizing official of the pending audit. Shortly thereafter, typically within days of receiving the written notification, the authorizing official will receive additional communication from HRSA, via electronic mail, to set up an initial call to discuss the details of the audit.[1]

KEY POINT

Managing the hospital's 340B program to be prepared for an audit at any time ensures that the details are well and completely managed. Regular "mock audits" are a useful tool to ensure readiness.

Figure 15-1 outlines the general timeline for a HRSA 340B audit. Timelines may vary depending on the auditor's workload, the nature of findings in the audit, and need for follow-up from the covered entity. If any follow-up requires a CAP and a proposal for repayment to a manufacturer, the audit may remain open until the CAP is complete and the audit findings are resolved.

To facilitate a covered entity's preparation of the audit experience, this section of the chapter will be divided into four sections:

1. Pre-audit interactions with HRSA
2. Information requests from HRSA
3. Onsite audit with HRSA
4. Post-audit interactions with HRSA

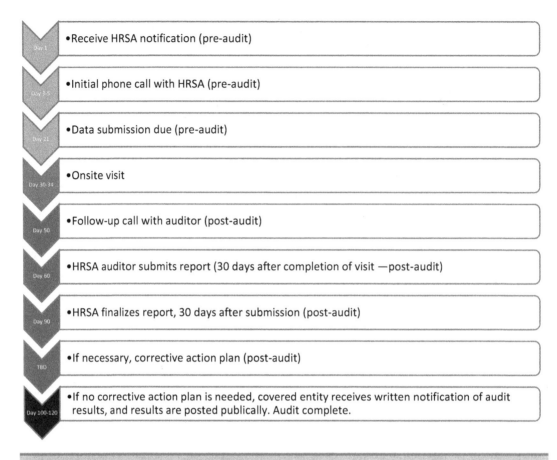

FIGURE 15-1. HRSA Audit Timeline

Pre-Audit Interactions with HRSA

HRSA sends the written notification to the authorizing official, which is followed up with an electronic mail from the auditor(s) who will conduct the onsite visit. This communication from the auditor is to set up an initial call with the covered entity and to confirm that the covered entity has received the audit notice. HRSA may use the initial notification and subsequent communication to emphasize the onsite audit's intent to review the covered entity's use of the 340B program. Specifically, HRSA may emphasize reviews for policies and procedures, the drug distribution system, group purchasing exclusivity compliance, patient definition, and duplicate discounts.

The timeline and dates for the onsite audit may be confirmed in this correspondence. During the correspondence, HRSA requests that the covered entity provide a primary agent, who need not be the authorizing official. The request for a primary agent is also based on the size of the covered entity. For large covered entities with multiple child sites and large contract pharmacy networks, multiple people may need to be present to represent different facets of pharmacy operations, 340B, policies and oversight, compliance, and recordkeeping. The primary agent's purpose is to minimize confusion caused by communication between multiple stakeholders and to streamline the upcoming visit. The primary agent is responsible for all communication with the HRSA auditor and to coordinate fulfillment of the various data requests and to coordinate the logistics of the auditor's visit. During the initial correspondence with the auditor, the covered entity should use the opportunity to obtain and confirm the details of HRSA's information request, which should be addressed in the initial call.

Pre-Audit Interactions with HRSA—Initial Call

In a short amount of time—typically less than 2 weeks after the covered entity receives written notification of the HRSA audit and the auditor e-mail to the authorizing official—the auditor and the covered entity will have an initial call. The intent of the initial call is to introduce the auditor and covered entity with the primary focus addressing the logistics of the onsite visit. Logistics include, but are not limited to, workspace for the auditor as well as computer and internet access, copy, fax, phone, and parking. Depending on the size and complexity of the covered entity, the audit may last 1 to 5 days. In rare situations, audits may extend past 5 days for large, complex covered entities that have multiple child sites and numerous contract pharmacies. Generally, prior to the call, HRSA will send a comprehensive information request to the covered entity.

On the initial call, covered entity attendees should include the authorizing official, the primary agent, and other pertinent staff who work with the covered entity's 340B program. Specific personnel will be dependent on the covered entity, but in all instances, they should include the members of the team who will be preparing the items for the data request and those who will meet with the auditor during the onsite visit.[1] Additional information regarding pertinent personnel is addressed in the *Audit Preparation, Planning, and Covered Entity Infrastructure* section. Also, the initial call is a prime opportunity to clarify with the HRSA auditor who from the covered entity may be present during the onsite audit. Covered entities may have individuals who are not considered pertinent personnel who may have reasons to attend the audit. Clarification and permission from the HRSA auditor should be received in advance of the onsite visit for personnel serving in recording roles, as well as learners and observers to be present during the audit. HRSA does not have any specific language permitting or forbidding this, but it is a reasonable auditor preference item.

During the initial call, the auditor will set the tentative agenda for the visit and specify areas to be addressed while onsite. This call provides an opportunity to clarify the scope of the audit and to outline the auditor's interest in seeing specific sites, understanding specific covered entity capabilities, and outlining logistics.[1] Except for smaller covered entities, the actual physical locations of child sites, retail pharmacies, and contract pharmacies can present a challenge to visit in an efficient manner. The initial letter to the authorizing official will identify the 340B identification number that is scheduled for audit. However, the covered entity should be prepared to address and review other 340B entities that may be associated with the address of the parent location, such as a Hemophilia Treatment Center, Ryan White program, or federally qualified health center. For example, a disproportionate share hospital (DSH) receiving notification of an upcoming audit may expect to have other 340B programs associated with the parent/child sites' address, covered entity name, and Medicare identification reviewed. Any information associated with the covered entity that is found on the HRSA 340B online database may be subject to review when the HRSA auditor is onsite.

The initial call is a key opportunity to clarify the information requests from HRSA because the pending visit requires the covered entity to submit specific information through a secure web site. Although 340B software vendors provide "standard" HRSA audit report packages and help desk support, the details of local 340B program implementation can dictate the way in which data are assembled and submitted. Clarifying the information request at this time, prior to the auditor arriving onsite, can minimize issues and delays in the onsite visit. Points for clarification regarding the information request should include where data should be submitted and the timeframe of the requests. HRSA generally indicates that the covered entity provide a secure location for data submission; cloud base portals that can securely handle large data files are recommended. When HRSA audits a covered entity, they typically audit a predefined timeframe, such as 6 months. The initial call is an opportunity to clarify the timeframe in question. If there are data limitations in the timeframe specified, it is prudent to inform the HRSA auditor as soon as possible. In addition, the initial call is an opportunity to clarify the auditor's preferred data format as well as how the information should be titled and labeled.

Information Requests from HRSA[1,12]

Prior to the initial call, the authorizing official or primary agent should ask the auditor for documentation regarding the information request. Questions about the information request can be clarified on the initial call as part of the pre-audit interactions with HRSA. The HRSA auditor will request that the information be uploaded to a secure cloud network location by a specified date prior to the onsite audit. The general outline of the information request is listed in **Table 15-1**. When uploading the above information to the secure cloud network, the covered entity should be in regular communication with the auditor. Notifications should be sent to the auditor when sections are uploaded. In addition, the covered entity should verify the auditor has access to the information. Prior to the onsite visit, the covered entity can expect correspondence with the auditor regarding the uploaded information.

The information request provides a template for the onsite visit agenda and who from the covered entity needs to be present during the specific times of the visit. In the balance of this section, additional details about what is expected for each component of the information request will be provided. Subject matter experts should be present and/or available during the onsite visit; the specific information will be highlighted as well in Table 15-1.

Gathering the required documents and data for the information request is challenging and time-consuming. The larger and more complex the organization, the more challenging the information retrieval can be. Datasets can be extremely large; in addition to being time-consuming to pull, the data should be reviewed and errors or gaps addressed prior to the upload. Data and information may need to be merged, cleaned, or modified prior to submission. Generally, the most time-consuming data to pull, review, and submit are the eligible medication orders and prescriptions, which will be discussed later in this chapter. Despite the challenges and the short amount of time allocated to gather all the appropriate information and data, covered entities need to meet HRSA's deadlines. Failure to do so can set the covered entity on a downward spiral going into the onsite audit. If the covered entity is struggling to meet the established timelines and deadlines, they are encouraged to engage in open dialogue with HRSA and attempt to resolve it.

Submitting poor and/or incomplete information and data are also a reflection on the covered entity and 340B program management. This may set the covered entity up for a challenging audit, because more time will be spent on cleaning up the submitted information while the auditor is onsite, rather than simply reviewing it. Poor or incomplete information and data may make it challenging for the auditor to discern facts and increases the likelihood of the audit resulting in findings. The findings may subject the covered entity to developing a CAP, encountering financial harm, and even expulsion from the 340B program, in addition to delaying the closing of the audit.

Policies and Procedures

When uploading the covered entity's policies and procedures, the date of the last document review needs to be present on the attachments. Ideally, the covered entity regularly reviews and updates policies and procedures. Other relevant dates on the policies and procedures are origin dates as well dates of subsequent changes to the documents. If the policies originate after the notification date of the HRSA audit letter, the covered entity should expect questions regarding timing. As stated earlier, the covered entity needs to be in a constant state of readiness for an audit. Uploading documents with origination dates after the HRSA audit letter notification date may signify to the auditor that the covered entity is being reactionary to 340B compliance under the threat of an audit rather than regularly and proactively attending to program maintenance. For the information request upload, the preferred document format for policies and procedures is either Adobe® Portable Document Format (PDF) or Microsoft® Word documents; however, while onsite, the HRSA auditor may ask the covered entity to show where the policies and procedures are posted on their intranet to confirm they are posted as well as to understand methods for communication throughout their organization.

Table 15-1. HRSA Information Request and Subject Matter Experts

HRSA Information Request	Covered Entity Subject Matter Expert(s)
1. Policies and procedures	■ Authorizing official ■ Listed primary contact ■ Internal audit and/or compliance staff ■ Procurement staff and/or drug distribution staff ■ Legal/contracting staff
2. Current Medicare cost report and trial balance	■ Finance staff specializing in CMS regulations and cost reporting
3. 340B medication orders or prescriptions for designated timeframe	■ Procurement staff and/or drug distribution staff ■ Staff who can navigate electronic medical record and/or paper patient chart
4. Authorized providers list	■ Human resources and/or credentialing office ■ Graduate medical education office
5. Covered entity's wholesaler and direct 340B medication purchases for designated timeframe	■ Procurement staff and/or drug distribution staff
6. List of contract pharmacies and contracts	■ Listed primary contact ■ Legal/contracting staff
7. Copies of self-disclosures made by covered entity	■ Internal audit and/or compliance staff ■ Individual(s) who have been in contact with HRSA and the manufacturers ■ Author of the corrective action plan(s)
8. Distributor and manufacturer direct purchase accounts for all parent and child sites	■ Procurement staff and/or drug distribution staff
9. Listing of eligible 340B locations within the parent and child sites	■ Finance staff specializing in CMS regulations and cost reporting
10. Listing of all Medicaid billing numbers and NPI numbers utilized to bill Medicaid for 340B	■ Finance staff, specializing in patient billing
11. Copies of contracts between the covered entity and state or local government to health services to low-income individuals	■ Program administrators ■ Legal/contacting staff ■ Government contacts
12. Copies of grant information or subgrantee documentation	■ Authorizing official ■ Listed primary contact ■ Grant administrator

CMS: Centers for Medicare & Medicaid Services, HRSA: Health Resources and Services Administration, NPI: national provider identifier

When reviewing the policies and procedures with the auditor, the covered entity should have subject matter experts present and/or available. Specifically, designees or subject matter experts for registration and recertification should be present. This includes the authorizing official and listed primary contact. In addition, if the covered entity has an internal audit group that actively reviews 340B compliance, they should be present to walk the auditor through how compliance to the policies is upheld, including self-disclosures. Operational and procurement staff who are involved in daily purchasing activities as well as inventory replenishment activities should be made available, as the auditor may have detailed questions. If the covered entity has a contract pharmacy, someone who is knowledgeable of the agreement(s) and transfer of data should also be present. Policies and procedures that the HRSA auditors target include, but are not limited to, the following:

- 340B registration and recertification
- Procurement
- Prevention of GPO violations
- Definition of covered outpatient medications and compliance with orphan drugs
- Compliance oversight
- Inventory replenishment
- Diversion and duplicate discount prevention
- Self-disclosure

Medicare Cost Report and Trial Balance

Depending on the timing of the audit, there may be a need to upload 2 years of Medicare cost reports and trial balances. This can be clarified during the initial call with the auditor. Generally, the auditor will state a specific timeframe that the covered entity will have to provide data, typically it is 6 months. If this timeframe overlaps two different timeframes of the cost report, there may be a need to upload multiple annual documents. Although rare, this situation is possible but can be clarified on the initial call with the auditor. In addition to the cost report and trial balances, the covered entity should consider creating and uploading a cross-walk document. Large covered entities with multiple child sites may have unique nomenclature on the cost report that may not easily flag eligible 340B areas. The cross-walk is intended to clarify nomenclature and assist the auditor where an eligible 340B area can be found on the cost report and trial balance.

When the auditor is onsite to review the cost report and trial balance, it is essential to have a subject matter expert navigate the documents seamlessly. The subject matter expert is generally someone from a covered entity's finance division who specializes in Centers for Medicare & Medicaid Services reporting for the institution. While interacting with the auditor, this subject matter expert should expect to map 340B parent and child site locations to the cost report and trial balance.

Eligible Medication Orders or Prescriptions

The covered entity should expect to spend a significant amount of time pulling, preparing, and reviewing the dataset that contains eligible medication orders or prescriptions. Although the dataset will cover a predetermined amount of time, the auditor will review only a random sampling of the data while onsite. The covered entity should clarify with the auditor what exactly needs to be pulled and for which patient care settings. It should be assumed that a covered entity will have to pull separate datasets for mixed-use areas as well as contract and retail pharmacies. Data elements that are generally required include, but are not limited to:

1. Medication/prescription identifying number
2. Acquisition price
3. Account medication was purchased through and the associated 340B location and identification

4. Quantity dispensed
5. Patient identification number
6. Payer
7. Ordering provider
8. Site 340B medication was administered, ordered, and/or prescribed
9. Determination if medication was actually dispensed, reversed, or returned to stock

In addition to uploading the requested datasets, the covered entity is expected to upload a document that describes how the data were pulled. Within this document, the covered entity is expected to address any data limitations. If data were excluded, it should be noted as well with justifications as to why.

During the onsite audit, the covered entity should expect to have a number of subject matter experts present during this portion of the audit. Although procurement staff and others who can effectively navigate the electronic medical records or paper documentation should be available, review of these data lead to questions about other information that was uploaded. Additional staff members who may be important to have around when reviewing the dataset include those who can verify authorizing providers and 340B eligible locations.

Authorized Providers

The covered entity is required to upload a file of all authorized providers who may have written an eligible medication order or prescription in the audit timeframe. If possible, the file sent to HRSA should have dates of employment for eligible providers. While the auditor is onsite, the covered entity can expect to produce documentation verifying provider eligibility, such as employment contracts or credentials. Covered entities that utilize trainees (e.g., medical residents, medical interns) will need to provide documentation for dates of employment if a trainee wrote a medication order or prescription.

While these individuals may not have to be present during the visit, it is recommended that the covered entity to have contacts in the credentialing office or human resources to verify eligible providers. Entities that utilize trainees should have contacts in the Graduate Medical Education (GME) office too. In preparation for the onsite audit, the covered entity should provide advanced notice to these contacts to be on stand-by in case any additional verification is needed.

Distributor and Direct 340B Purchases

HRSA will request that the covered entity provide a comprehensive list of all 340B drug purchases for the audit timeframe. All 340B purchases for the parent and child sites are expected to be uploaded. The intent of these data is to validate that a 340B product was purchased and dispensed in a 340B-eligible area during the data review portion of the audit. Purchase anomalies, such as inventory adjustments, should be included in the uploaded data. Although not required, it may be helpful to also include GPO and wholesaler acquisition cost (WAC) purchase data; this can be clarified on the initial call. Procurement staff should be made available and be ready to discuss when a specific purchase was made. The covered entity should also expect the auditor to verify procurement policies and procedure adherence when reviewing the purchases. Including the GPO and WAC purchase data in the upload may be helpful in addressing the auditor's questions about new medications that were purchased and dispensed for the first time during the audit timeframe. Expect the auditor to target high-cost medications during the audit.

Contract Pharmacies

Details regarding implementation, operations, and compliance for contract pharmacies are found in Chapter 9. For the onsite audit, the covered entity should provide a listing of all contract pharmacies. In addition, the covered entity should upload all agreements that identify each individual contract pharmacy. During the portion of the audit in which the HRSA database is validated, contract pharmacies will be reviewed. Agreements for individual contract pharmacies and addresses on the HRSA database need to match. The covered entity may be asked to take the auditor to visit a contract pharmacy listed on the database.

Self-Disclosures[6]

HRSA requires the covered entity to provide information, such as any self-disclosures, for the specified timeframe of the audit. Although the covered entity may not have had a self-disclosure during the specified timeframe, any self-disclosure filed by the covered entity is subject to review. A covered entity that is fortunate enough not to have a self-disclosure can expect questions on how the covered entity may respond if a violation was found.

During this discussion, a review of policies and procedures should be expected. If the covered entity has a self-disclosure on file with HRSA, a detailed discussion regarding the identification of the breach may occur. In addition, any subsequent changes made to policies and procedures will likely be discussed. CAPs for the self-disclosure will need to be uploaded and are open to review during the audit. Copies of all correspondence to HRSA and the manufacturers should be uploaded to HRSA in advance of the audit. Individuals who have been in correspondence with HRSA and manufacturers should be available for follow-up questions. Subject matter experts listed in policies and procedures may be asked to highlight changes that the covered entity made as a result of the self-disclosure.

Distributor and Direct Purchase Accounts

HRSA requests a list of all medication purchase accounts to be uploaded. Any purchase account that services a covered entity's parent or child site needs to be submitted. This includes 340B accounts, GPO accounts, and WAC accounts. Each account should be labeled for the type of contracts it contains (e.g., 340B, GPO, WAC). Ideally, a pure outpatient setting should have mirroring 340B and WAC accounts, while a mixed-use area should have 340B, WAC, and GPO accounts. Procurement staff should be made available and be ready to discuss when each account is used. The covered entity should also expect the auditor to verify procurement policies and procedure adherence when reviewing the accounts.

340B-Eligible Locations

During the onsite audit, the covered entity should expect to review 340B-eligible locations during the HRSA database review as well as during the cost report and trial balance review. As addressed in the *Medicare Cost Report and Trial Balance,* a covered entity is highly encouraged to create a cross-walk document that ties any 340B-eligible location back to the cost report and trial balance. This document will be helpful during the navigation of the medication and prescription files during the onsite visit. A subject matter expert who can identify the 340B-eligible locations and utilize the cross-walk to the Medicare cost report and trial balance is essential for the onsite audit.

Medicaid Billing and National Provider Identifier Numbers

A list of Medicaid billing numbers and national provider identifier (NPI) numbers will have to be uploaded prior to the audit. In addition, when uploading the medication order and prescription data, these data should include the Medicaid billing and/or NPI numbers. If the medication order and prescription data do not contain this information, the covered entity must be prepared to identify what Medicaid billing and/or NPI number is associated with the medication dispense. In addition, it is essential for the HRSA database to list the covered entity's Medicaid billing and/or NPI numbers. Failure to do so will subject the covered entity to additional scrutiny during the onsite audit. Generally, the authorizing official and/or primary agent for the covered entity are needed during the audit to attest to the Medicaid billing and/or NPI numbers. Additional subject matter experts may be needed during the onsite data review.

State and Local Contracts to Cover Low-Income Patients

If the covered entity has state and local government contracts to provide healthcare services to low-income individuals, the agreements will need to be uploaded. Supplemental documentation supporting the agreements will also need to be uploaded. This includes, but is not limited to, CMS waivers and eligibility criteria. When the auditor is onsite, the covered entity should have those people involved with the program available, including government contacts, if questions arise or additional clarification is needed.

Grant and Subgrantee Documentation

HRSA audits of grantees will focus on relevant grant or subgrantee documents. These documents will need to be uploaded prior to the visit. It should be noted that HRSA may choose to audit a grantee while auditing a covered entity that shares the same address of a grantee. For example, a DSH that has received notice of an upcoming audit should expect a review of any grantee program that is associated with the address of the parent or child sites. In any scenario, the grantee contact should be made available during the covered entity audit.

Onsite Audit with HRSA[1,11]

Once the HRSA auditor is onsite, the audit officially begins. Ideally, the covered entity has clarified expectations and settled logistics on the initial call. High-performing covered entities have uploaded the information requests in a timely fashion, updated the HRSA database, and have been in a constant state of readiness for the onsite audit. As the onsite audit nears, the HRSA auditor will contact the primary agent to validate logistics for the visit. Upon arrival to the covered entity, the auditor will meet with the primary agent and other relevant staff and conduct introductions and clarify the agenda for the audit. The agenda for the onsite audit is intended to be informal and does not dictate time constraints on what needs to be covered when. Generally, a typical onsite audit loosely follows the agenda below:

1. Introductions
2. Capitalized Medicare Cost Report and Trial Balance
3. Policies and procedures review
4. Medication order and/or prescription review
    a. Drug purchases and inventory management
    b. Dispensing review
    c. Site and provider eligibility review
5. Contract pharmacy review and visit
6. Parent/child site visits
7. Wrap-up, question and answer session

In anticipation of the audit, the covered entity should attempt to secure a room that is capable of having numerous computers and projectors presenting simultaneously. A good portion of the audit is a review of the submitted information and data. At times, different submitted data elements are cross-referenced to other data elements. The ability to easily point between multiple screens as opposed to toggling between applications and data elements enables the covered entity to display all the relevant information at the same time in an efficient manner.

Introductions

During the initial introductions, all relevant contacts, subject matter experts, and associated staff should be present. At this time, the auditor will state their preference for conducting the audit and specifically who can be present. After the introductions, the auditor will clarify the covered entity's parent and child sites through a comprehensive HRSA database review. During this review, it is essential that staff from the covered entity knowledgeable about the parent and child sites, as well as the database, are present. It may be helpful during this portion to have a computer and projector set up, so the database can be viewed on a wider screen. Also, consider having paper copies of the HRSA database available, as it may be easier to quickly navigate the document compared to accessing it via a computer.

Medicare Cost Report and Trial Balance Review

On completion of the introductions and review of the HRSA database, the auditor will likely review the Capitalized Medicare Cost Report and Trial Balance. As previously stated, utilizing a subject matter expert (e.g., someone from finance with knowledge of CMS and the cost report) will facilitate this interaction. The cross-walk of eligible locations listed on the HRSA database that links to the lines in the cost report and trial balance will assist in expediting this process. During this portion of the audit, keep both an electronic *and* paper copy of the relevant documents.

Policies and Procedures Review

For this portion of the audit, the auditor reviews a HRSA checklist compared to the covered entity's policies and procedures. Staff who is present should be expected to walk the auditor through how the policies are applied at the covered entity. In addition, the auditor may propose a hypothetical scenario in which procurement staff is asked to justify purchases, applying the relevant policies and procedures. Also, scenarios regarding duplicate discount may be discussed in which the covered entity walks the auditor through how Medicaid is notified if a product dispense is 340B or not.

Medication Order and/or Prescription Review

A significant portion of the onsite visit will probably be dedicated to medication order and/or prescription dataset review. Having multiple computers and projectors for presenting the data and information would be ideal. During this part of the audit, the HRSA auditor will request data from the following sources of information:

1. 340B medication orders or prescriptions for designated timeframe—export of the electronic medical record and/or copies of the patient chart
2. Policies and procedures
3. Authorized provider list
4. Covered entity's distributor and direct 340B medication purchases for designated timeframe
5. Distributor and manufacturer direct purchase accounts for all parent and child sites
6. Listing of eligible 340B locations within the parent and child sites
7. Listing of all Medicaid billing numbers and NPI numbers utilized to bill Medicaid for 340B

This portion of the audit generally has two components; if applicable, there is a review of mixed use dataset and a review of the contract pharmacy and/or retail pharmacy dispense dataset.

During this comprehensive data review, the auditor will have selected a random sample of medication orders and/or prescriptions. The covered entity should be prepared to perform an order review in which the medication order and subsequent dispensing or administration are traced back to the provider who wrote the order, where the order was written and dispensed, when the medication was purchased, what account the medication was purchased, and how it was billed. In addition, the tracer will allow the auditor to determine if the covered entity's policies and procedures have been applied appropriately.

As the medication order and/or prescription information is projected, an individual from the covered entity who is comfortable and familiar with the electronic medical record or paper chart should navigate. This individual can highlight the medication order number or prescription number, ordering provider, origin of the order, dispense location, and any billing modifiers that flag dispenses as 340B or non-340B. Another individual can navigate the provider file, identifying that the provider is authorized. To validate both the order origin and dispense location as authorized, screens or handouts with the HRSA database and list of eligible locations should also be projected or on hand. Ideally, another individual is in front of all the projected screens, flagging out the relevant data for the auditor. The exercise is intended to be intense, but if the covered entity is prepared and knowledgeable about the data, it is possible to navigate this section efficiently. It should be expected that this portion of the audit will take anywhere between 4–16 hours. Covered entities that have submitted poor or incomplete data should expect this section to be challenging and time-consuming.

Contract Pharmacy Review and Visit

Covered entities that do not utilize contract pharmacies can expect to skip this portion of the audit. Covered entities that utilize contract pharmacies should expect to review and validate the HRSA database with the auditor to ensure that the contract pharmacies are appropriately listed. In addition, during the *Medication Order and/or Prescription Review,* the auditor will likely pull additional dispenses from contract pharmacies and apply the same tracer methodology. Lastly, the auditor will also conduct a review of the contracts to ensure that they are appropriate, the designated pharmacies are listed on the HRSA database, and the covered entity's policies and procedures are being followed correctly.

Parent/Child Site Visits

The HRSA auditor will want to see how 340B compliance at the covered entity is applied and upheld in real time. Covered entities should expect to arrange visits for the HRSA auditor to the parent site, child sites, covered entity pharmacies, as well as contract pharmacies. During these visits, front-line staff may be requested to walk the auditor through day-to-day 340B operations regarding procurement, 340B determination, and validation. All staff who handle and dispense 340B product should feel comfortable speaking with the auditor about daily practice.

Wrap-up, Question and Answer Session

After completing the onsite audit, the auditor will conduct a wrap-up meeting, complete with a question and answer session. The auditor will state a tentative timeline for next steps as well as review facts. The auditor is not permitted to share opinions about what potential findings HRSA or OPA may identify from their report. At this time, the auditor will share the facts that he or she found during the visit as well as highlight items that were missing. If gaps or questions were identified during previous portions of the audit, this is an opportune time to provide data or relevant information to mitigate the gaps and address any unanswered questions. During this session, the auditor may ask for additional documentation to be uploaded too. The auditor will also use this time to clarify a point of contact for follow-up questions, after he or she leaves the covered entity and begins to prepare the report.

Post-Audit Interactions with HRSA[1,11]

As the onsite audit concludes, the HRSA auditors will follow up with the primary agent on the next steps as well as clarify any points from the audit. The covered entity should expect written communication correspondence via electronic mail and verbal communication over the phone to clarify questions and follow-up. This correspondence will take place in less than 30 days from the completion of the onsite audit; generally, this takes place 10–20 days after the onsite audit. As addressed in *Onsite Audit with HRSA,* the auditor is submitting facts that were gathered while onsite. The auditor is prohibited from making statements regarding the covered entity's audit findings. It should be noted that the timelines stated in this section are to serve as a guide and should be considered best case scenarios.

Once the HRSA auditor gathers and clarifies the information and facts gathered from the onsite audit and follow-up correspondence, their report will be submitted to HRSA or specifically to OPA. Their report is generally submitted within 30 days of the completion of the onsite audit. OPA then has 30 days upon receipt of the HRSA auditor's report to review and respond to the covered entity. If OPA determines that the covered entity did not have any findings of concern regarding the integrity of the 340B program, the audit is considered closed. The covered entity will receive written notification that there were no findings as well as documentation that the audit has been closed. The HRSA web site will be updated shortly after the audit is closed to indicate that the covered entity was audited, had no findings, and the audit is considered complete and closed.

When OPA identifies violations in the 340B program, the covered entity will receive notice of the findings. Findings can range from minor infractions (e.g., omissions from the HRSA database) to severe (e.g., violation of GPO prohibition or failure to uphold the integrity of the 340B program). The latter finding might result from an institutional failure to keep records sufficient to permit an audit, among other items. A list of common findings can be found in **Table 15-2.** The covered entity is required to respond to the findings in writing. Covered entities that choose to accept the audit findings are subject to preparing a CAP, which documents actions that the covered entity will undertake to prevent the cause of the finding from occurring again. As part of the CAP, the covered entity is expected to present documentation of changes such as updates of policies and procedures or database updates. After resolution of the findings, HRSA will post the final audit results online and send notification to the covered entity that the audit is closed.

KEY POINT

Following completion of the onsite audit, prepare to respond to a HRSA report of findings such as potential challenges and appeals. Audited covered entities typically provide 30 days to respond, including appeals and corrective action plans.

A covered entity has the option of challenging findings. Challenges must be submitted in writing with appropriate documentation to support the reversal of the finding. If the finding is not overturned, the covered entity is permitted to continue to challenge. After resolving the findings, HRSA will post the final results online and send notification to the covered entity that the audit is closed.

AUDIT PREPARATION, PLANNING, AND COVERED ENTITY INFRASTRUCTURE

A covered entity that continually embraces the mindset that an audit is forthcoming—as opposed to a covered entity hoping an audit will not occur, or believes an audit can be managed to avoid problem areas in their 340B program—is best prepared to handle the response to an audit notification. Building a program that has the resources, oversight, and infrastructure are the keys to a successful audit. Early adoption of the "forthcoming audit" mindset is essential, because the audit process itself offers very limited time to address program gaps, build solutions, and prepare for success once notification is received.

Developing broad-based oversight for the 340B program that includes a committee of key stakeholders across the organization is critical. Based on the size of a covered entity, it may be necessary to establish multiple 340B committees. Larger, and potentially more complex organizations will need subject matter experts in addition to the authorizing official. Examples of committees and attendees can be found in **Table 15-3.**

Table 15-2. Common HRSA Violations and Findings[2,3]

Common HRSA Violations/Findings	Corrective Action Plan
Lack of, or incomplete policies and procedures	Provide HRSA with supplemental documentation of policies and procedures
HRSA database omissions or failure to terminate information from database, including contract pharmacies	Update HRSA database
GPO prohibition violation	Manufacturer repayment; provide HRSA with supplemental documentation of revised policies and procedures
Duplicate discount violation, including contract pharmacies	Manufacturer repayment; provide HRSA with supplemental documentation of revised policies and procedures
Diversion, dispensing 340B medication to ineligible patients, including contract pharmacies	Manufacturer repayment; provide HRSA with supplemental documentation of policies and procedures

GPO: group purchasing organization, HRSA: Health Resources and Services Administration

Table 15-3. 340B Committees and Attendees[12]

340B Committee	Attendees
340B Oversight	▪ Authorizing official
	▪ Listed primary contacts from the HRSA web site
	▪ Chief Executive Officer
	▪ Chief Operating Officer
	▪ Chief Financial Officer
	▪ Governmental affairs contact
	▪ Public relations contact
	▪ Pharmacy leadership, including but not limited to Chief Pharmacy Officer, Operations Leadership, Ambulatory Leadership
	▪ Legal counsel
	▪ Finance contacts, including but not limited to CMS content experts and patient billing experts
340B Operations	▪ Pharmacy leadership, specifically operations leadership from both the mixed-use and retail settings
	▪ Procurement staff
	▪ Patient billing staff
	▪ Electronic medical record content experts

HRSA: Health Resources and Services Administration

Appropriate policies and procedures related to the audit itself have been addressed in this chapter as a focal point of an audit. However, having policies and procedures alone is not sufficient to pass an audit. A covered entity must verify that they are being followed. A failure to follow policies and practices outlined in the covered entity's policy manual increases the risk of an audit finding. Ascertaining that the covered entity is meeting their policies and procedures can be accomplished through a variety of mechanisms, including but not limited to internal audits and utilization of external consultants to review the covered entity's 340B program compliance. As gaps in policies and procedures are identified, covered entities need to be nimble enough to make adjustments and apply new ones. If adjustments are made due to internal audits or external consultants' recommendations, the changes must be documented. The following section will high-light tools that a covered entity can utilize to be in a constant state of audit readiness.

Using Internal Audits as a Preparation Tool[10]

Internal audits are a "best practice" and should be a key part of a covered entity's 340B program oversight and audit preparation strategy. Successful internal audits will require assigned staff time to ensure audits remain a priority. There are multiple components to a comprehensive internal audit process, with frequency of tasks ranging from daily completion to quarterly and annual review. Some audit components are relevant to all 340B program areas, while others are specific to the retail pharmacy or mixed-use settings. Components of audit elements can be found in **Table 15-4**.

Some providers may practice at multiple sites within a health system, which may or may not be on the Medicare cost report; thus, they have the potential to write medication orders that are both eligible and ineligible for 340B. If automated split-billing software is used, the covered entity should verify that it is able to recognize the origin of electronic prescriptions accurately. Pharmacy employees responsible for manually determining an order or prescription's 340B eligibility should be aware of this requirement. If the covered entity is aware of providers that practice in eligible and ineligible locations, these providers should be a focus of internal auditing efforts. Likewise, if a health system allows nonemployee physicians to utilize its facilities, care should be taken to ensure orders written by these providers are not considered 340B eligible. Lastly, the covered entity should verify that all 340B orders are written within a provider's scope of practice. A licensed provider may legally prescribe beyond their scope of practice, but the prescription is not 340B eligible.

Additional steps are required to complete internal audits of orders from mixed-use areas. Mixed-use areas include operating rooms and other procedural areas that see admitted and non-admitted patients. For these orders, the patient's admission status at the time the order was written and dispensed should be verified. This information should be available within the health system's electronic medical record. The methods and process to access this information for audit purposes should be documented as it is a requirement of any external 340B audit.[13]

Patient tracers are used to verify that proper and accurate patient and prescription identification and management practices are present throughout a covered entity's 340B program. A *patient*

Table 15-4. Internal Audit Elements[10]

Internal Audit Element	Frequency of Audit
Policy and procedure review, complete with patient tracer	Every 6–12 months
Review of parent/child status and publication on the HRSA database	Quarterly
Purchasing data review	Every 6–12 months
Authorized provider review	Quarterly, monthly if possible
Split-billing integrity review	Quarterly
Patient billing data review, specifically inclusion of billing modifiers on eligible transactions	Quarterly
Correspondence with Medicaid to review duplicate discounts	Quarterly
Cost report and trial balance review and mapping to the HRSA database to verify eligible areas	Quarterly

HRSA: Health Resources and Services Administration

tracer involves the validation of all auditable components of a drug dispensing or drug administration activity. Patient tracers include:

- A review of the relationship of the provider to the organization
- The relationship of the patient to the provider
- Confirmation of a qualifying patient care encounter
- Verification of outpatient status at time of dispense
- Confirmation that proper modifying codes have been applied to the claim.

The number of patient tracers to be completed is dependent on the pharmacy's total volume, available resources, and department-specific targets. A covered entity may choose to trace either a specific number of processed claims or a percent of total claims. A target of 3–5% of total claims traced is reasonable. Priority should be given to high dollar claims, but low dollar claims cannot be ignored, as these will certainly be included in any external audit. All errors discovered during tracers should be corrected immediately. If an error is made during a manual process, the individual responsible for the error should be provided with feedback. Errors should be logged to discover trends and adjust systems to prevent future reoccurrences.

Covered entities are also encouraged to seek outside assistance to be compliant with the 340B program.[13] Third-party auditors can offer a variety of resources and tools to assist with compliance and should be considered. Even covered entities with strong internal audit processes may benefit from an outside perspective. Covered entities concerned about feedback from third-party auditors being negatively portrayed by HRSA, may consider conducting the audit under attorney-client privilege. No matter how effectively and appropriately a program is run, it still needs to be prepared. Hiring a consultant can provide insight and resources to ensure the audit goes well, but if a consultant is hired to support an audit for a neglected program or one with gaps or challenges, it is generally too little, too late.

KEY POINT

A well-run program can benefit from consultants and external support. However, hospital leadership should build compliance and operations knowledge to support a high-performing program that will successfully complete a HRSA audit.

Audit Discovery and Reporting[7,14]

A tightly run 340B program with strong program oversight and regular internal audits should generally find modest exceptions or issues to be addressed to stay compliant. However, in some instances, a lapse in 340B program compliance at a larger scale or scope may be discovered. This internal audit discovery may rise to the level of a material breach. Material breaches may also be found during an external audit. When a material breach is discovered, the entity should carry out the necessary steps to correct the situation under policies developed to support compliance and integrity.[6,7,10] The policies should outline thresholds to disclose material breach to a manufacturer and HRSA and consider HRSA's requirements for completing a CAP. Criteria for disclosing noncompliance may be determined, as outlined earlier in the chapter. These thresholds should be reasonable, and the organization's policy must be followed as written.

If material breach occurs and disclosure is required, a template is available through Apexus.[7] When disclosing a breach to HRSA, the statement should include a description of the breach, the timeframe, and the reason the breach occurred. The statement must also include a list of the parties impacted by the breach and a detailed action plan to correct the breach and prevent future breaches. Manufacturers impacted by a material breach must be contacted too. If there are multiple manufacturers, each disclosure statement should be manufacturer-specific and provide details that pertain only to them.

All disclosures made to HRSA and manufacturers should be kept on file for the life of the entity's 340B program, and the file should be readily retrievable in the case of an audit. The file should also contain any correspondence received from the manufacturer, especially if the correspondence contains agreements related to corrective actions or repayments. If multiple attempts are made to contact a manufacturer to determine corrective action, documentation of each attempt should be kept on file. Copies of checks written to manufacturers should also be in this file.

SUMMARY

HRSA and covered entities must work together to uphold the integrity of the 340B program. Although the focus of the chapter was HRSA covered entity audits, integrity measures such as annual recertification and self-disclosures were also covered in detail. The rationale for reviewing annual recertification and self-disclosures is that they make up a significant component of the HRSA covered entity audit.

If anything can be ascertained from this chapter, it is the following: *A constant state of readiness is the best mechanism to achieve a successful audit.* Regular self-audits and mock audits—combined with attention to HRSA's current approach and requirements—can lead to a successful audit result, even if findings occur. A well-run program will see limited financial and punitive impact beyond remedying program gaps identified in the audit process. To adapt to the potentially changing dynamics of 340B compliance and be better positioned, covered entities should adopt the mentality that (1) an audit is inevitable, (2) it is prudent to be prepared at all times through regular internal reviews, and (3) using external consultants is advisable.

REFERENCES

1. Health Resources and Services Administration; program integrity. http://www.hrsa.gov/opa/programintegrity/index.html. Accessed November 4, 2017.

2. Health Resources and Services Administration; program integrity: FY16 Audit Results. https://www.hrsa.gov/opa/programintegrity/auditresults/fy16results.html. Accessed November 4, 2017.

3. Health Resources and Services Administration; program integrity: FY15 Audit Results. https://www.hrsa.gov/opa/programintegrity/auditresults/fy15auditresults.html. Accessed November 4, 2017.

4. Apexus: Registration/Recertification. https://www.340bpvp.com/resource-center/faqs/registration--recertification/. Accessed November 4, 2017.

5. Health Resources and Services Administration; annual recertification. https://www.hrsa.gov/opa/recertification/recertification.html. Accessed November 4, 2017.

6. Health Resources and Services Administration; self-disclosure process. http://www.hrsa.gov/opa/selfdisclosures/selfdisclosure.html. Accessed November 4, 2017.

7. Apexus 340B University Establishing Material Breach Threshold Tool. https://docs.340bpvp.com/documents/public/resourcecenter/Establishing_Material_Breach_Threshold.pdf. Accessed November 4, 2017.

8. Apexus: Medicaid/Duplicate Discounts. https://www.340bpvp.com/resource-center/faqs/medicaid--duplicate-discounts. Accessed November 4, 2017.

9. Health Resources and Services Administration; self-disclosure. https://www.hrsa.gov/opa/updates/september2014.html. Accessed November 4, 2017.

10. Apexus 340B University: 340B Compliance Self-Assessment: self-audit process. https://docs.340bpvp. com/documents/public/resourcecenter/dsh_340b_compliance_selfassessment_datatransactions.pdf. Accessed November 4, 2017.

11. Testoni M. What should a 340B covered entity expect during a typical HRSA audit? *PPP*. 2014 11(9). Available at: https://www.pppmag.com/article_print.php?id=1571. Accessed November 4, 2017.

12. Apexus: 340B Compliance for the C-Suite. https://docs.340bpvp.com/documents/public/resourcecen-ter/340BCompliance_CSuite.pdf. Accessed November 4, 2017.

13. Hicks D, et al. Engaging and working with pharmacy consultants. *Am J Health-Syst Pharm*. 2016; 73:150-155.

14. Apexus: 340B Self Disclosure to HRSA, suggested template. https://docs.340bpvp.com/documents/ public/resourcecenter/ALL_Entities_Self_Reporting_340B_Non_Compliance.docx. Accessed November 4, 2017.

CHAPTER 16

Manufacturer Considerations and Perspectives on the 340B Program

Marcus Farbstein, MBA, RPh

The intent of this chapter is to provide a pharmaceutical industry viewpoint to a broad array of stakeholders. It is not intended as a guide for manufacturers implementing their program participation or as the definitive manufacturer perspective on the 340B program. Information and opinions are based on the author's opinions and published government reports, industry studies, and think-tank information and statistics. Due to the nature of the 340B program, all of the analysis is open to interpretation; contrasting and potentially conflicting data and perspectives; and alternative viewpoints.

In general, pharmaceutical industry executives support programs that provide access to care and pharmaceuticals for underserved, needy, and disadvantaged patients. Health Resources and Services Administration (HRSA) grant programs serve the neediest individuals with the greatest health risks. Access to 340B drugs with significant discounts allows these programs to stretch their limited grant dollars. Likewise, hospitals that are deeply invested safety net providers in their communities benefit from the same discounts under the 340B program to stretch resources to provide access to care.

When the 340B program was enacted in 1992, health policy makers, professional and trade organizations, hospitals and healthcare providers, and the pharmaceutical industry paid it little attention. The 340B program appeared to be a niche program providing support for federal grant program awardees serving uninsured and indigent patients in underserved communities. In the year following its enactment, fewer than 100 disproportionate share hospitals (DSHs) enrolled in the program. **Figure 16-1** illustrates the growth of hospitals in the 340B program from inception through 2011 (after that growth leveled off). The 2015 Medicare Payment Advisory Commission (MedPAC) report to Congress on the Overview of the 340B Drug Pricing Program stated that in 2014, there were 14,061 hospitals and affiliated sites in the 340B program, comprising 2,140 hospital organizations.[1] The growth of the 340B program and the nature of its impact in the marketplace had extended beyond what even the most ardent boosters might have anticipated. The current estimate is that more than 40% of U.S. hospitals participate in the program.

340B PROGRAM PERSPECTIVES

Focusing on the 340B program today, the pharmaceutical industry's interests and concerns may be grouped into five broad areas:

1. The growth of the program and appropriate use and access to 340B-discounted drugs.
2. Concern about future guidance, regulations, and challenges to HRSA authority.

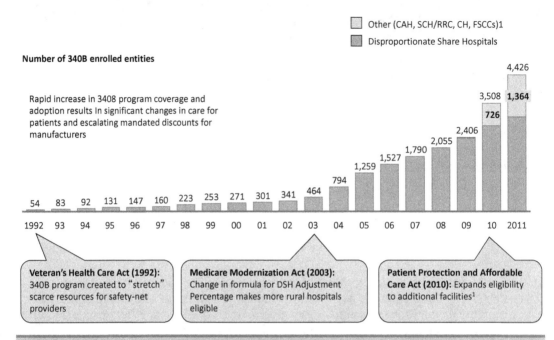

Number of 340B enrolled entities

Other (CAH, SCH/RRC, CH, FSCCs)1
Disproportionate Share Hospitals

Rapid increase in 3408 program coverage and adoption results In significant changes in care for patients and escalating mandated discounts for manufacturers

| | | | | | | | | | | | | | 794 | 1,259 | 1,527 | 1,790 | 2,055 | 2,406 | 3,508 726 | 4,426 1,364 |

54 | 83 | 92 | 131 | 147 | 160 | 223 | 253 | 271 | 301 | 341 | 464

1992 93 94 95 96 97 98 99 00 01 02 03 04 05 06 07 08 09 10 2011

Veteran's Health Care Act (1992): 340B program created to "stretch" scarce resources for safety-net providers

Medicare Modernization Act (2003): Change in formula for DSH Adjustment Percentage makes more rural hospitals eligible

Patient Protection and Affordable Care Act (2010): Expands eligibility to additional facilities[1]

FIGURE 16-1. Rapid Growth in Enrollment, First 20 Years of the 340B Program

3. The transfer of 340B discount proceeds to third parties through business arrangements such as contract pharmacies.

4. Implementing complex 340B program requirements correctly.

5. Managing refunds triggered by prior period restatements.

Examples of the facts underlying these concerns are outlined in the following discussion.

A study published in *Health Affairs*, stated the following:

> Hospital-affiliated clinics that registered for the 340B program in 2004 or later served communities that were wealthier and had higher rates of health insurance compared to communities served by hospitals and clinics that registered for the program before 2004. Our findings support the criticism that the 340B program is being converted from one that serves vulnerable patient populations to one that enriches hospitals and their affiliated clinics.[2(p1786)]

Adam Fein, a pharmaceutical industry analyst and consultant, reported in the blog *Drug Channels* that the 340B prime vendor Apexus supplied data that purchases in the 340B program reached at least $12 billion in 2015, 67% higher than 2013 purchases.[3] In comparison, over the 10-year period from 2005 to 2015, total hospital drug purchases grew by 31%, while 340B purchases grew 400%.[3,4]

HRSA has offered a number of significant 340B program rules addressing the areas of ceiling price calculations and penalties imposed on drug manufacturers, the 340B program administrative dispute resolution process, and Omnibus Guidance that addresses a number of areas including site eligibility, program integrity, and definition of eligible patients. Depending on how HRSA finalizes its guidance, stakeholders might challenge the rules. Recent litigation related to interpretation of the orphan drug rule and HRSA's authority to impose rules not sanctioned by Congress questioned how guidance imposes an immediate and significant burden on manufacturers. HRSA must consider their mandate and areas of regulatory authority and the risk of litigation from covered entities or manufacturers that would forestall implementation of rule making of a guidance document or regulatory proposal.

In all the discussion and debate about how the 340B discount should be used to extend and augment patient care services and support safety net providers, manufacturers, public policy makers, and regulators are not able to identify, participate in dialogue related to, or to direct or circumscribe the transfer of revenue or other benefits of the 340B program discount to third parties. The 340B discount is substantial enough to generate interest in its broad application to covered entity programs and to support the development of a 340B "industry" of consultants, software, and service companies providing support for covered entities to effectively tap 340B value, broadening the scope of the 340B program use.

KEY POINT

Over the past 25 years, the 340B program has become complex and the savings has grown to be substantial. It is substantial enough to support the development of a 340B industry of consultants, software, and service companies providing support for covered entities to capture savings while remaining compliant with current rules.

Examples include, but are not limited to:

- Commercial insurance companies negotiating contracts with differential reimbursement for 340B entities armed with the knowledge that 340B hospitals are receiving deep discounts for clinic-administered drugs and retail prescriptions.

- Pharmacy chains developing their retail networks for 340B contract pharmacy relationships, including discount-based fees and larger networks to capture 340B-eligible patients and prescriptions across broad geographic areas.

- Third-party administrators (TPAs) using sophisticated pharmacy claim screening tools to identify and capture prescriptions for patients of covered entities in contract pharmacy networks.

- 340B TPAs capturing after-the-fact claims in contract pharmacy relationships. The disconnect supported by the post claim 340B process sidesteps the National Council for Prescription Drug Programs (NCPDPs) 340B identifier. This may lead to payers and pharmacy benefit managers (PBMs) continuing to collect manufacturer rebates on 340B prescriptions, a form of *double discounting*.

The 340B program continues to grow and evolve with many varied players vying to participate and extract value for covered entities, their partners, and themselves.

Additional Perspectives from Government Agencies and Congress

Several government agencies and members of Congress have weighed in on the current state of the 340B program. In February 2013, *The New York Times* reported on congressional reaction to press coverage of windfalls to DSHs, quoting letters from Senator Charles E. Grassley, "If 'nonprofit' hospitals are essentially profiting from the 340B program without passing those savings to its patients, then the 340B program is not functioning as intended."[5]

In November 2015, a Health and Human Services (HHS) Office of the Inspector General (OIG) report stated the following:

Medicare Part B paid covered entities a total of $1.3 billion (58%) more than the cost of the drugs. In 2013, covered entities retained $1.3 billion in Part B payments because of the spread between Medicare payment amounts and 340B ceiling prices. The 340B statute does not restrict how covered entities may use these funds."[6]

The Government Accounting Office (GAO) published a report in June 2015 stating that 340B covered entities,

…were generally larger and more likely to be teaching hospitals compared with non-340B hospitals. They also tended to provide more uncompensated and charity care than non-340B hospitals; however, there were notable numbers of 340B hospitals that provided low amounts of these types of care. For example, 12 percent of 340B DSH hospitals were among the hospitals that reported providing the lowest amounts of charity care across all hospitals in GAO's analysis.[7]

Another area of manufacturer concern is around implementation of 340B program requirements. Manufacturers devote significant time and resources to managing the 340B program requirements. Tracking all sales and returns under commercial contracts and discounts, including various rebates to support correct calculation of a 340B price, is a daunting task. Data retrieval and validation require resources and careful analysis. Most manufacturers utilize internal legal resources and outside counsel to evaluate their standard operating procedures.

KEY POINT

Manufacturers devote significant effort to comply with 340B program pricing requirements. Tracking all sales, returns, and discounts under commercial contracts to support correct calculation of a 340B price is a daunting task. Making the 340B prices available to 340B covered entities each quarter is resource intensive.

Factors including prior period adjustments further challenge extending correct 340B pricing in the supply chain to permit 340B covered entities access to the products they need. Reclamation and rebate adjustment in the Medicaid Rebate Program is straightforward, because rebate invoices can be adjusted and rebates are retrospective. The 340B program presents unique challenges because the discounts are offered at time of sale and are not easily adjusted retrospectively. Manufacturers have discussed this issue with HRSA for some time. Some accommodations and mechanisms have been developed, but standard guidance would benefit from clarification.

Congress enacted the 340B program over two decades ago. In the process of drafting the program, it borrowed a qualification method that employed a hospital's inpatient utilization tracked by the DSH calculation to support enrollment in an outpatient program. The use of a hospital's Medicare cost report to determine 340B eligibility and outline 340B-eligible service areas (i.e., individual clinics must appear on a reimbursable line) was not foreseen when Centers for Medicare & Medicaid Services (CMS) developed the cost report.

Further, definitions of covered outpatient drugs and pricing calculations were tied to the methods and definitions used in the Medicaid Drug Rebate Program (MDRP). No other federal pricing program stipulates quarterly recalculations and then requires a rebate mechanism. The calculation of 340B prices and the MDRP calculation are covered in Chapter 10. The combination of the unique elements of the 340B program along with the use of definitions and methods from other CMS and Medicare programs has muddied the administration of the 340B program and created unintended consequences and complexity.

> ### KEY POINT
>
> The unique elements of the 340B program, combined with the definitions and methods borrowed from other CMS and Medicare programs, has complicated the administration of the 340B program.

SHIFTING SITES OF CARE

Many factors contribute to the shift from community-based physician practices to the hospital. Hospitals can bill at a higher rate for services, accrue economies of scale for back office functions, and realize margin on physician-administered drugs. These financial incentives are offset by rising costs, alternative payment models proposed by CMS and commercial payers, and coverage gaps for patients. One of the topics debated in the oncology practice community is the impact of the 340B program on oncology care delivery. According to data assembled by the Community Oncology Alliance, since 2008, hospitals have acquired 609 community oncology practices.[8] This shift represents more than half of the community oncology practices that closed or merged over the 8-year period. 340B program discounts add to the business incentives for participating hospitals to acquire community oncology practices due to substantial margins realized on drugs purchased at the 340B price, which can exceed 50%.

RULES VERSUS GUIDANCE

HRSA's Office of Pharmacy Affairs has published and presented their thoughts and opinions at conferences on many aspects of the 340B program since its inception. The Office of Pharmacy Affairs (OPA) web site has links to *Federal Register* notices, frequently asked questions (FAQs), and interpretive rules, statements, and guidance. Although these statements have evolved and changed over the course of time, most have been accepted and incorporated into 340B program practices. However, in October 2015, the D.C. District Court ruled that HRSA had overstepped its authority in the matter of orphan drug access for newly designated covered entities.

The Office of the *Federal Register* outlines the rule making and definitions as follows:

> Agencies get their authority to issue regulations from laws (statutes) enacted by Congress. An agency must not take action that goes beyond its statutory authority or violates the Constitution. Agencies must follow an open public process when they issue regulations, according to the Administrative Procedure Act (APA). This includes publishing a statement of rulemaking authority in the Federal Register for all proposed and final rules.

> Interpretive rules, policy statements, and other guidance documents may be issued anytime after a final rule is published to help the public understand to how a regulation applies to them and affects their interests. There is a key distinction between an interpretive rule and a final "legislative" or "substantive" rule. The interpretive rule or policy statement must not set new legal standards or impose new requirements.[9]

Although the pharmaceutical manufacturer and 340B covered entity communities have generally supported HRSA's guidance, HRSA's authority and scope for rule making is limited. In areas where all parties do not concur, it is likely that rules and guidance may be subject to litigation by either manufacturers or covered entities. This challenging situation means that many areas of the 340B program are likely to lack detailed guidance for the foreseeable future.

KEY POINT

In areas where all parties do not concur, it is likely that rules and guidance may be subject to litigation by either manufacturers or covered entities. This challenging situation means that many 340B program areas will likely lack detailed guidance for the foreseeable future.

Manufacturers encounter a variety of challenges and details in implementing the 340B program. The following sections outline this in more detail.

MANUFACTURER PARTICIPATION IN THE 304B PROGRAM

Manufacturers are required to participate in the 340B program as a result of Section 602 of Public Law 102-585, the Veterans Health Care Act of 1992. All drug pricing and rebate programs are interlocked, meaning that a manufacturer must participate in either all of the programs or none of them. As a result, virtually every manufacturer participates in the 340B program. Participation is governed by a *pharmaceutical pricing agreement (PPA)*, which is a contract between the government and the manufacturer. There are separate PPAs for 340B, Medicaid Rebate, Medicare Part D, and the VA's federal supply schedule contracts. HRSA posted this notice on their web site for manufacturers:

> In accordance with the guidance found in the May 7, 1993, Federal Register, Section 340B provides that a manufacturer who sells covered outpatient drugs to eligible entities must sign a pharmaceutical pricing agreement . . . with the Secretary of Health and Human Services . . . in which the manufacturer agrees to charge a price for covered outpatient drugs that will not exceed the average manufacturer price (AMP) decreased by a rebate percentage.[10]

A *covered outpatient drug*, defined in section 1927(k) of the Social Security Act, includes most FDA-approved prescription drugs, over-the-counter drugs written on a prescription, and insulin. Vaccines and drugs billed as part of a bundled payment are not eligible for 340B pricing.

The 340B price is also known as the *340B ceiling price*. A manufacturer cannot charge a covered entity more than this price. Manufacturers are free to offer a lower price, also known as a *sub-ceiling price*. Sub-ceiling prices are most often provided in competitive therapeutic classes. Of note, per OPA guidance, if a manufacturer offers a price that is incorrect and higher than the ceiling price, the manufacturer must make restitution with a refund. However, if the price offered is below the ceiling and is offered in error, the manufacturer is not permitted to request a refund from the covered entity.

Manufacturers are required to submit documentation of AMP and rebate calculations to CMS for purposes of verifying Medicaid rebate amounts. This information is also shared with OPA to validate 340B prices. AMP and rebate data are considered proprietary, so OPA can verify only the final 340B price. Manufacturers are required to retain records of price history and calculations of required discounts from the date of product introduction or back to the inception of the MDRP.

GENERAL CONSIDERATIONS

Given the size and complexity of the program, manufacturers have an obligation and a strong incentive for correct program implementation. Similar to covered entities, HRSA has the power to conduct audits of manufacturers. Unlike covered entities, violations of the 340B pricing requirements can result in significant monetary penalties above restitution. Most manufacturers have detailed policies and procedures in place that conform to standard operating procedures; many will have these systems validated as part of their internal financial audit.

MONITORING 340B ELIGIBILITY AND SALES

Manufacturers can and should have systems in place to monitor the distribution and sales of their products to covered entities. Typically, manufacturers work closely with distributors to validate customer eligibility. Distributors have robust systems in place to match customer ship-to locations with the verified eligibility database that OPA maintains.

When the distributor submits a chargeback to the manufacturer, they should validate the transaction with eligibility in OPA's database. Analysis of chargeback volume is one way to evaluate 340B compliance.

OPA is obligated to monitor and verify eligibility annually for covered entities. Each covered entity must stipulate that every child site meets the criteria as attested to in the hospital's Medicare cost report.

340B PRICING ISSUES

Manufacturers face a variety of unique challenges in the 340B program. Unlike other government pricing programs or commercial contracts, the 340B price must be calculated, submitted, and implemented every quarter. Although it is also true that Medicaid rebates are calculated every quarter, they are reconciled and invoiced retroactively. The retroactive rebate process allows for adjustments and evaluation of eligibility with sufficient time to manage the process.

340B prices lag Medicaid by two quarters out of necessity, as real-time data for the calculations are not available. For example, sales transactions that occur in the first quarter generate AMP and best price data submitted to CMS and used to calculate 340B prices during the second quarter ultimately are implemented for the third quarter. This process then moves forward quarter by quarter, always with a two-quarter lag.

The transfer of pricing files between manufacturers and distributors and subsequent uploading into purchasing and ordering platforms can introduce clerical and accounting errors. This scramble occurs 15 to 30 days prior to the beginning of every quarter.

OPA maintains a price verification system to help adjudicate inquiries from covered entities seeking to confirm that correct prices are available.

PRICING CALCULATIONS

Every manufacturer calculates the 340B price quarterly using a statutory formula that essentially provides the Medicaid rebate as an upfront discount. The calculation is the AMP minus the unit rebate amount (URA). The minimum discount was raised from 15.1% to 23.1% as part of the Affordable Care Act (ACA). For branded drugs, price increases above consumer price index for urban areas (CPI-U) incur an inflation penalty which is why the average discount in the program exceeds the minimum discount. Manufacturers must maintain and include all price increases in their calculations starting in 1993 or from product introduction if introduced later. With the passage of MDRP legislation in 2015, generic drugs and over-the-counter products calculate their respective 340B ceiling price as AMP minus 13% and were not been subject to the inflation penalty until January 2017.

PENNY PRICING

Penny pricing is a contentious topic for manufacturers. In some circumstances it is possible for the URA to exceed AMP, which results in a negative 340B price using the calculation above. Neither the 340B statute nor the PPA provides direction regarding this anomaly. Although HRSA's penny pricing policy is not stated in statute or regulation, HRSA says that it has been communicated to manufacturers and has been a routine practice since the program started.[11] A number of alternatives have been proposed via comments in the *Federal Register*. As a result of HRSA's undetermined authority, individual manufacturers may not follow the HRSA policy guidance under advice of their counsel.

In the past, penny-priced products led to covered entities ordering greater quantities of product than were purchased in the previous quarter. In a policy clarification, HRSA has provided guidance about reasonable orders of quantities and allocation of product in this situation to prevent shortages.[12] Similarly, if there is a bona fide shortage of a product, the manufacturer can develop a plan for nondiscriminatory, restricted distribution to all purchasers, including 340B covered entities, or a product allocation program. The plan should be shared with OPA and can be posted on their web site.

CORRECTING 340B PRICES AND PROVIDING REFUNDS

Manufacturers are compelled to have systems in place to manage and process orders, contracts, pricing, compliance, etc. The goal is to make sure the right price is available for the appropriate customer in the correct distribution channel. Inevitably, there are errors—human, system, and distributor, to name a few. *What happens when such an error is discovered in the 340B environment?*

If the incorrect price is detected within 30 days (depending on distributor contracts), the manufacturer can utilize a credit-rebill for the chargeback—effectively correcting the error in real time when the distributor credits the customer. If the pricing error is discovered later, the remedy is more complicated. The manufacturer might need to consider a judgment call regarding materiality. Actions to make corrections for small, short-term overcharges might differ from more substantial overcharges over longer periods. Even small price discrepancies might accrue to a significant sum when sales volume is large. OPA encourages manufacturers to contact them to discuss the problem and map out corrective action. Typically OPA requests that the manufacturer post a notification letter on the HRSA web site with information about how covered entities may receive a refund if one is owed.

All the corrective actions are stipulated for incorrect prices above the ceiling price. OPA has made it clear that if a manufacturer mistakenly charges a price below the ceiling, a refund from the covered entity cannot be sought. This is deemed to be a voluntary price concession.

Manufacturers have been managing the Medicaid rebate program longer than the 340B program. Each state Medicaid program supplies product utilization outlining the units dispensed and submits an invoice for the rebate on a regular basis. It is common practice for manufacturers to make adjustments to the URA retroactively as commercial rebate programs can trigger tiered discounts at the end of a quarter or year impacting the rebate calculation. These adjustments can lead to a restatement, which means that the 340B price from several quarters earlier is now effectively above the ceiling price offered at that time. The challenge is that the 340B program is an upfront discount and that transaction has closed.

From a practical standpoint, the majority of restatements are pennies or fractions of pennies. HRSA has reviewed and discussed this dilemma as it applies to 340B sales for years. A method to consider how to address small-scale restatements may be clarified in future regulation or guidance, but one of the challenges has been how to process a refund to covered entities, irrespective of the amount. There are three available mechanisms to process a refund to a covered entity:

1. A credit-rebill can be issued through the distributor, practical only for a short time window after a sale is made.

2. The manufacturer can issue checks. This method is very expensive, time- and resource-intensive. In addition, hospitals and clinics have difficulty in attributing, managing, and handling refund checks.

3. The 340B prime vendor has developed a mechanism to process refunds using a credit back through the distributor. This model can also aggregate small adjustments and process them quarterly or annually, potentially solving the materiality concern.

Distribution of Drugs under the 340B Program

Manufacturers have many different options to handle their product distribution. Systems and processes have evolved over time with contracts, costs, infrastructure, and pedigree requirements all impacting distribution. Most products are distributed through the full-line pharmaceutical wholesale channel, but specialty distribution is gaining wider use. A number of manufacturers still sell direct to some customer classes. In an environment supporting diverse specialty and traditional pharmaceutical offerings, the choice of a distribution channel is likely to be product-specific. Manufacturers understand the requirement to make the products available at 340B price through whatever channel they select and cannot discriminate against covered entities by creating distribution barriers. Under OPA guidance, manufacturers are not required to alter their distribution model for 340B customers.

RISK EVALUATION AND MITIGATION STRATEGIES PROGRAMS

Risk evaluation and mitigation strategies (REMS) programs are beyond the scope of this discussion. REMS programs are FDA-approved and come in many unique forms by design. A REMS program is specific to the benefits, concerns, and risks of the designated product. REMS programs do not preclude delivery of the covered drugs to or through 340B covered entities. However, covered entities must meet all of the REMS programs' requirements. Although HRSA's authority is not clear in regard to drugs where REMS performance is a requirement, manufacturers may engage with OPA to outline their approach to the specific therapeutic needs imposed. HRSA has not posted formal guidance, but has concurred when the plans to address covered entities are nondiscriminatory and has posted letters and notices addressing specific limited distribution agreements that include REMS drugs.[13]

WHOLESALE DRUG DISTRIBUTION VERSUS SPECIALTY DRUG DISTRIBUTION

Economics, particularly with lower-volume high-cost products, has driven the shift to specialty distribution in the last several years. Although this is not a 340B issue per se, it has an impact on cost and availability of 340B drugs especially for hospitals. Keep in mind that the traditional wholesale model has two key components: a prompt-payment discount (typically 2%) and a volume-based discount to the end customer. The prompt-payment discount is derived from the wholesale acquisition cost (WAC), which might be double or even higher for deeply discounted products.

The manufacturer can negotiate a completely different contract in the specialty distribution model. The contract may be based on revenue milestones and handling considerations such as cold chain or secure delivery. Fees and discounts to the distributor are generally much lower than the standard wholesale terms above. On the opposite side of the equation, the specialty distributors have increased top line revenue because they generally do not offer the bundled discount/ rebate as part of the wholesale contract. For full-line distributors, savings accrued from the traditional non-specialty book of business generated may be considered in offsetting higher cost/lower yield specialty distribution.

MANUFACTURER PERSPECTIVES ON THE 340B PRIME VENDOR PROGRAM

The 340B prime vendor program (PVP), envisioned as a de facto distributor for covered entities purchasing drugs under the 340B program, was included in the 340B program's original legislation. It slowly transformed into a negotiating entity offering a broad range of services. Manufacturers may take advantage of the program's safe harbor feature to offer 340B sub-ceiling prices in competitive markets. All 340B PVP-negotiated sub-ceiling prices are not subject to MDRP best price provisions or to inclusion in the Veterans Administration's (VA) non-federal AMP calculation (the required pricing vehicle for the VA). Apexus is currently the government's exclusive contractor for the 340B pricing program. Apexus can also provide a manufacturer support to offer voluntary inpatient pricing to 340B covered entities, although this is not common.

CONTRACT PHARMACIES

In 1996, OPA responded to a request from several covered entities to establish a contract pharmacy relationship. The response created a model to solve one of two potential problems: either the covered entity did not have the ability to set up an outpatient retail pharmacy or the covered entity served a large area where patients experienced a hardship in reaching the primary site. HRSA's original guidance limited the covered entity to a single off-site contract pharmacy. By 2010, there were over 2,000 registered contract pharmacy relationships.

The situation changed dramatically with the new HRSA contract pharmacy guidance published March 5, 2010 in the *Federal Register*. Under the new guidance, covered entities were permitted to contract with multiple pharmacies, as long as they adhered to instructions that helped to prevent diversion and duplicate discounts and the policies set forth in a restatement of patient definition.[14] As of July 2014, there were 15,330 unique pharmacy locations, which accounted for 25% of total U.S. retail, mail, and specialty pharmacy locations.[15]

The large network of retail, specialty, and mail order pharmacies operating in concert with 340B covered entities presents many challenges to manufacturers. The sheer number of sites operating as surrogates for 340B covered entities makes it difficult to monitor. A given covered entity can have hundreds of contract pharmacy sites. A single mail order pharmacy may have a 340B contract pharmacy relationship with more than 500 unique covered entities. Neither HRSA nor manufacturers have the capacity to audit even a fraction of these locations. A concern is growing that diversion of 340B drugs and duplicate discount challenges may be taking place, either intentionally or unintentionally.

KEY POINT

The large networks of retail, specialty, and mail order pharmacies operating under contract with 340B covered entities presents a significant challenge to manufacturers. The sheer number of sites makes it difficult to manage and monitor.

Manufacturers find it nearly impossible to monitor or track sales into contract pharmacies because the record of sale, the chargeback from the distributor, documents the purchaser's bill-to address, not necessarily the ship-to address. Chargeback and other sales tracking systems are designed to validate the 340B sale to the covered entity, not to track distribution to a secondary location.

HRSA guidance outlines the use of a ship-to/bill-to procedure. The covered entity purchases the drug; the manufacturer/wholesaler must bill the covered entity for the purchased drug, but ships the drug directly to the contract pharmacy. The covered entity is responsible for compliance with the contract pharmacy arrangement(s) and must maintain ownership of the 340B drugs at all times.[16]

The covered entity, per HRSA guidelines, is responsible for handling the product as it maintains the title. It is required to annually review the contract pharmacy relationships during recertification and audits, which provides some measure of oversight. However, a covered entity's priority is not to protect the manufacturers' interest but to maintain its internal integrity.

DIVERSION OF 340B DRUGS TO INELIGIBLE PATIENTS

Diversion of 340B drugs may take several forms:

- A 340B-priced drug dispensed or administered in a noneligible area or service (e.g., an inpatient setting or an ineligible clinic location).
- A 340B-priced drug dispensed to an ineligible patient in a retail pharmacy or administered in a clinic or outpatient setting.
- A 340B drug may be transferred to a third party or a non-eligible location in a covered entity.

A straightforward example of diversion would be for a covered entity to resell 340B-purchased product. Documented instances of all types of diversion have appeared in HRSA audits and covered entity self-disclosures. In one instance, a hospital worked with an affiliated physician to deliberately divert 340B drugs to non-340B physician providers by marketing and selling to oncology practices in adjoining states. A manufacturer detected the diversion of the 340B-priced product through examination of purchasing patterns and verification of covered entity practices.

Manufacturers are becoming increasingly vigilant in 340B program management by monitoring ordering patterns, verifying eligible covered entities, and developing best practices. Covered entities should manage their 340B programs to provide consistent and transparent procurement and supply chain management to reduce variations, which might be associated with or appear to reveal diversion of 340B drugs. Further, consistent with HRSA's statements, covered entities should be prepared to provide good-faith answers to manufacturer queries regarding 340B-related purchases.

KEY POINT

Covered entities should manage their 340B programs to provide consistent and transparent procurement and supply chain data. Transparency and consistency reduce the likelihood that variance may be seen as a potential marker of a poorly administered program or to represent potential diversion of 340B drugs.

MEDICAID AND 340B DUPLICATE DISCOUNTS

Monitoring for duplicate discounts is one of the most difficult program compliance practices to validate. A *duplicate discount* occurs when a manufacturer provides a discounted 340B price and a Medicaid drug rebate for the same drug. 42 USC 256b(a)(5)(A)(i) prohibits duplicate discounts; that is, manufacturers are not required to provide a discounted 340B price and a Medicaid drug rebate for the same drug. Covered entities must have mechanisms in place to prevent duplicate discounts.[17] In addition to the complexities in sales tracking outlined above, every state manages its own Medicaid rebate program, processing invoices and sometimes providing dispensing data that can be matched to providers.

Covered entities must indicate how they will implement their 340B program for purposes of billing Medicaid in the OPA database. The covered entities must be included in the HRSA exclusion file to prevent Medicaid rebates on those units if they intend to bill Medicaid for drugs purchased at 340B prices. Covered entities are permitted to carve out Medicaid, which means they purchase drugs at WAC only for dispensing to Medicaid patients. In this scenario, the state will request a rebate for drugs purchased outside the 340B program.

States have the authority to request rebates for patients in managed Medicaid programs. These units are more difficult to track, and covered entities often do not know which patients are in a managed Medicaid program.

Connecting all the dots can be a challenge and may not be easily detected without an audit. In instances when a duplicate discount occurs, financial harm occurs to the manufacturer because it has to pay a rebate on the same unit sold at the 340B price which can add up to more than the original cost of the drug.

ORPHAN DRUGS

The ACA added four new categories of covered entities to the 340B program: critical access hospitals, rural referral centers, sole community hospitals, and certain free-standing cancer hospitals. For these four categories of covered entities, pricing is not available for "a drug designated by the Secretary under section 526 of the Federal Food, Drug, and Cosmetic Act for a rare disease or condition." Treatment of orphan drugs in the 340B program has had many twists and turns, ultimately resulting in litigation that invalidated HRSA's proposed guidance. Details are outlined in Chapter 3, and the impact to covered entities is addressed in Chapters 11 and 12.

On October 14, 2015, the U.S. District Court for the District of Columbia granted Pharmaceutical Research and Manufacturers of America's motion for summary judgment against HHS. The court ruled that an "interpretive rule" was contrary to the language of the 340B statute. Essentially, the ruling sends a signal that HRSA has limited scope to promulgate rules. If HRSA issues "guidance," which is a lower level of instruction, it is open to interpretation.

After the October 2015 federal court decision, a manufacturer's prerogative to withhold pricing on orphan drugs from these covered entities is clear. However, because the language of the statute addresses orphan drugs by redefining them as excluded from the definition of covered outpatient drugs, manufacturers can provide individual contracts to the covered entities listed above. Due to HRSA giving manufacturers sole discretion, some manufacturers have chosen to offer discounts on orphan drugs to these hospitals.[18]

Manufacturer Audits of 340B Covered Entities

The concept of manufacturer audits of 340B covered entities has been discussed since the program's inception. Manufacturers have had a long-standing reluctance to embark on audits. Their reasons include an early lack of clarity about justification for an audit, concerns about creating an adversarial relationship with customers, the cost of hiring an external accounting firm, and the recovery of loss based on improper 340B activity that was limited to a refund of the discount. Manufacturers encouraged HRSA to conduct audits to reveal program weaknesses and covered entities' potential violations of program rules and guidance.

MANUFACTURER AUDIT GUIDELINES

HRSA published manufacturer audit guidelines in December 1996. The full notice defined the general concept of a manufacturer audit within a narrow scope.

> Covered entities which choose to participate in the section 340B drug discount program shall comply with the requirements of section 340B(a)(5) of the PHS Act. Section 340B(a)(5)(A) prohibits a covered entity from accepting a discount for a drug that would also generate a Medicaid rebate. Further, section 340B(a)(5)(B) prohibits a covered entity from reselling or otherwise transferring a discounted drug to a person who is not a patient of the entity. The participating entity shall permit the manufacturer of a covered outpatient drug to audit its records that directly pertain to the entity's compliance with section 340B(a)(5)(A) and (B) requirements with respect to drugs of the manufacturer.[19]

A manufacturer that suspects a violation of the program can contact OPA for guidance. Typically, this contact starts an informal dispute resolution process. Manufacturers are permitted to audit only for violations of the duplicate discount prohibition or diversion to an ineligible recipient (entity or patient). This process is a communication between the covered entity and the manufacturer usually without OPA involvement. If the informal process does not lead to an agreeable resolution or if the covered entity refuses to engage in good faith, it can constitute justification for an audit as outlined in the *Federal Register*:

> A manufacturer shall conduct an audit only when it has documentation which indicates that there is reasonable cause. "Reasonable cause' means that a reasonable person could believe that a covered entity may have violated a requirement of section 340B(a)(5) (A) or (B) of the PHS Act (i.e., accepting a 340B discount on a covered outpatient drug at a time when the covered entity has not submitted its Medicaid billing status to the Department or transferring or otherwise reselling section 340B discounted covered drugs to ineligible recipients).[19]

To initiate an audit, the manufacturer then must do several things:

■ Submit a justification to OPA identifying probable cause.

■ Engage an accounting firm capable of conducting an audit under federal government standards.

■ Determine whether to engage other manufacturers to participate in the audit.

Perhaps due to the highly complex process, issues, and costs involved, it was not until the spring of 2012 when the first manufacturer, Genentech, requested permission to conduct an audit of a covered entity. The author managed the process for the first three manufacturer audits.

The auditing accounting firm is charged with researching the suspected violation for the products involved and the time period stipulated. Because they must see internal documents and even patient records, strict confidentiality is maintained. Manufacturer representation is limited to introductions at the beginning of the audit and during the exit conference. The auditor then prepares a formal report for OPA and the covered entity outlining any relevant findings and documenting inappropriate discounts received. The covered entity can respond to the audit findings and must refund improper discounts and could be sanctioned by OPA.

If a violation is uncovered either during an informal dispute process or audit, the covered entity is required to refund the unearned discount received. Generally, this is simply an offer of a refund check.

COVERED ENTITY SELF-DISCLOSURE

HRSA recommends that a covered entity establish and document criteria that signify when a material breach of compliance has occurred. For situations that are a material breach, the covered entity should take steps to inform HRSA while it moves to correct the issue. This self-disclosure can have a similar result to an audit and, in fact, could be the result of a covered entity's internal audit. Usually a manufacturer will receive an "offer to repay" letter notifying them that a refund is available and that a corrective action plan was filed with OPA.

Generally, manufacturers will not accept a refund without proper documentation. They need to know what happened, the period of time, the products involved, and the number of units. The manufacturer may seek to validate the amount of the discount per unit or seek a statement regarding the conduct of the audit or compliance with 340B rules going forward. Manufacturers should review the documentation provided; validate the offer, if possible, with their own analysis; and determine if additional information is needed. Depending on the amounts involved, some manufacturers may decline the refund offer.

SUMMARY

Since the inception of the 340B program in 1993, the program has grown tremendously. The hospital segment grew from fewer than 100 to over 2,000 facilities and healthcare systems. Contract pharmacies were piloted in 1996 to assist organizations that did not have a retail outlet or were geographically challenged. Fourteen years later, under a more open model, these arrangements have grown to larger networks across communities designed to capture revenue for covered entities. New legislation expanded the types and number of covered entities eligible to participate. **Figure 16-2** illustrates the timeline of changes and expansion of the program.

Manufacturers face many challenges as they work to ensure compliance with the demands and provisions of the 340B program. Some of these resonate with covered entities such as retaining experienced, knowledgeable personnel. Other demands— such as the ceiling price calculation or following product distribution through the various sales channels and reconciling chargebacks and credits—are more opaque.

For some manufacturers, the 340B program represents a large segment of business and associated risk. Other manufacturers might have more modest involvement with a single product. All of the 340B rules apply in either case. All participants are on notice that they are subject to audit, which raises the bar to increase transparency.

The HRSA Office of Pharmacy Affairs is working toward a method to verify every quarterly price. In general, manufacturers look on this favorably, but perhaps have some trepidation related to the confidentiality of their AMP and/or best price that might reveal commercial discounting strategies.

At the root of the very complex healthcare system that includes the distribution and pricing of pharmaceuticals is the need to serve patients. All 340B program participants should recognize that collaboration promotes access and, by extension, facilitates treatment options. When we recognize the challenges we face in each of our roles imposed by a legislated program such as 340B, we will hopefully partner more effectively.

340B Drug Pricing Program Growth

The 340B Drug Pricing Program has changed and evolved over time. The timeline below illustrates the high points:

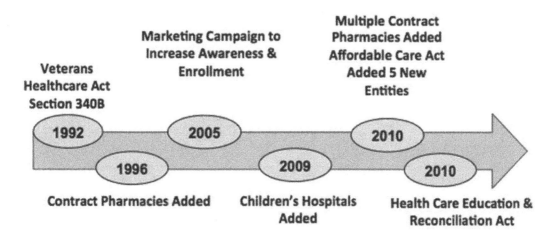

FIGURE 16-2. 340B Drug Pricing Program Growth

REFERENCES

1. Medicare Payment Advisory Commission. Report to the Congress Overview of the 340B Drug Pricing Program. http://www.medpac.gov/docs/default-source/reports/may-2015-report-to-the-congress-overview-of-the-340b-drug-pricing-program.pdf?sfvrsn=0. Accessed October 10, 2017.

2. Conti RM, Bach P. The 340B drug discount program: hospitals generate profits by expanding to reach more affluent communities. *Health Aff.* 2014; 33:1786-1792.

3. Fein A. Drug channels July 19, 2016, reality check: 340B is 4% (not 2%) of the U.S. drug market—and growing quickly. http://www.drugchannels.net/2016/07/reality-check-340b-is-4-not-2-of-us.html. Accessed October 10, 2017

4. Fein A. Drug channels February 23, 2016, 340B purchases hit $12 billion in 2015—and almost half of the hospital market. .http://www.drugchannels.net/2016/02/340b-purchases-hit-12-billion-in.html. Accessed October 10, 2017.

5. Pollack A. Dispute develops over drug discount program. *The New York Times,* February 12, 2015. http://www.nytimes.com/2013/02/13/business/dispute-develops-over-340b-discount-drug-program.html?_r=0. Accessed October 10, 2017.

6. Office of the Inspector General, Department of Health and Human Services. Part B payments for 340B-purchased drugs. November 2015. https://oig.hhs.gov/oei/reports/oei-12-14-00030.pdf. Accessed October 10, 2017.

7. United States Government Accountability Office. Medicare Part B drugs action needed to reduce financial incentives to prescribe 340B drugs at participating hospitals. June 2015. http://www.gao.gov/assets/680/670676.pdf. Accessed October 10, 2017.

8. Community Oncology Alliance. 2016 Community Oncology Alliance Practice Impact Report. http://www.communityoncology.org/2016-coa-practice-impact-report/. Accessed October 10, 2017.

9. Office of the Federal Register. A guide to the rulemaking process. https://www.federalregister.gov/uploads/2011/01/the_rulemaking_process.pdf. Accessed October 10, 2017.

10. Department of Health and Human Services, Health Resources and Services Administration. Health-care Systems Bureau OMB No. 0915-0327; general instructions for completing the pharmaceutical pricing agreement (PPA). http://www.hrsa.gov/opa/manufacturers/pharmaceuticalpricingagreement.pdf. Accessed October 10, 2017.

11. Department of Health and Human Services, Office of the Inspector General. Review of 340B prices. July 2006. https://oig.hhs.gov/oei/reports/oei-05-02-00073.pdf. Accessed October 10, 2017.

12. Department of Health & Human Services, Health Resources and Services Administration. 340B Drug Pricing Program Notice Release No. 2011-2, Clarification of Penny Pricing Policy. http://www.hrsa.gov/opa/programrequirements/policyreleases/pennypricingclarification112111.pdf. Accessed October 10, 2017.

13. Celgene Corporation. Notice Regarding Limited Distribution Network for Revlimid (lenalidomide), Pomalyst (pomalidomide) and Thalidomid (thalidomide). http://www.hrsa.gov/opa/programrequirements/manufacturerletters/2015/celgeneletter.pdf. Accessed October 10, 2017.

14. Department of Health and Human Services, Health Resources and Services Administration. Notice regarding 340B drug pricing program—contract pharmacy services. *Federal Register*. 2010 (March 5). 75;43:10272-10279. https://www.gpo.gov/fdsys/pkg/FR-2010-03-05/pdf/2010-4755.pdf. Accessed October 10, 2017.

15. Fein AJ. Challenges for managed care from 340B contract pharmacies. *J Manag Care Spec Pharm*. 2016; Mar 22(3):197-203.

16. Department of Health and Human Services, Health Resources and Services Administration Department of Health & Human Services, Health Resources and Services Administration. Contract Pharmacy Services. http://www.hrsa.gov/opa/implementation/contract/. Accessed October 10, 2017.

17. Department of Health and Human Services, Health Resources and Services Administration. Duplicate Discount Prohibition. https://www.hrsa.gov/opa/program-requirements/medicaid-exclusion/index.html. Accessed October 10, 2017.

18. Department of Health and Human Services, Health Resources and Services Administration. Orphan Drugs. http://www.hrsa.gov/opa/programrequirements/orphandrugexclusion/index.html. Accessed October 10, 2017.

19. Department of Health and Human Services, Health Resources and Services Administration. Manufacturer audit guidelines and dispute resolution process 0905–ZA–19. *Federal Register*. 1996 (December 12). 61;240:65406-65410. http://www.hrsa.gov/opa/programrequirements/federalregisternotices/disputeresolutionprocess121296.pdf. Accessed October 10, 2017.

CHAPTER 17

Future-proofing Your 340B Program

Andrew L. Wilson, PharmD, FASHP

Throughout the history of the 340B program, the Health Resources and Services Administration (HRSA) Office of Pharmacy Affairs (OPA) has made a sustained effort to clarify the rules, boundaries, and guidelines for covered entities' and manufacturers' participation. However, due to the limited nature of HRSA authority and the changing healthcare environment in which 340B operates, the resulting guidance, frequently asked questions (FAQs), and standards provide an outline but fall short of definitive and permanent guidance. HRSA's singular attempt to produce a broad "Mega Guidance" document was a casualty of the Trump administration's approach to regulatory reform.

Because HRSA has limited insight and no oversight of the operating requirements and business results of a hospital's 340B program, most guidance documents touch lightly on the daily complexities of health-system pharmacy and supply chain management, except for elements of eligible patient identification. FAQs, guidelines, and best practices offered by HRSA directly and through Apexus, the 340B prime vendor, constitute the largest body of written guidance. A substantial portion of the guidance exists only as FAQs and tools on the Apexus web site. These unofficial documents are subject to withdrawal or change by HRSA without formal notice. In some instances, the guidance is reactive; that is, it represents a response to a frequent question from 340B covered entities or may be a recurrent audit finding of concern to HRSA. The diversity of systems and practices mean that implementing a given practice or policy may vary widely between covered entities, and HRSA may seek to describe the specific actions or activities to meet guidance in more detail.

The consequence of this compliance framework along with the variation in health-system goals, diverse pharmacy software, and operations choices has led to the growth of a large network of "experts" including leading 340B peers, 340B consultants, 340B software and service industry leaders, and the officers and staff of various 340B and 340B-related groups. Varying perspectives, experience, and goals across the group lead to diverse opinions and recommendations, reflecting a variety of perspectives on risk, compliance, and business objectives. The 340B network provides support through user group meetings, webinars, online interest groups, and active consulting and outreach. These groups support the interpretation and actualization of the 340B guidelines by covered entities.

GUIDANCE WHEN IMPLEMENTING A PROGRAM

Given the general nature of formal guidance and the more informal authority of various tools and support documents, specific "how to implement and manage a 340B program" advice remains mixed. For the purposes of this discussion, consider that advice comes from two camps:

1. Experts in 340B with deep 340B knowledge, but modest or limited non-340B information technology (IT) supply chain knowledge and experience. This group includes 340B consultants, 340B industry experts, and 340B interest group staff.

2. Experts in the healthcare supply chain and informatics (e.g., supply chain professionals, IT professionals) with modest or limited 340B knowledge and experience. This group includes supply chain consultants, supply chain industry experts, and providers of medical record and financial software.

Each party attempts to optimize their primary area of expertise, while avoiding roadblocks and problems in their area of lesser interest and expertise. This places two burdens on the health-system pharmacy team overseeing the supply chain and patient care operations. *First*, they must serve as the source of 340B expertise; *second*, they must make certain that the resulting 340B-responsive processes and solutions are effective and efficient. In addition, the pharmacy leader may need to referee areas where the two approaches collide.

The 340B Program Handbook's chapter authors are experienced and familiar with the challenging discussions and compromises to be made in achieving balance. In the past, when 340B was lightly structured and infrequently audited, decisions were typically made to optimize patient care delivery or business results with modest 340B consideration. In the current situation of deeper and more complex 340B program guidance with regular HRSA audits, the converse is true. Hospitals often sacrifice the utility of supply chain efficiencies to preclude real and imagined 340B compliance concerns and undergo the potential loss of 340B savings. This approach mitigates the effectiveness of supply chain programs that address everything from inventory control to centralization of packaging and distribution services to efforts addressing drug shortages.

The volume of dialogue on *"How did you interpret 340B rules when implementing this (automation/software/supply chain) program?"* in electronic communications and at pharmacy and supply chain meetings is a telling indicator of the scope of the challenge. HRSA's use of peer-to-peer consulting addresses practical guidance segmented by covered entity type, and Apexus Answers offer some additional support; however, in sum, neither fully resolves the business versus compliance balance for an individual 340B covered entity.

HRSA's more recent active use of 340B audit standards—to foster a shared 340B community understanding grounded in HRSA's use of specific information and data elements to signify compliance—has assisted in building common ground. However, changing evidence required and clarified standards fosters a need to stay in touch to sustain and interpret the most recent view.

340B PROGRAM SUCCESS STRATEGIES

Although not exhaustive, the list of ten practices below should ensure that your 340B program remains viable, performs well, and provides a sustained and meaningful contribution to the mission of the covered entity.

KEY POINT

A strong policy and practice backbone, combined with documentation, is a critical element of success.

1. ***Participate in and communicate with the 340B community***. The first activity to undertake in maintaining a healthy 340B program over the long term is to stay current and maintain a continuing, active connection to the 340B community, including conversations about recent HRSA audits, updates to FAQs, and other HRSA guidance. This should

include participation in user groups for 340B software and for supply chain services, electronic medical record (EMR) software, and automation. Participate in and foster detailed dialogue and development of clear goals, standards, and processes to meet 340B objectives and support a well-functioning supply chain. 340B covered entities should drive key elements of their vendors' interpretation of 340B rules and understand their local application. As a presenter stated at a recent 340B meeting, the number one HRSA audit finding is "My software wasn't doing what I thought that it was." Passively accepting a vendor tool as 340B-compliant and well-functioning when implemented in your facility is a recipe for mediocrity at best and an audit finding at worst.

A variety of 340B organizations and activities are available in which to participate. A thoughtful approach spans the full spectrum from the pharmacy buyer and business manager through pharmacy leadership, finance, and administration. Meetings, newsletters, blogs, and relationships through consultants, group purchasing organizations (GPOs), and others should be elements of this effort.

2. ***Communicate internally***. Internal communication regarding 340B goals, objectives, and performance is also crucial, so develop a 340B program oversight structure that includes compliance, finance, IT, pharmacy leadership, and others to oversee 340B program function and results. As in the quote from the pundit above, 340B program results might currently meet expectations, but setting appropriate expectations is the first step. Covered entities over the recent past have focused on compliance, perhaps setting aside operational efficiency and business results as a secondary priority. The oversight committee engaging broad leadership understanding and executive support should thoroughly and thoughtfully examine this balance. The discussion of risk tolerance is not based solely on how closely the rules are followed, but also considers the systems, processes, quality checks, and other safeguards in balancing results. When this leadership conversation is fully explored, it also provides a framework for quality assessment along with an opportunity to assess the impact of program changes from the simple change of a software setting, to contracts with payers and the government, through wholesale policy changes by HRSA, Centers for Medicare & Medicaid Services (CMS), or Congress.

3. ***Hire and train 340B program staff***. Many methods are available to hire, train, and support qualified staff to support a compliant, high-performing 340B program. Training options include online offerings from Apexus that can lead to a 340B credential; in-person sessions held by Apexus, 340B Health (https://www.340bhealth.org), and others; and training provided by consultants and software vendors. As with any function requiring expertise and compliance knowledge, new staff and current pharmacy staff with 340B responsibility should be supported in enrolling and successfully completing such programs.

340B training programs are focused on compliance and broad categories of practices and activities that support the program. Hospitals are well advised to be certain, in addition to the training outlined above, that 340B program staff are trained in other elements of good practice and regulatory compliance in other areas. The 340B program functions within the larger healthcare delivery system and supply chain. The rules of the State Board of Pharmacy, U.S. Drug Enforcement Administration, U.S. Food and Drug Administration, "Track and Trace," and others also apply. A competently managed supply chain team must be prepared to acquit itself well on all regulatory and compliance dimensions. Ensuring a 360-degree view of compliance combined with operational and business achievement is vital.

4. ***Record program and software settings, policies, and practices***. The paucity of detail and the sheer scope of options and combinations, combined with the variance among vendor solutions in 340B software and tools, require that covered entities keep their wits about them. Covered entities must keep up-to-date on subjects that support thoughtful policies, practices, and software settings, along with active monitoring for changes in the

340B program universe and in information technology feeding 340B program functions or that utilize 340B information. Their vigilance includes monitoring changes and updates in the hospital's electronic medical record (EMR), finance, and patient billing software; supply chain and inventory software; and distributor ordering portals. This oversight might extend to include testing and regular quality assurance activities. Even a modest change or update in any 340B-connected system or practice can cause a malfunction or a change in business results. Casual selection or update of software settings should be discouraged. Likewise, a change or update to a policy or practice should lead to an internal review of settings and functions and also result in an internal communication utilizing the oversight structure outlined above.

5. *Audit annually*. An annual audit of contract pharmacy is an element of HRSA's audit standards. HRSA's focus is on compliance, duplicate discount, and the potential for diversion of 340B drugs; however, a well-run 340B program also audits the business elements beyond the 340B compliance requirements. The application of a similar audit strategy to the broader program is a key to success. This review should include mixed-use areas, clinics, retail and specialty pharmacies owned by the hospital, and other areas where 340B is a component of the supply chain or patient care delivery.

   Covered entities are advised to include more frequent audits of data management in all areas to ensure that complete, correct, reliable, and accurate data are passing to the systems that support 340B. Regular review of error reports from software vendors should include root cause analysis in addition to corrections and updates. As discussed earlier, a review should be undertaken whenever a system on which 340B depends is updated, upgraded, or changed. As outlined below, business results are often an early sign of a gap or change.

6. *Review program business results and benchmark*. 340B program results can be viewed through a variety of lenses and metrics. However, weekly and monthly reviews of business results, including purchases by category (wholesale acquisition cost [WAC], 340B, GPO) and the savings associated with the program, should be a regular element of internal discussions and review. For more detail, see Chapter 14.

7. *Evaluate and select business partners thoughtfully*. In the 340B program, where the rules are guidelines open to some level of interpretation, selecting business partners with aligned views and a deferential approach to 340B compliance risk as viewed by the covered entity is critical. Hospitals typically think of their 340B third-party administrator (TPA) for contract pharmacy as a vital choice reflecting this element. However, the retail pharmacy partner, the split-billing software vendor, pharmaceutical distributor, and others should also be aligned. In many cases, multiple automation, software, finance, and 340B vendors need to align and work together to ensure success. Hospitals must share protected health information (PHI) with some vendors to achieve 340B goals. Investing the effort to understand the approach of partners to 340B in addition to the core business processes is time well invested. Regular examination of supply chain and 340B program results speak for themselves, but a regular review of contracts, business associate agreements (BAAs), contract pharmacy agreements, and other relationship documents is also essential.

8. *Calculate 340B proceeds and track how they are used*. The results of management and monitoring of 340B business activities can provide clear insight into the savings and revenue impact of 340B on a covered entity hospital. Although HRSA has not tracked these results and many hospitals are circumspect about discussing 340B proceeds publicly, it is important to ensure that a detailed and quantitative understanding of 340B financial results are brought to any discussion of business performance. In addition, as guidance and regulatory changes are proposed, ready access to a detailed accounting of 340B program costs, savings, and results—along with their support of the hospital's programs and mission—will permit responsive comments to regulators, hospital leadership, and in many cases, the hospital's board. As 340B has progressed to a financially impactful program beyond the

pharmacy, an internal answer to the question regarding use of proceeds is interesting, while an answer to the question *"What will happen if a change occurs in 340B?"* has become critical.

9. ***Monitor proposed regulatory and guidance changes***. *A simple prescription, but one well aligned with all the items above:* Stay in touch with proposed 340B program and 340B program-related changes. Many legislative and regulatory changes are 340B-program-specific, while others occur in related programs (Medicaid, Medicare, etc.). However, the diverse and complex nature of hospital care delivery combined with the complex nature of 340B make engagement of the hospital's government affairs team essential. Although the government affairs team may not be 340B experts, assigning them to keep a "weather eye" open to changes—combined with alignment with hospitals' 340B experts, state and national hospital organizations, and 340B organizations—will add a key dimension to an otherwise modest corner of the pharmacy and hospital regulatory landscape. If the hospital is to benefit from a broader understanding of regulatory policy and practice, it must be prepared to understand the impact of potential changes in 340B rules guidance or law.

10. ***Develop a trusted advisor relationship***. Organizations often do not fully appreciate their internal experts. This is likely doubly true for 340B experts. The 340B program is complex, arcane, and in many instances an insider's game to recall and understand the important details. Trusted advisors can be outside consultants, leaders in organizations, peers, and leaders in other 340B organizations. They may even be leaders within the organization with a broader view—strategic planning, public policy, or community affairs that provide an objective, but knowledgeable external view. Taking a few steps back to assess the 340B program from a different perspective can permit action to mitigate or avoid an adverse audit finding, select and work more effectively with a 340B business partner, respond to a 340B program challenge, and prioritize options for growth and change. The complexity of 340B program implementation in hospitals isn't widely appreciated until it encounters trouble or fails. Finding a trusted advisor to assist in keeping the conversation focused and on target is beneficial.

SUMMARY

The 340B program is a substantive benefit to participating hospitals serving the indigent and vulnerable, and a key element of care delivery in the U.S. healthcare system. It was not always so. However, as is the case with many government programs, the larger healthcare environment drives the larger perspective. As 340B has grown, it has become a target of criticism, a linchpin in hospital financial status, and an object of proposals for improvement or reform.

KEY POINT

A thoughtful 340B hospital invests in the quality and integrity of the current 340B program, works to protect it in its current form, and considers the future.

A thoughtful approach respects that change may come from outside the 340B program and may result from change in the larger healthcare environment. 340B program participants should prepare to defend the effectiveness of the 340B program in supporting hospitals serving indigent and vulnerable patients, but also prepare to assess and respond to changes from wherever they originate. A thoughtful and detailed appreciation of current 340B program investment and impact, along with a vigilant and active scan of the healthcare environment, will serve a 340B hospital in meeting the coming challenge.

INDEX

A